128.8

ROBERT M. GUERNSEY

D1133530

MARIHUANA

ON

TRIAL

In 1937, Congress, through pressure by the Federal Bureau of Narcotics, passed judgment on marihuana, rendering it illegal. The legislatures of various states seconded this judgment, many with even harsher laws.

Today that judgment is being called into question. Lawyers are challenging it in the courts. And there is growing evidence that an entire generation of Americans is challenging it in practice.

This volume is designed to illumine the facts long obscured by the marihuana myth. Presented on these pages is the famous LaGuardia report on marihuana. The impassioned defense of the drug by Allen Ginsberg. The historical realities by Dr. Norman Taylor. The testimony of noted physicians, psychiatrists, sociologists. And much, much more—

Everything, in fact, that you need to make up your own mind.

"A highly interesting and controversial book"
—*Washington Star*

SIGNET Books of Special Interest

☐ **THE HIPPIE PAPERS by Jerry Hopkins.** An eye-opening collection of outspoken articles from the nation's underground press of subjects ranging from drugs to free love, from Vietnam to police brutality. (#Q3457—95¢)

☐ **THE HIPPIES by Burton Wolfe.** At once highly critical and deeply sympathetic, this is an in-depth examination of the hippie kingdoms—its "government," its organizing principle, its leaders and members, the drug scene, the communes, the poverty, the disease. (#T3453—75¢)

☐ **TURNING ON by Rasa Gustaitis.** The author, a noted journalist visited Esalen, took an LSD trip, freaked out with the gypsies, participated in various sense-awakening therapies and visited hippie communes, and describes her experiences in this intelligent book. (#Q4243—95¢)

☐ **MY SELF AND I by Constance Newland.** The intimate, completely frank record of a woman's experiment with LSD, the controversial "mind-expanding" drug. (#T2294—75¢)

THE NEW AMERICAN LIBRARY, INC., P.O. Box 999, Bergenfield, New Jersey 07621

Please send me the SIGNET BOOKS I have checked above. I am enclosing $_____(check or money order—no currency or C.O.D.'s). Please include the list price plus 15¢ a copy to cover mailing costs.

Name_____

Address_____

City_____State_____Zip Code_____

Allow at least 3 weeks for delivery

→ THE
MARIHUANA
PAPERS

Edited by DAVID SOLOMON, 1925-

Introduction by Alfred R. Lindesmith, PhD

A MENTOR BOOK from
NEW AMERICAN LIBRARY
TIMES MIRROR

Copyright © 1966 by David Solomon

All rights reserved. This book, or parts thereof, may not be reproduced without permission in writing from the publisher. For information address The Bobbs-Merrill Company, Inc., 4300 West 62 St., Indianapolis, Indiana 46268.

Library of Congress Catalog Card Number: 66-25282

This is an authorized reprint of a hardcover edition published by The Bobbs-Merrill Company, Inc.

Fifth Printing

 MENTOR TRADEMARK REG. U.S. PAT. OFF. AND FOREIGN COUNTRIES
REGISTERED TRADEMARK—MARCA REGISTRADA
HECHO EN CHICAGO, U.S.A.

SIGNET, SIGNET CLASSICS, SIGNETTE, MENTOR and PLUME BOOKS
are published by The New American Library, Inc.,
1301 Avenue of the Americas, New York, New York 10019

First Printing, April, 1968

PRINTED IN THE UNITED STATES OF AMERICA

The Marihuana Papers is dedicated
 to my mother Ida,
who first created my consciousness,
and to wife Pat and daughters Kim and Lin,
who have nurtured its expansion.

Acknowledgments

The Editor wishes to acknowledge his appreciation and gratitude to the following authors, publishers, and publications for permission to include the selections listed below:

The selection by Théophile Gautier is translated by Ralph J. Gladstone. Copyright © Ralph J. Gladstone, 1966.

The selection by Charles Baudelaire is from *The Essence of Laughter and Other Essays*, edited by Peter Quennell and translated by Norman Cannon. Translation copyright © 1956, Norman Cannon. British edition copyright © 1956, Weidenfeld and Nicolson, Ltd.

The selection by William Burroughs, copyright © 1963, is reprinted with the author's permission. The quotation appearing in the editor's Introduction to that selection is reprinted with the author's permission from "Deposition: Testimony Concerning a Sickness," *Evergreen Review*, January/February 1960. Copyright © 1960 by Grove Press, Inc.

The selection by Norman Taylor is from *Narcotics, Nature's Dangerous Gift to Man*. Copyright © 1963, Norman Taylor; published by Dell Publishing Company, Inc.

The selection by Alfred Lindesmith is from *The Addict and the Law*. Copyright © 1965, Alfred Lindesmith; published by Indiana University Press.

The selections by Howard S. Becker are from *Outsiders*. Copyright © 1963 by the Free Press of Glencoe, a division of The Macmillan Company, The Crowell-Collier Publishing Company.

The selection by George Morris Carstairs is reproduced by permission from the *Quarterly Journal of Studies on Alcohol*, Volume 15, pages 220–237, 1954. Copyright © 1954 by Journal of Studies on Alcohol, Inc., New Brunswick, N.J.

The selections by Victor Robinson and W. Reininger are reprinted with the permission of Ciba Pharmaceutical Company from *Ciba Symposia*, Volume 8, Number 5–6, August-September 1946.

The selection by François Rabelais is from *Pantagruel*, Chapters 49–52, Book III; translated by Samuel Putnam; published by Covici-Friede, 1929, and reprinted by permission of Crown Publishers.

38206

The selection by Paul Bowles is from *100 Camels in the Courtyard*, published by City Lights Press. Copyright © 1962 Paul Bowles; reprinted with the author's permission.

The selection by Terry Southern (copyright © 1960 Terry Southern) is from *Evergreen Review* and is reprinted with the author's permission.

The original selection by Allen Ginsberg is published with the author's permission. Copyright © Allen Ginsberg, 1966.

The selection by Sheldon Cholst appeared in *Residu* and is published with the author's permission. Copyright © Sheldon Cholst, 1965.

The original selection by Timothy Leary is published with the author's permission. Copyright © Timothy Leary, 1966.

The selection from *The Marihuana Problem in the City of New York* has been reprinted with the permission of Ronald Press. Originally published by Jaques Cattell, 1944.

The selection by Samuel Allentuck and Karl Bowman is from *The American Journal of Psychiatry*, Volume 99, Number 2, September 1942, and is reprinted with permission of the authors and the *Journal*.

The selection by George Tayleur Stockings is from the *British Medical Journal*, June 28, 1947, and is reprinted with the permission of the author and the *Journal*.

The selection by Lloyd J. Thompson and Richard Proctor is from the *North Carolina Medical Journal*, October 1953, and is reprinted with the permission of the authors and the *Journal*.

The selection by Robert Walton is from *Marihuana*, published by J. B. Lippincott, 1938. Reprinted with permission of the author and publisher. Copyright © Robert Walton, 1938.

The selection by William H. McGlothlin is printed with the permission of the author. Copyright © 1965 William H. McGlothlin.

Table of Contents

BOOK TWO: LITERARY AND IMAGINATIVE PAPERS

BOOK THREE: SCIENTIFIC PAPERS

THE MARIHUANA MYTHS

A recent *Playboy* cartoon by Donald Reilly depicts a conventional-looking couple standing expectantly before their college-age son. The husband, portly and respectable, holds a newspaper loosely by his side while his matronly wife, her hands clasped demurely, shyly addresses the young man: "Dear, your father and I would like some pot." So would millions of other Americans who are beginning to hear and learn that marihuana is both pleasurable and harmless.

Playboy presumably ran the cartoon described above precisely because marihuana *is* becoming increasingly popular today, a phenomenon reflected by the current ground swell of news reports, magazine articles, television programs, and sociological studies dealing with the herb and its growing legion of devotees.

Marihuana comes from the flowering tops and leaves of the hemp plant, *Cannabis sativa,* which was cultivated—as a source of rope and cloth fibers, bird seed, certain essential oils, and medicinal products—in the United States and Central and South America for centuries, and in Europe, Asia, and Africa for thousands of years. Before the Civil War, hemp rope rigged the world's sailing ships and hemp fabric covered our pioneers' wagons. Until 1937 it was available for prescription as a legitimate therapeutic device and was listed in the official *U.S. Pharmacopoeia* as tincture of *cannabis.* Several large drug companies, including Parke-Davis, manufactured this liquid extract of marihuana, but the product was withdrawn from the market largely because of the harassing restrictions of the Marihuana Tax Act of 1937.

With its origins in botanical antiquity, marihuana—or hemp, as it is called when grown as a source of fibers and seeds— is one of the oldest domesticated plants known to man. Before the passage of the Marihuana Tax Act and the development of synthetic fibers, it had long been a major crop in Kentucky, Virginia, Wisconsin, Indiana, and other corn-belt states. Early English settlers were even offered special incentives by the Crown for growing hemp. It has been said that George Washington raised it at Mount Vernon: Once, during one of his many extended absences, Washington was reported to have expressed the wistful hope that he would be able to return to his plantation in time for the September hemp harvest.

George Washington was not alone. Hemp was a cash crop for most Colonial and post-Revolutionary planters, and after cotton, the South's most important agricultural product. Before the Civil War, indignant Southern hemp growers lobbied for and got a full congressional investigation when it was learned that the United States Navy dared award a large contract to suppliers of Russian-grown hemp on the grounds that it possessed greater tensile strength than the domestic variety.

During World War II, the cultivation of hemp was briefly encouraged by the federal government because sources for sisal rope had been cut off by the Japanese occupation of the Philippines. After the war, with foreign fiber sources augmented by the emergence of such synthetics as nylon, the market for domestic hemp largely disappeared.

Officialdom evinced little or no concern over marihuana until the 1930s, when its use began to spread to more dominant social groups, especially those elements that had become economically déclassé by the depression. Many people now began to discover that it was far cheaper to smoke the dried leaves of the hemp plant than to drink liquor—which, unlike marihuana, was both socially acceptable and federally taxed. Alcohol, interestingly enough, had only been officially rehabilitated in 1933 by the repeal of the unworkable Volstead Act of 1919. More people were finding out by direct experience, moreover, that marihuana, far from possessing any of the notoriously toxic properties of alcohol, was a mildly stimulating and relaxing herb that was completely nonaddictive and could be used for social purposes without appreciably reducing the efficiency of one's physical and mental faculties.

Before the Marihuana Tax Act, poor, segregated minority groups, especially Mexican-Americans and urban Negroes, used marihuana's consciousness-expanding properties as an economical euphoriant: its preparation does not entail fermentation or distillation; hence it is far cheaper to produce than alcoholic beverages. And because the plant thrives, requires practically no cultivation, and needs only drying to prepare it for use, it was often home-grown in rural areas.

Obviously, the popular discovery of marihuana as a safe euphoric was imminent. Why the public emergence of that fact represented such a problem to authorities is a tantalizing question. It is hard not to speculate (as some prominent sociologists have done privately) that the upsurge of the use of marihuana in the thirties was opposed primarily by pressure groups in both the federal government and the newly revived liquor industry. The suggestion that the ban on marihuana might have been in part a result of a powerful liquor lobby does not seem improbable when one considers that a substantial public shift to marihuana might have created considerable competition to the sale of alcoholic beverages.

Despite its increasing popularity in the thirties, however, most middle-class Americans still had no contact with marihuana and knew little, if anything, about it. But the anxiety-producing stresses of the depression had made the country panic-prone. Deprived of the facts and primed on hysteria-provoking, apocryphal horror stories given to the press by the Federal Bureau of Narcotics, Americans were sold a mythological bill of goods. They were told that marihuana was a "killer drug" that triggered crimes of violence and acts of sexual excess; a toxic agent capable of driving normal persons into fits of madness and depraved behavior; a destroyer of the will; a satanically destructive drug which, employing lures of euphoria and heightened sensuality, visited physical degeneration and chronic psychosis upon the habitual user.

The most unprincipled aspect of this yellow journalism played upon the public's concern for the health and safety of their children: front-page headlines and feature articles in popular magazines such as the now defunct *Literary Digest* depicted insidious pushers selling marihuana everywhere, including in high schools throughout the nation, thus precipitating wild orgies and outbursts of crime and violence.

The outcome was predictable: the federal legislation that was passed at the end of the 1937 congressional session was virtually scare-enacted. Accepting uncritically the testimony and recommendations of the Federal Bureau of Narcotics, Congress equipped the Marihuana Tax Act with sharp teeth: five years' imprisonment, a $2,000 fine, or both, were the penalties provided for possession of even a minute quantity of the herb.

In 1930—the year the Federal Bureau of Narcotics was established—only sixteen states had laws prohibiting the use of marihuana, and those statutes were generally mild and rarely enforced. By 1937, largely as a result of almost eight years of persistent efforts by the Bureau, almost every state legislature had been pressured into adopting a standard bill making marihuana illegal. With the passage of the 1937 federal legislation, then, the plant's legal fate was effectively sealed. The Federal Bureau of Narcotics had created a villainous bête noir out of whole cloth, which it then heroically proceeded to slay in a campaign that today seems more noteworthy for its zeal than for its principles.

With the mass media inciting the public and demanding that the authorities take action under the new laws, the expected national crackdown exploded early in 1938. Thousands of persons, mostly members of ethnic minorities, were arrested and jailed; tons of marihuana were theatrically confiscated and destroyed by glory-seeking law-enforcement officials, more often than not to the pre-arranged pop of photographers' flash bulbs.

In New York City, however, the marihuana hysteria ran into trouble from an exceptional political figure. Mayor Fiorello LaGuardia, whose political integrity was something of a rarity, declined to hunt herbal witches. Refusing to accept uncritically the charges brought against marihuana, he demanded facts, not legends. In his Foreword to *The Marihuana Problem in the City of New York,* commonly referred to as the Mayor's Report, he declared:

> As Mayor of the City of New York, it is my duty to foresee and take steps to prevent the development of hazards to the health, safety, and welfare of our citizens. When rumors were recently circulated concerning the smoking of marihuana by large segments of our population and even by school children, I sought advice from The New York Academy of Medicine, as is my custom when confronted with problems of medical import. On the Academy's recommendation I appointed a special committee to make a thorough sociological and scientific investigation, and secured funds from three Foundations with which to finance these studies.
>
> My own interest in marihuana goes back many years, to the time when I was a member of the House of Representatives and, in that capacity, heard of the use of marihuana by soldiers stationed in Panama. I was impressed at that time with a report of an Army Board of Inquiry which emphasized the relative harmlessness of the drug and the fact that it played a very little role, if any, in problems of delinquency and crime in the Canal Zone.
>
> • • •
>
> I am glad that the sociological, psychological, and medical ills commonly attributed to marihuana have been found to be exaggerated insofar as the City of New York is concerned.

In 1938, the internationally renowned New York Academy of Medicine provided Mayor LaGuardia with a committee of impartial scientists, pledged to make a comprehensive series of sociological, medical, and psychological studies of the alleged marihuana problem in the City of New York. Although the subsequent report, which appears in shortened version in this anthology, is frequently alluded to by researchers, the general public has rarely heard of it. This hidden classic (most medical libraries do not have copies) contains the findings of a team of twenty-eight leading physicians, psychiatrists, research chemists, pharmacologists, and sociologists. Published in a limited printing in 1944, their conclusions were based on exhaustive studies over a period of years, studies that included intensive community research as well as controlled hospital and laboratory experiments.

When the Report was issued, it flatly contradicted the mythology then officially being disseminated as fact. Summing up 212 pages of comprehensive documentation, George B. Wallace, MD, chairman of the Mayor's Committee on Marihuana, cited the study's conclusions:

In most instances, the behavior of the [marihuana] smoker is of a friendly, sociable character. Aggressiveness and belligerency are not commonly seen . . .

The marihuana user does not come from the hardened criminal class and there was found no direct relationship between the commission of crimes of violence and marihuana. "Tea-pads" have no direct association with houses of prostitution, and marihuana itself has no specific stimulant effect in regard to sexual desires.

There is no organized traffic . . . among New York City school children, and any smoking that occurs in this group is limited to isolated instances.

Smoking marihuana can be stopped abruptly with no resulting mental or physical distress comparable to that of morphine withdrawal in morphine addicts.

•   •   •

Marihuana does not change the basic personality structure of the individual. It lessens inhibition and this brings out what is latent in his thoughts and emotions but it does not evoke responses which would otherwise be totally alien to him.

•   •   •

No evidence was found of an acquired tolerance for the drug.

•   •   •

From the study as a whole, it is concluded that marihuana is not a drug of addiction, comparable to morphine, and that if tolerance is acquired, this is of a very limited degree. Furthermore, those who have been smoking marihuana for a period of years showed no mental or physical deterioration which may be attributed to the drug.

The lessening of inhibitions and repression, the euphoric state, the feeling of adequacy, the freer expression of thoughts and ideas, and the increase in appetite for food brought about by marihuana suggest therapeutic possibilities. . . .

The comprehensive and detailed evidence contained in the Mayor's Report was bitterly assailed by both the American Medical Association and the Federal Bureau of Narcotics. Nevertheless, it has come to be regarded by scientists as the most detailed and accurate study yet conducted.

Another contributor to this anthology has written extensively regarding the therapeutic possibilities of marihuana, which Dr. Wallace referred to in his summary of the Mayor's Report. In the chapter "Therapeutic Application," by Dr. Robert Walton, the medical uses of marihuana are soberly assessed:

The therapeutic application of cannabis is more a matter of history than of present-day practice. Synthetic analgesics and hypnotics have almost entirely displaced these preparations from their original field of application. The newer synthetics are more effective and reliable and, in addition, have been more intensively exploited by commercial interests. Cannabis preparations have come to occupy so minor a place among modern medicinals that it has been suggested that they be abandoned altogether, this latter point of view being based on the assumption that they represent a menace from the standpoint of the hashish habit. Such an action would certainly be too drastic in view of the circumstances. For one thing, the therapeutic use of cannabis and the hashish habit are almost entirely unrelated. The drug has been readily available in this country for almost a century without developing more than a very occasional, isolated instance of hashish abuse. The marihuana habit came into this country by other channels, although it is true that once established as a practice, some few individuals have made use of the "drug store" preparations. The 1937 Federal legislative acts should be wholly effective in making these preparations completely unavailable for any further abuse of this sort. More stringent regulations making the drug unavailable for medical and scientific purposes would be unwise, since other uses may be developed for the drug which will completely overshadow its disadvantages. The drug has certain remarkable properties and if its chemical structure were determined and synthetic variations developed, some of these might prove to be particularly valuable, both as therapeutic agents and as experimental tools.

. . .

Although hemp preparations may have been used by the ancients to produce anesthesia, these drugs were not introduced generally into medicine until about 1840. At this time, O'Shaughnessy, Aubert-Roche, and Moreau de Tours observed its use in India and Egypt and proceeded to experiment with its therapeutic possibilities. After using it in different sorts of conditions, they were each enthusiastic in representing it as a valuable therapeutic agent. Their activities resulted in a very widespread and general use of the drug in both Europe and America. During the period 1840-1900 there were something over 100 articles published which recommended cannabis for one disorder or another.

. . .

Among the miscellaneous conditions for which it has been used and recommended may be mentioned cough, fatigue, rheumatism, rheumatic neuralgia, asthma, and delirium tremens.

. . .

In combating pain of various causes, cannabis preparations might be expected to be reasonably effective. See declared that it "gives relief from pain and increases the appetite in all cases, no matter on what causes the pain and loss of appetite may depend."

Hare says [that] "during the time that this remarkable drug is relieving pain, a very curious psychical condition sometimes manifests itself; namely, that a diminution of pain seems to be due to its fading away in the distance, so that the pain becomes less and less." Mercer says that it does not arrest pain but has a "special power over spasmodic pain." Wood says that "as an analgesic it is very much inferior to opium but may be tried when the latter is for any reason contra-indicated. In full doses, in neuralgic pains, it certainly often gives relief." Aulde says that "as a remedy for the relief of supraorbital neuralgia no article affords better prospects than cannabis." . . . Osler and McCrae have said that for migraine, *Cannabis indica* is probably the most satisfactory remedy.

Concerning the use of marihuana in mental conditions, Dr. Walton writes:

Moreau de Tours was the first to advocate using the hashish euphoria as a means of combating mental conditions of a depressive character. He reported a number of case histories of maniacs and melancholics which were improved after such therapy. . . . There have been a few other observations agreeing in general with Moreau de Tours and there have been some who reported adversely on such treatment. Straub recently suggested that small doses of a properly standardized preparation may possibly prove useful in depressive melancholias. Edes found it benefited patients who complained of unpleasant, tiring dreams, and Birch used it in the treatment of chronic chloral and chronic opium poisoning.

Other medicinal uses mentioned by Dr. Walton for marihuana include the drug's value in uterine dysfunction, specifically painful and excessive menstruation as well as impaired menstruation. Moreover, as a therapeutic device used in labor and childbirth, Dr. Walton cites several sources, including the following, which appeared in the *Journal of the American Medical Association:*

The sensation of pain is distinctly lessened or entirely absent and the sense of touch is less acute than normally. Hence a woman in labor may have a more or less painless labor. If a sufficient amount of the drug is taken, the patient may fall into a tranquil sleep from which she will awaken refreshed. . . . As far as is known, a baby born of a mother intoxicated with cannabis will not be abnormal in any way.

Dr. Walton's research into the therapeutic history of marihuana is confirmed by another contributor to this anthology, Victor Robinson, MD. Dr. Robinson, both a physician and a chemist, was one of this country's leading experts on marihuana. In 1946 *Ciba Symposia* devoted an entire issue to articles on cannabis written by him. The following material is taken from one of those essays, "Concerning *Cannabis Indica.*"

In the most ancient of all medical works, the *Susruta Samhita,* hemp is recommended for catarrh. A sanskrit work on *materia medica, Rajbulubha,* alludes to the use of hemp in gonorrhea. In the first century, Dioscorides—the most renowned of the ancient writers on materia medica—recommended the seeds in the form of a cataplasm to soothe inflammation. Galen wrote that it is customary to give hemp to guests at banquets to promote hilarity and happiness. At the beginning of the third century, the Chinese physician Hoa-Thoa used hemp as an anesthetic in surgical operations.

In medicinal doses cannabis has been used as an aphrodisiac, for neuralgia, to quiet maniacs, for the cure of chronic alcoholism and morphine and chloral addiction, for mental depression, hysteria, softening of the brain, nervous vomiting, for distressing cough, for St. Vitus' dance and for epileptic fits of a most appalling kind. It is used in spasm of the bladder, in migraine and tetanus. It is a uterine tonic, and a remedy for the headaches and hemorrhage occurring in the final cessation of the menses. According to Osler, cannabis is sometimes useful in locomotor ataxia. Christison reports a case in which cannabis entirely cured the intense itching of eczema, while the patient was enjoying the pleasant slumber which the hemp induced. It is sometimes employed as a hypnotic in those cases where opium, because of long continued use, has lost its efficiency. As a specific in hydrophobia it was once claimed to be marvelous, for Dr. J. W. Palmer wrote that he himself had seen a sepoy, an hour before furiously hydrophobic, under the influence of cannabis drinking water freely and pleasantly washing his hands and face. . . .

Marihuana has, of course, been employed for millennia as a folk euphoriant and medicinal agent by peoples of diverse cultures. Although many governments have attempted to eradicate its use by declaring it illegal, in those areas where it has become part of the cultural pattern (as in Africa, India, Asia, and Latin America) no authority has been able to suppress it for long. According to United Nations statistics, in 1951 there were 200,000,000 marihuana users throughout the world. That figure is undoubtedly higher today.

Almost twenty-five years ago, the Mayor's Report noted that the use of marihuana was largely limited to working-class Negroes and other minority groups. Today, marihuana smoking in large United States urban centers, despite its illegality, has become a moderately common phenomenon among such disparate groups as bond salesmen, advertising copywriters, financial analysts, doctors, chemists, TV producers, actors, film technicians, civil service employees, welfare workers, writers, editors, secretaries, newspapermen, publishing executives, teachers, suburban housewives, classical and jazz musicians, and even members of the police department.

The important point is that in contemporary America the employment of marihuana has ceased to be a subcultural affair limited to the underprivileged and the undereducated. It has become a custom that is rapidly expanding through the byways of the middle and upper classes. Today it is evident that the use of marihuana is rapidly spreading among the privileged and the literate, college student and professor alike, and finding warm and broadening acceptance by creative people of all ages in the arts, sciences, and professions who no longer wish to limit themselves to the psychologically numbing effects of alcoholic beverages. Moreover, the increasing popularity of marihuana smoking, especially among younger adults, indicates a growing awareness that in a world beset by such spectres as exploding bombs and populations, mass hunger, race hatred, contaminated waters, droughts, floods, polluted air and paranoid politicians, so benevolent an herb as marihuana hardly deserves exclusion from one's internal fallout shelter.

The editor of this book takes the point of view that the use of marihuana should be legalized. Science has demonstrated that the plant possesses a wide variety of therapeutic applications, and investigation has proved that its popular use is harmless to the individual and to society.

Legalization should be two-fold. First, marihuana should be accorded the medical status it once had in this country as a legitimate prescription item. After 1937, with the passage of the Marihuana Tax Act and subsequent federal and state legislation, it became virtually impossible for physicians to obtain or prescribe marihuana preparations for their patients. Thus the medical profession was denied access to a versatile pharmaceutical tool with a history of therapeutic utility going back thousands of years.

Second, since it is in no demonstrable way poisonous and harmful, as are nicotine and alcohol, marihuana should be granted at least the same public availability and legal status as tobacco and liquor.

Ultimately, prohibitive legislation will not determine the fate of marihuana. Notwithstanding its illegality, more and more Americans are becoming aware that not only is it superior to alcohol as a euphoriant, but it has none of alcohol's notoriously destructive physiological and social properties. That knowledge will exercise greater authority in the future than any current restrictive laws.

The Marihuana Papers, then, have been compiled with the express purpose of supplying the accurate and authoritative information needed to perform the belated rites for the marihuana myths. In addition to changing people's minds about marihuana, it is further hoped that this anthology will serve as a basic factual manual for that growing number of concerned, courageous Americans who, in recognition of the plant's many virtues, risk official disapproval by openly arguing and campaigning for its legality.

DAVID SOLOMON
New York City, 1966

N.B. *Since both marihuana and marijuana are acceptable spellings of the word, the editor has chosen to retain the original orthographic preferences of the authors represented in this collection.*

It should be noted, as well, that the term hashish refers to the resinous substance exuded by the flowering tops of the hemp (cannabis sativa) *or marihuana plant. Since it derives from the same herb, hashish is equivalent to marihuana in its chemical composition and psychological effects.*

INTRODUCTION

The attempt to suppress the use of marihuana in the United States through police power and by means of heavy penalties shows no signs of succeeding. For several years, it appeared that the zeal of police in pursuing and apprehending marihuana users was declining. The Federal Bureau of Narcotics reported 1,288 marihuana cases in 1952; by the end of 1960, this total had shrunk to 169, although during the same period the Bureau's budget and staff were considerably enlarged. Since 1960, however, it has become apparent that the popularity of marihuana has dramatically increased, especially among young people of middle class background.

In 1937, when the federal antimarihuana law was enacted, marihuana was viewed as the "new drug problem" and, as Mr. Solomon has indicated in his foreword, was ballyhooed and exploited to the full by the mass media. The campaign that led to the 1937 measure was spearheaded by the Federal Bureau of Narcotics and especially by its chief, Harry J. Anslinger. At the hearings on the measure before the House Ways and Means Committee in April and May of 1937, and later in the same year before a subcommittee of the Senate Committee on Finance, Mr. Anslinger proudly told the story of his campaign and took credit for much of the publicity that had been given the "marihuana menace." At these hearings the marihuana user was described as a violent criminal given to rape, homicide, and mayhem. Continued use of marihuana, it was said, led to insanity.

At the House hearings of 1937, Representative Dingell of Michigan asked Mr. Anslinger: "I was just wondering whether the marihuana addict graduates into a heroin, an opium, or a cocaine user?"

Mr. Anslinger replied: "No, sir; I have not heard of a case of that kind. I think it is an entirely different class. The marihuana addict does not go in that direction."

A few months later he again made this point before the Senate subcommittee:

"There is an entirely new class of people using marihuana. The opium user is around 35 to 40 years old. These users are 20 years old and know nothing of heroin or morphine."

There was only one dissident voice at the 1937 hearings, that of Dr. William C. Woodward of the American Medical Association. Although he did not speak officially for the AMA, Dr. Woodward suggested that the measure was being enacted too hastily, that the menace was exaggerated, that more study was needed, and that "primary data" from government agencies such as the Bureau of Prisons, the Children's Bureau, and other sources should be collected and analyzed. He was badgered, browbeaten, given a very bad time, and his testimony finally ignored. Comic relief was afforded when congressmen heard from commercial growers of hemp that marihuana seeds are fed to birds; the lawmakers wanted to know what the effects were on the birds.

Eighteen years later, in the Congressional hearings that led to the 1956 Narcotic Control Act, it was evident that Mr. Anslinger had drastically changed his views on the marihuana question. He played down the connection between marihuana use and crime, emphasizing instead that marihuana was dangerous primarily because it sometimes led to heroin addiction. He pointed out that marihuana was not an addicting drug and noted that marihuana users were not being counted in the Bureau's national survey of addiction.

Senator Price Daniel asked the following question:

"Now, do I understand it from you that, while we are discussing marihuana, the real danger there is that the use of marihuana leads many people eventually to the use of heroin, and the drugs that do cause complete addiction; is that true?"

Mr. Anslinger, forgetting his 1937 line, agreed. "That is the great problem and our great concern about the use of marihuana, that eventually, if used over a long period, it does lead to heroin addiction."

When congressmen asked him if it were not true that the most heinous crimes were often committed under the influence of the weed, Mr. Anslinger admitted that this did sometimes occur, but marihuana, he said, was not a "controlling factor" in crime.

If it is true that marihuana users were not switching to heroin in 1937, it seems probable that it was the 1937 antimarihuana law itself that brought about the change. With the risks increased, prices and profits on the now illicit commodity went up, with the result that merchants who had earlier handled one or the other of these drugs, but not both, now began to handle both of them. The marihuana user thus found himself able to purchase heroin from merchants who had previously sold only marihuana.

Before the publication of the LaGuardia Report in 1944,

there were rumors that the study would be suppressed. The 1942 article by Allentuck and Bowman, which appears in this anthology, prompted Mr. Anslinger to write a letter of protest which was published in the *Journal of the American Medical Association* of January 16, 1943. In this letter he cited references to support the idea that the use of marihuana leads to insanity. It being freely predicted in the 1930s that the nation's mental hospitals would shortly begin to be crowded with mentally deteriorated or psychotic marihuana users.

On April 28, 1945, the *Journal* took the unusual step of editorially assailing the newly published LaGuardia Report, with which Allentuck and Bowman had been associated. The language and logic of the editorial are more like those of a police handout or of a prohibition tract than of medical science. The editorial lamented the comment by *Down Beat* on the LaGuardia Report: "Light Up, Gates, Report Finds 'Tea' a Good Kick." It supported the idea that marihuana is a potent cause of crime and mental deterioration, and suggested the absurd notion that scientific and technical papers on the marihuana question are important factors in law enforcement and in the use of the weed by adolescents.

Subsequent developments have clearly shown that the LaGuardia study is far closer to the realities of the situation than was the viewpoint represented by the JAMA editorial. Despite sharply increased use in recent years, mental hospitals, for example, have not been inundated by marihuana users; and even the police themselves have to a considerable extent swung over to the Report's position that marihuana use is trivial as a cause of crime, and that the "marihuana problem" is as nothing compared with the "alcohol problem."

By and large, the use of marihuana has in the past tended to be concentrated in the lower, underprivileged classes, whereas alcohol is used in all strata. This sociological fact may account in considerable part for the persistence of the marihuana myths, for it means that most writing on the weed and its effects has been done by persons of the middle and upper classes, who themselves use alcohol rather than marihuana, who often have had no direct experience with marihuana or with the social types who use it, and who consequently tend to forget about alcohol when they express their disapproval of the alleged effects of the weed on persons of the lower strata.

Hindu society provides an instructive example of a very different evaluation of alcohol and marihuana from that to which we are accustomed. Hindus tend to associate the use of alcohol with meat eating and, not without reason, sexual immorality. The aversion to alcohol is supported by reference to the sacred literature. On the other hand, marihuana, in the form of ganja, bhang, or charas, is not religiously or socially tabooed to anywhere near the same extent and is actually frequently prescribed in religious practice and social custom. In short, the status of marihuana in relation to alcohol tends to be the opposite of what it is in Western society. It would be rash indeed to believe that it would be to India's advantage to outlaw marihuana and encourage the use of alcohol.

The histories of alcohol and marihuana suggest that these substances, and others like them, have a psychological value which is beyond the control of legislation and which tends to nullify attempts at prohibition. The destiny of marihuana, like that of alcohol, will probably be determined by the efficiency with which it meets certain common human psychological needs. If, for example, it is a less dangerous and generally more effective intoxicant than alcohol, no conceivable legislation can alter this fact or prevent it from becoming known. Much of the literature on marihuana is designed primarily to frighten adolescents, but the latter are much less influenced in these matters by what they read or by what adults tell them than they are by what they themselves experience and by what they learn from each other.

There are more and more indications that the inappropriateness of present United States policy with respect to marihuana is coming to be widely acknowledged, and the need for a genuine legislative examination of this matter is becoming increasingly evident. The 1937 legislation was passed by Congress largely at the behest of the Federal Bureau of Narcotics without any genuine inquiry into the facts. By 1951, marihuana was customarily lumped with other drugs such as heroin, morphine, and cocaine, and the penalties attached to its use were made more severe along with the others. The story was repeated in the 1956 Narcotic Control Act, when the penalties for marihuana violators were again sharply increased with no more than a casual legislative glance at the actual problem and without even the pretense of an inquiry. When a legislative investigation into the marihuana question is finally made, materials of the sort presented in this book should contribute to the formulation of a wiser and more realistic policy.

ALFRED R. LINDESMITH, PhD
Professor of Sociology
Indiana University

BOOK ONE

Historical, Sociological, and Cultural Papers

CHAPTER ONE

THE PLEASANT ASSASSIN:
The Story of Marihuana

Dr. Norman Taylor

This witty, perceptive essay is a literate and knowledgeable compendium of historical and scientific material on marihuana by one of America's foremost botanists. Dr. Taylor served as curator of both the Brooklyn and the New York Botanical Gardens for twenty-five years. He is the author of eighteen popular books and standard reference works on gardening and wild flowers, including the famous 1,225-page Encyclopedia of Gardening. *He has also been editor for Botany, Ornamental Horticulture, and Forestry for* Webster's New International Dictionary *and has contributed to the* Encyclopaedia Britannica *and* The Book of Knowledge. *In addition, Dr. Taylor has published dozens of botanical monographs in various scientific journals and has led botanical explorations throughout the Caribbean, South America, and Mexico.*
Dr. Taylor's essay is remarkable for its eloquent and principled stand in opposition to the marihuana myths.

New and lurid words are no mystery to those who invent them. What are *gates, reefers, greeters, muggles, mooters, Indian-hay,* or *goof-butts?* And just what is *marihuana?* Only the last is in Webster, but all these words are known to millions.

This gutter jargon of New Orleans and New York is merely a crop of new words for a very old plant, long and correctly known as Indian hemp. It was even properly christened by

31

Linnaeus, in 1753, as *Cannabis sativa*. But few ever heard of *Cannabis* or Indian hemp, although the Greeks had a word for it—and so did the Persians, Arabs, Hindus, and Chinese.

In whatever language, the words all apply to a single species of plant—a tall, decidedly weedy annual herb, first cousin to the fig tree and the hop, and having more than a bowing acquaintance with the stinging nettle. But botanical affinities matter less than what the plant has meant to uncounted millions. For every race and creed, from ancient China to Harlem, has used it in some form. Before the current crop of slang, the literate knew, perhaps a little vaguely, that *hashish* came from Indian hemp, but few connected hashish with marihuana, and no wonder. For the latter is a Mexican-Spanish word first used for a poor grade of tobacco, only later—and much more widely—applied to this plant which antedates Greece or Rome.

When the Indian hemp, under its new name of marihuana, appeared in Texas and New Orleans, it immediately sprang into prominence because of the vituperation poured upon it. It would have been an old story to the Hindus, the Chinese, and the Narcotics Commission of the United Nations. They knew, as we did not, that the history of Indian hemp goes back three thousand years before Christ, and that the plant has survived all wars, many famines, and every attempt to exterminate it—even our own.

The plant has suffered more from its friends than its enemies. One of its greatest exponents has left his name fantastically linked with one of the chief products of Indian hemp—hashish. The story is a bit legendary, for it deals with the time just before the First Crusade. And it is not very pretty, for its hero was neither gentle nor polite, nor Christian, and almost certainly he could not read. Such handicaps mattered less then than now, and any story of marihuana would be no story at all without him.

Far below lay the frozen sea of a salt desert, terrible by day, but soon to be drowned in the opalescent splendor of moonlight. Long shadows were already creeping up the side of the fortress as Hasan-i-Sabbah made Alamut safe for the night—safe, if a fortress can be by merely bolting the door.

Quiet reigned within, but not peace, for the peace of Allah does not come readily to the uneasy. And to Hasan and his band of fanatics much had happened and was to happen.

They were, of course, brave men. No others could have taken this mountain fortress, so near Baghdad and Basra. Why be uneasy? Had they not won a haven just where Hasan wanted it, right on the caravan route to Mecca? And wasn't there a beautiful mosque nearby, built by the great Haroun al-Raschid?

Even before Mecca became a shrine the caravans from the magical East passed close by, the long strings of camels plowing through the frosty blindness of the desert.

But Hasan was uneasy and so were the more speculative of his followers. They had no fear of the desert, or of mountains still higher than Alamut. Had they not been born in far-off Khurasan, close up to the immensity of the Himalayas? And hadn't all of them roamed the awful desert between, where nothing grows in the salt sand but tamarisk and the manna bush? Perhaps they scarcely knew why they were uneasy, but they should have known. For into that fortress they carried, with their courage and their arms, something far more serious than weapons—an idea.

Now, ideas are apt to be dangerous, especially to fierce men who, like Hasan, have long known the peace of the mountains and the isolation of the desert. Not the kindly sands of Arabia or Morocco, but the blinding salt sands where the date palm grows only in the oases and the bleached bones of camels mark the track. Hasan knew this desert perfectly, knew its curious crescent-shaped ripples and dunes, and the storms of dust for weeks on end. And upon this desert, in the year 1090, came his idea.

At first it was wholly religious. Like all good Moslems he had fumed at the dominance of Arabian and Turkish caliphs. And he would have naught to do with those weak Moslems who followed Fatima, or worse still, the bastard spawn of those caliphs who succeeded Mahomet. Already the Moslem world was split by these sects. But Hasan decided there was room for another, and he founded one dedicated to his idea. This split the Moslem world so that the Christians won Jerusalem on their first crusade, which happened to coincide with the rise of Hasan.

While the Christians couldn't keep the Holy City, they carried back to Europe a host of Moslem lore. Only three concern us here. One was the brand-new idea of Hasan's which was secret assassination. The second was the name of his band —the Assassins, a term unknown before that. The third was the product of a strange plant from China or India, which was hashish.

Many, including Marco Polo, have implied that Hasan's technique of secret murder could only have been accomplished by men well stoked with hashish. But this ignores the fact that Hasan invented the method from the loftiest motives—to purge the Moslem world of false prophets. He did considerable purging until Genghis Khan killed off twelve thousand of the Assassins in one session, toward the end of the thirteenth century.

Long before that, when Hasan was in his prime, his most dastardly deed was the secret murder of his friend Nizam-al-Mulk. That the latter was educated, a statesman and author, a founder of observatories, hospitals, and universities, did not spare him from the Assassins, who, to make doubly sure, subsequently murdered his son.

At this late date it may be impossible to separate fact from fiction. It does seem reasonably certain that the term *Assassin* and *hashish* either are derived from or are corruptions of Hasan's full name, which was *Hashishin*. He is, with a little more certainty, credited with being the Old Man of the Mountain. There we must leave him, with the reservation that the connection between *hashish, assassin,* and the wicked *Hasan* seems to be more than an etymological accident.

The evil reputation of hashish was fanned by lurid tales of the Assassins. They were credited with decorating their revolting deeds of atrocity with the debauchery assumed to be inherent in hemp. It is this, fortified many years after by the effusions of Baudelaire, Gautier, Dumas, not to mention our own Bayard Taylor and Fitzhugh Ludlow, that has made hemp a symbol of sin.

Is it necessarily and always so? For centuries before Hasan, and ever since, the plant has been used by uncounted millions. They find it a very pleasant assassin indeed, for it kills care, gloom, and apprehension. They think of it—and many of them are by no means ignorant—as the least harmful flight from reality. Naturally they have little patience with those, usually knowing far less, who are only able to make of hemp some monster of evil. Where the truth lies depends a little on some imponderables.

While Hasan was holding his fortress, long caravans passed below it, laden with the spoils of the East. They were then near the end of an all but incredible journey, having survived the passes of Afghanistan, the frozen steppes of Pamir, and the salty deserts of Transcaspia. If Allah were good, and only the sanctioned prayers were omitted, they would soon be in Baghdad, unpacking their fantastic freight.

To Baghdad nothing was improbable. Ever since its founding, had it not been the very threshold of Asia, the last remote outpost of Europe? Marco Polo had not yet told his tales about it, but when he did they turned out to be no more fantastic than the facts. Center of the luxury and learning of the Moslem world, it was a princely city, fabulously rich, the very navel of the Arabian Nights. But, like Hasan, it lacked peace, and was ripe for any messenger who brought it.

Such a messenger arrived one day, very long ago, just when

will probably never be known, and perhaps it does not matter. His message, to a population to whom Mahomet had forbidden wine, was one of the most welcome in the world. What he brought was a little packet of rather crumbling blackish-yellow resin, magical beyond the dreams of Allah. It was far more potent than our marihuana for it was hashish, derived from Indian hemp, and it came almost certainly from beyond the Himalayas. To Moslems no song of India was so sweet. To understand why, and to appreciate why it has since gone around the world, we must go back to China, very far back, where hemp was used centuries before the Christian era.

Males and Females

The ancient Chinese, especially the Emperor Shen Nung, were startlingly modern about drugs and medicines. They gave us ephedrine, which they called *mahuang,* and about 2737 B.C. Nung wrote a pharmacy book. In it he was far more observant about Indian hemp, knew its love life, and had more understanding about its use than most of us.

Today only a handful of botanists know that *Cannabis sativa* grows in two forms. One is a tall and comparatively colorless male plant, which yields in its stem a cordage fiber known as hemp. The other and shorter form of the hemp plant is the quite dynamic female. It never bears male flowers, but among the female clusters there lurks a resin which has worried some and pleased others ever since an inquisitive native discovered its extraordinary properties. No one knows when that was, but it must have been long before the intelligent Shen Nung wrote his pharmacopoeia. He seems to have guessed the female Indian hemp was destined to bring a kind of euphoric happiness to countless millions from that day to this. This troubled him, for China, even then, had its stern moralists. To them, as to many today, to be a little happy is suspect, and to be very happy is quite certainly sinful. Hence they were soon calling this resinous female the "Liberator of Sin."

There seems little need for those ancient Chinese to have smirched female hemp with its first recorded stigma. For they could easily have grown only the male plant and hence produced more rope than sin. What females they did grow, however, were mostly devoted to producing a medicine which we still use. Shen Nung prescribed this for "female weakness, gout, rheumatism, malaria, beri-beri, constipation, and absent-mindedness." Today, after five thousand years of trial and error, modern medicine confines its use "to relieve pain, especially headache, encourage sleep and to soothe restlessness." The drug known to doctors as *Cannabis indica,* is produced exactly as it was in ancient China, for our pharmacopoeia says it must come from the "dried flowering tops of the pistillate (female) plants of *Cannabis sativa."*

Centuries after the Chinese were calling the female of Indian hemp "The Delight Giver," the plant crept into India. It was certainly known there before 800 B.C., but where it acquired the name "Indian" hemp will probably never be known. Dr. W. H. Camp of the University of Connecticut points out that it was not originally wild there, and it may never be possible to say where it first grew. There is some evidence that it originated in Pamir. This is near enough to Hasan's fortress so that science may yet bolster medieval surmises as to the origin of the term *hashish.*

Regardless of hemp's nativity, it is the history of India that reveals the real story of the plant. The kaleidoscopic facets of its culture, use, and abuse, together with a close intertwining of religion and philosophy, are recorded in everything from the Vedas to a modern bazaar. In India the culture of hemp became almost a science and its use very close to epicurean.

Actually, growing male and female hemp plants is no mystery. To produce seed the sexes must be grown in sufficient proximity so that reproduction may be given a chance. Pollination is easy, for it depends upon the wind. All males, except those grown for fiber or needed for fertilization, are cut down. For it is only the female flower cluster that produces enough resin to be beguiling, and quite special skills have been developed to promote its secretion. When fully ripe, and in the presence of great heat, the female flower clusters, and even the top of the plant, are covered by a sticky golden-yellow resin, with an odor not unlike mint. Yellow at first, it ultimately turns blackish. It is this which contains that distillation of nature which disturbed the Chinese moralists, while the more tolerant and thoughtful Hindus called it "The Heavenly Guide," "Poor Man's Heaven," and the "Soother of Grief." The plant can be grown in any region with hot summers.

This sticky resin, closely allied to the substance on hops which makes but a little soporific; is so precious that growers have made its horticulture and harvesting almost as fantastic as the effects of hashish itself. In Nepal, where the finest hemp was formerly grown, the plants were set out in long rows, spaced so that mature flowering tops would just touch. Some resin develops even before the tiny greenish flowers are ready to bloom. To prevent its loss would be easy by simply cutting off the tops of such precocious plants. But that would mean losing the resin of the main crop. To overcome this dilemma, and capture all the resin, completely naked men were driven at intervals pell-mell through the hot steaming rows of hemp, and what stuck to them was scraped off. If this seems a little exhausting under a tropical sun, it was scarcely improved by the fact that the workers were forced to thrash their arms about so that every inch from the waist up would have its clinging coat of resin.

These amenities of hemp culture seem to have developed at least the rudimentary germs of hygiene, for later on the naked runners were made to catch the resin on large leather aprons. But even this refinement did not satisfy the more fastidious Hindus, who demanded a product a little less mixed with the effluvia of the workers. And so something like modern methods of collection became general. Resin is now coaxed out of the cut flower clusters with all the care that the most finical could demand. Spread between snowy cheesecloth, it is pressed out and then scraped off the cloth.

This resin, wrung from the reluctant females with so much care, is the quintessence of the Indian hemp, known for centuries to the Hindus as *charas* (also *churus,* or *churrus*). Ever since the days of Hasan we know it only as hashish.

Bhang and Ganja

So potent is hashish that its continued and excessive use, it has been claimed, leads straight to the lunatic asylum, as some believe it did for Baudelaire.* But since he also suffered from syphilis, hemp may have an alibi in his case. Hashish, by some accounts dangerous when used immoderately, is also so expensive that only the rich can afford it. If it were the only hemp product, its use would be confined to this minority. But Nature and man's ingenuity have provided far cheaper and milder flights from reality than hashish; it is these that have sent hemp all over the world.

Two other hemp products seem, in comparison to charas, absurdly easy to produce. Uncultivated or dooryard plants are cut without extracting the resin and from the cut tops a decoction in milk or water is brewed. This is the celebrated *bhang* of India. When tobacco pipes were brought from the New World, bhang was often dried and smoked, in which form it is a little more potent than as an infusion. Bhang is about the cheapest method of using hemp, and is still scorned by all but the very poorest in India. It is, under the name of *marihuana,* practically the only hemp product used in America.

* Editor's note: Although the literature on *cannabis* has occasionally made reference to a causal relationship between the excessive use of hashish and insanity, such claims have never been scientifically authenticated.

To the more reflective Hindu, bhang is a crude substitute, a little like the difference between flat beer and fine old bourbon. Hindus have known a finer product for centuries. Somewhere in the early history of hemp, they set out to find something better than bhang. Very carefully selected plants were cultivated and their tops harvested. The quality and amount of the resin is much better than in bhang, and to this improved product the term *ganja* was applied. The word is known throughout the world, except in America, where we seem to be content with the second-rate bhang.

Ganja is so much better than bhang that its use became popular with everyone except those who could afford only the cheaper product. It, too, is made into an infusion, but more generally smoked; and it enters into a lot of popular feminine sweetmeats—delectable dainties generally known as *majun* or *majoon*. Ganja palaces sprang up in Calcutta and Bombay, every bazaar sold it, the government finally taxed it, and its use spread westward. It crept along both sides of the Mediterranean and ultimately reached Paris, where, however, hashish (charas) was preferred by the coterie of writers who first became articulate about hemp to the modern world. Their reputation for excess and their ecstatic praise of hashish, quite as much as modern American propaganda against marihuana, inevitably led to anxious inquiry into the "morals" of hemp.

Before attempting to answer the moral question, it is only fair to try to understand the motives of those responsible for the present perfection of hemp products. For centuries nearly every system of Indian philosophy or religion is inextricably bound up with Indian hemp. At least sixteen hundred years ago cultivated Hindus set out to explore the emotional and fantastical properties of hemp. Nothing that has happened since has improved upon those researches, although we do know a little more about the chemistry of the various products. Their object was to produce some flight from reality, less harmful than most others, and to produce an effect different from any other.

It is scarcely surprising that such a quest should arouse violent and emotional thinking, especially in America. The worst possible interpretation was heaped upon it by those who think of hemp only in terms of "vice." One Pacific Coast publishing company went to town on the subject. And even some men of science came perilously near to substituting emotion for thought. Dr. Robert P. Walton's book on marihuana has the first three chapters devoted only to this phase of the long saga of hemp. To those who prefer to let judgment wait upon evidence, let us attempt a dispassionate appraisal of the Indian hemp. And because it will make that appraisal somewhat easier to follow, it is well to recapitulate.

Indian Hemp: Named *Cannabis sativa* by Linnaeus in 1753. A tall, annual weedy herb; the male and female flowers on separate plants. Stems of the male plants yield hemp. The resinous exudation from the female flower clusters and from the tops of female plants yields the various products below. The plant is often called simply *hemp.*

Bhang: A decoction or a smoking mixture derived from the cut tops of uncultivated female plants. The resin content is usually low. Sometimes the word *bhang* is also applied to these inferior plants.

Marihuana: A Mexican-Spanish name for bhang. The term was originally confined to Mexico, and is the only one used for Indian hemp in America, except for the vernacular of the streets.

Ganja: A specially cultivated and harvested grade of the female plants of Indian hemp. The tops are cut and used in making smoking mixtures, beverages, and sweetmeats without extraction of the resin. The plants grown for ganja, which was a licensed agricultural industry in India, are those from which is derived:

Charas (also called *churus* or *churrus*): The pure, unadulterated resin from the tops of the finest female plants of Indian hemp, usually those grown for ganja. But in charas the resin is always extracted. It is known to us only by the name of *hashish,* and from it medicine derived the drug known as *Cannabis indica.*

There are hundreds of other terms for hemp in all languages. Pedantry could dig up scores from almost any reference book, but these few are all that are necessary to discuss the questions of addiction and of whether or not hemp is really dangerous; to determine whether or not this undeniable assassin of care, gloom, and apprehension is tied up with crime and vice.

Concerning the effects of no other plant is there such a mass of written evidence, and the most important of this originated with the English. At Simna, in 1894, there was published the *Report of the Indian Hemp Drug Commission,* in seven volumes comprising over three thousand pages. This will probably always be the classic work on hemp. The inquiry, which lasted nearly two years, was carried through with typical British impartiality. They found teeming millions growing the plants, smuggling of charas was rife, and the licensed dealers in ganja were evading the tax. But far more important than these administrative details, the commission, after meticulous examination of eight hundred doctors, coolies, yogis, fakirs, heads of lunatic asylums, bhang peasants, tax gatherers, smugglers, army officers, hemp dealers, ganja palace operators, and the clergy, admitted three things:

1. "There is no evidence of any weight regarding mental and moral injuries from the moderate use of these drugs.
2. "Large numbers of practitioners of long experience have seen no evidence of any connection between the moderate use of hemp drugs and disease.
3. "Moderation does not lead to excess in hemp any more than it does in alcohol. Regular, moderate use of ganja or bhang produces the same effects as moderate and regular doses of whiskey. Excess is confined to the idle and dissipated."

What the report didn't say, and what some Indians thought was the real motive for the inquiry, was that the cost of hemp products, except charas, was one-twentieth that of good Scotch whisky, from which a large tax revenue was derived. The commission's proposal to tax bhang was, however, abandoned. Practically, it would amount to our attempts to tax moonshiners if they were as common all over the country as they are in the Tennessee mountains. One of the commissioners, invited by the Englishmen to sit with them—a certain Oxford graduate, Raja Soshi Sikhareswar Roy—objected to the proposed tax on grounds that would raise only an incredulous smile at the U.S. Treasury. His argument was that Moslem law and Hindu custom forbade "taxing anything that gave pleasure to the poor. So do the Vedas."

More recent evidence on the effects of hemp has been collected by Professor Walton. He concludes that "the development of any specific fundamental organic change resulting from the chronic use of these drugs has yet to be demonstrated."

That was written in 1938. Still more recent and a much more complete study of the "marihuana problem" was issued by the New York Academy of Medicine at the request of the mayor of New York. That report, issued in 1944, is an exhaustive study of the medical, sociological and addiction problems of marihuana by a corps of experts. It is not without significance that their conclusions are almost precisely similar to those of the Indian Hemp Drug Commission issued fifty years ago. The Academy's main points may be briefly summarized thus:

1. Smoking marihuana does not lead directly to mental or physical deterioration.
2. The habitual smoker knows when to stop, as excessive doses reverse its usually pleasant effects.
3. Marihuana does not lead to addiction (in the medical sense), and while it is naturally habit-forming, its withdrawal does not lead to the horrible withdrawal symptoms of the opiates.
4. No deaths have ever been recorded that can be ascribed to marihuana.
5. Marihuana is not a direct causal factor in sexual or criminal misconduct.
6. Juvenile delinquency is not caused by marihuana smoking, although they are sometimes associated.
7. "The publicity concerning the catastrophic effects of marihuana smoking in New York is unfounded."
8. It is more of a nuisance than a menace.

Only a year before this, Colonel J. M. Phalen, the editor of the *Military Surgeon,* in response to frightened inquiries about our soldiers using marihuana in Panama, headed his editorial "The Marihuana Bugaboo." He wrote, in part, ". . . that the smoking of leaves, flowers and seeds of *Cannabis sativa* is no more harmful than the smoking of tobacco or mullein or sumac leaves." He then went on to warn the anxious that "the legislation in relation to marihuana was ill-advised . . . it branded as a menace and a crime a matter of trivial importance."

The uproar over these two reports was prodigious. Harried feature writers for the newspapers and magazines saw one of their most juicy and lurid topics snatched away from them —if the Colonel and the Academy were right. Gone was the linking of marihuana with sex perversion, gang wars, rape, theft, murder, juvenile delinquency, and whatever sensational nonsense they could dream up. Even the staid *Journal of the American Medical Association* hurled a few invectives at the Academy warning that "Public Officials will do well to disregard this unscientific study and continue to regard marihuana as a menace wherever it is purveyed." We have done so ever since, and Mr. Anslinger, former U.S. Commissioner of Narcotics, in his book, *The Traffic in Narcotics,* issued in 1953, writes of the Academy's report, "The Bureau immediately detected the superficiality and hollowness of its findings and denounced it."

Where the error appears to lurk is that marihuana smoking by weak and maladjusted youths is sometimes or even often *associated* with crime, but not the *cause* of it. Mental and spiritual maladjustment, neurotic or psychopathic individuals, poverty, overcrowding and the slum conditions of Negroes and Puerto Ricans in Harlem provide an ideal environment for nursing crime. And the Academy found that a large proportion of marihuana smokers were Negroes or Puerto Ricans. They also found that a lot of smokers were perfectly respectable individuals who, through boredom, wanted to become "high," preferably in one of their "tea-pads" which in some cases are reasonably innocent if rather crude clubs. They almost never mix hard liquor with marihuana as alcohol tends to destroy the effects of the drug.

As to being a sex-excitant, marihuana appears to be just the reverse. These denizens of "tea-pads" appear to know this quite well. If they had ever heard of Théophile Gautier, the most literate hashish-eater in the world, they would heartily agree with this statement, "A hashish-eater would not lift a finger for the most beautiful maiden in Verona."

But the marihuana problem still plagues us. Reformers listen less to unpalatable facts than to their inner urge to justify their quite often ignorant zeal. It is thus, in spite of the evidence, as difficult to curb reformers as to pull up all hemp. They keep harking back to the past, especially to Fitzhugh Ludlow and Bayard Taylor.

"The Lullaby of Hell"

Fitzhugh Ludlow, friend of Mark Twain, used hashish for years and wrote a book about it. He there quotes the phrase which titles this section. It was bequeathed to him by a couple of fiends conjured up during one of his protracted bouts of hashish-eating. Similar and more awful terrors are strewn through the literature of hashish, from a Hindu who wrote in the first century of our era to the effusions of Gautier, Baudelaire, Dumas, and the clique that formed "Le Club des Hachichins" in Paris of the 1850s. Such distortions have little to do with the age-old moderate use of hemp, for hashish is a potent extract to whose excessive use only few are devoted.

It is quite otherwise with bhang and ganja. Statistically, it might be proved that the ganja-using Orient is not particularly crowded with lunatics; in this country the much-berated marihuana has not noticeably filled our asylums. What hemp offers as a flight from reality is best understood from those who use it. One of them, writing very long ago, put the matter clearly:

To the Hindu the hemp plant is holy. A guardian lives in the bhang leaf. . . . To see in a dream the leaves, plant or water of bhang is lucky. . . . A longing for bhang foretells happiness. . . . It cures dysentery and sunstroke, clears phlegm, quickens digestion, sharpens appetite, makes the tongue of the lisper plain, freshens the intellect, and gives alertness to the body and gaiety to the mind. Such are the useful and needful ends for which in His goodness the Almighty made bhang. . . . It is inevitable that temperaments should be found to whom the quickening spirit of bhang is the spirit of freedom and knowledge. In the ecstasy of bhang the spark of the Eternal in man turns into light the murkiness of matter. . . . Bhang is the Joy-Giver, the Sky-Flier, the Heavenly Guide, the Poor Man's Heaven, the Soother of Grief. . . . No god or man is as good as the religious drinker of bhang. The students of the scriptures at Benares are given bhang before they sit to study. At Benares, Ujjain and other holy places, yogis, bairagis and sanyasis take deep draughts of bhang that they may center their thoughts on the Eternal. . . . By the help of bhang ascetics pass days without food or drink. The supporting power of bhang has brought many a Hindu family safe through the miseries of famine. To forbid or even seriously to restrict the use of so holy and gracious an herb as the hemp would cause widespread suffering and annoyance and to large bands of worshipped ascetics deep-seated anger. It would rob the people of a solace in discomfort, of a cure in sickness, of a guardian whose gracious protection saves them from the attacks of evil influences. . . . So grand a result, so tiny a sin!

A somewhat different interpretation, obviously more in harmony with American marihuana reformers, is quoted by Oman. He cites a missionary whose Christian zeal prompted him to write, "A great number of Hindu Saints [sic] live in a perpetual state of intoxication, and call this stupefaction, which arises from smoking intoxicating herbs, *fixing the mind on God*."

To the modern man, perhaps disenchanted with the impact of reality, such ecclesiastical quibbling merely befogs the issue. He may wonder how 400,000,000 people can be wrong for such a long time.

It is, of course, impossible to describe a sensation if one has never felt it, any more than one can be really lucid about the odor of a perfume. But in spite of the essential futility of words, millions have been written on the effects of hemp. From among those who have used the plant, one of the better attempts at description is by Bayard Taylor, the translator of *Faust*. Mostly in a spirit of inquiry and to relieve his curiosity, he decided to try hashish. He wrote:

The sensations it then produced were those, physically, of exquisite lightness and airiness—mentally of a wonderfully

keen perception of the ludicrous, in the most simple and
familiar objects. During the half-hour in which it lasted, I
was at no time so far under its control that I could not with
the clearest perception, study the changes through which I
passed. I noted, with careful attention, the fine sensations
which spread throughout the whole tissue of my nervous fibres,
each thrill helping to divest my frame of its earthly and material nature, till my substance appeared to me no grosser
than the vapors of the atmosphere, and while sitting in the
calm of the Egyptian twilight, I expected to be lifted up and
carried away by the first breeze that should ruffle the Nile.
While this process was going on, the objects by which I was
surrounded assumed a strange and whimsical expression. . . .
I was provoked into a long fit of laughter. The hallucination
died away as gradually as it came, leaving me overcome with
a soft and pleasant drowsiness, from which I sank into a deep,
refreshing sleep.

For ganja and bhang, too, the descriptions inevitably mention this feeling of lightness and gaiety, of perfect consciousness during the waking moments, and final sleep only when
too much is used. Moderate users of marihuana confirm this.

W. B. O'Shaughnessy quotes a retiring young Scottish student who tried hemp. "He became like a rajah for three hours,
talked as he never had . . . about everything he never had or
expected to have. It terminated nearly as suddenly as it commenced, and no headache, sickness or other unpleasant symptoms followed."

All competent observers agree that this quality of bringing
euphoric happiness to the harassed is pre-eminent in hemp.
Nothing else except alcohol and perhaps the peyotl can approach it in this respect.

Some have charged hemp with being an aphrodisiac, but
there is no scientific warrant for this. It is quite true that certain
ganja smoking mixtures and some of the more delectable
feminine sweetmeats had other things added to them. But this
stimulation of waning ardor can scarcely be charged against
hemp. Needled ganja is in precisely the same category as
cantharides, yohimbine, and the not too well disguised euphe-
misms of modern glandular therapy. The plain fact seems to
be that pure ganja has the reverse effect, and is taken by Indian priests to quell libido.

Bhang and ganja in the Old World, marihuana in the New,
will never be put down by all the propaganda against them,
whether true or false. Exhilaration of spirit, the flights of
pure imagination, the feeling of ascending as though one
floated above reality, the freedom from serious aftereffects,

and most of all the lack of permanent damage—it is these that make the extermination of hemp seem quite hopeless, even to those dedicated to that enterprise.

Doubts do not deter those who feel that all aspects of hemp are inherently wicked. No one can defend its wholesale and deplorable abuse by thoughtless and excitement-craving school children, any more than one can condone their abuse of tobacco and alcohol. But adult and moderate use is just as intolerable to the true reformer. Yet one of the more reasonable of these, Professor Walton, says that hemp "still flourishes in every country in which it has once been established. This is despite the fact that, in some of these countries, attempts have been made for almost a thousand years to stamp out the practice."

In spite of this, hemp has been attacked hopefully by doctors, the police, and hosts of self-appointed reformers. To an intelligent Hindu, this seems the crudest of nonsense. Even the British government authorities in India ended their report on hemp by saying, "It is neither practicable nor desirable to depart from the traditional policy of tolerating the moderate use of . . . ganja and bhang even for non-medical purposes, whilst taking every possible measure to prevent abuse."

That was written a few years before the cohorts of American weed-pullers really began to put on steam. Now there are marihuana laws in most states, with penalties ranging from heavy fines to ten years in jail (Oregon). But those who wish to enjoy the plant react to such laws as though they well knew the story of the Djoneina Garden in Egypt. The Mohammedan ladies of that gorgeous pleasure retreat were fond of growing hemp and feeding its products to their clientele. How long this had been going on no one knew. But in 1402 there came a reformer, and he ordered that all hemp must be rooted out of the garden. To fortify the law he ordered that any damsel "caught with ganja would be subjected to the extraction of her teeth." This seems drastic enough, but the old chronicle relates, without comment, that in a few years "the custom came back with renewed vigor."

If this is to be the fate of hemp in America, and all signs suggest that it is, the solution is obvious. It is far better to be realistic about it, as the British were in India, where ganja palaces were taxed and ganja growers licensed. Then we could get rid of criminal purveyors, spend no money for enforcement, tax the business, and so avoid the worst excesses of Prohibition. Hemp would then, like tobacco and alcohol, become another measure of character, not a cockpit of controversy.

Meanwhile, as the controversy rages, one likes to think of

some Mexican peon twanging a plaintive guitar up in the free cloudless air of his desert mountain. He will, likely as not, be singing of this still more plaintive cockroach who wouldn't walk without . . .

> *La cucaracha, la cucaracha,*
> *Ya no puede caminar,*
> *Porque no tiene, porque le falta*
> *Marihuana que fumar.*

Guitar-playing boys on Mexican mountains do not offhand seem to have much affinity with jazz leaders in any big city. But all authorities agree that jam sessions and even more serious music are often spiked by marihuana. Nor are other forms of creative art free from this taint—even movie stars. One of the best "box-office" men in the business has served a jail term for the possession of marihuana—and he is still one of the highest paid actors!

According to Mr. Anslinger, we are thoroughly reprehensible for not shunning every movie in which he stars. In his *The Traffic in Narcotics,* the former U.S. Commissioner of Narcotics writes, "But, consider how the public reacts respecting glamorous entertainment characters who have been involved in the sordid details of a narcotic case. Is there a spontaneous reaction which drives them out of the show business as might have been done a generation ago? Not at all. There seems to be some sort of public approval of these degenerate practices. The character is not ostracized. Instead he or she immediately becomes a box-office headliner."

This was written long after the Federal Bureau of Narcotics boasted that, cooperating with state and city authorities, there had been destroyed sixty thousand tons of marihuana. But the plant is still with us, for such zealous and continuing destruction of hemp has not stopped marihuana smoking. In fact, the attempt at eradication has provoked the derisive comments of those who think the British plan in India and the report of the New York Academy of Medicine make more sense than pulling up weeds.

One of the most percipient of these skeptics is Dr. Robert S. deRopp, who, in his *Drugs and the Mind,* quotes the opinion of many "that marihuana never hurt anybody and that the Narcotics Bureau would do better to devote its time and energies to the control of the really dangerous drugs, morphine, heroin and cocaine, instead of chasing after a relatively innocuous weed."

While the United Nations *Single Convention on Narcotic*

Drugs, 1961, does not, of course condone the use of marihuana, it appears to realize that its worldwide popularity will
not make its eradication either easy or speedy. On page 31 it
says that "The use of Cannabis (hemp) for other than medical
and scientific purposes must be discontinued as soon as possible, but in any case within twenty-five years." That is a rather
optimistic timetable, matched against three thousand years of
use by untold millions.

CHAPTER TWO

THE MARIHUANA PROBLEM:
Myth or Reality?

Dr. Alfred R. Lindesmith

Dr. Alfred R. Lindesmith has long been considered one of America's most perceptive and enlightened experts on the sociology of illegal drugs. He has published dozens of articles on the subject in many general and learned journals, and has edited and written several books on the subject. The following essay has been selected from The Addict and the Law.
Dr. Lindesmith's scholarly, persistent, and courageous role as critic extraordinaire *of the myth- and panic-oriented Federal Bureau of Narcotics has won him the admiration and respect of America's intellectual community, a respect that has never been accorded the uninformed inquisitional bureaucrats who have directed that outmoded federal organization. A professor of Sociology at Indiana University, Dr. Lindesmith is a proponent of the medical rather than the punitive approach to such drug problems as opiate and barbiturate addiction. Since it cannot be demonstrated that marihuana is addicting or physically harmful, he argues that it should be completely separated—in both the popular and the official mind—from such acutely toxic substances as heroin, barbiturates, and amphetamines.*

The primary fact about marihuana, which ought to be taken into account by legislators but is not, is that it is not a habit forming drug. By this is meant that the regular use of marihuana does not produce tolerance, and its abrupt cessation does not lead to withdrawal distress. As a consequence the problem of controlling or regulating its use is sharply different from that presented by the genuine drugs of addiction, i.e., the opiates such as heroin and morphine and their synthetic equivalents. Nevertheless, by federal legislation in 1951 and 1956, the increased penalties imposed on opiate users and peddlers were also applied to the users and distributors of marihuana. This extension was made casually with little discussion or investigation and with no apparent appreciation that the use of marihuana is something almost totally different from the use of heroin.

Effects of Smoking Marihuana

Marihuana is ordinarily used in this country by smoking. The effects it produces are experienced as exhilaration, loss of inhibitions, a changed sense of time, and other psychological effects which have sometimes been described and extravagantly praised by those who have experienced them. These effects are in a general way comparable to the stimulating effects produced by alcohol in the sense that they are intoxicating, although they differ qualitatively from those of alcohol.

Intrinsically, however, marihuana is less dangerous and less harmful to the human body than is alcohol. It is, for example, not habit-forming, whereas alcohol is. While the alcoholic commonly substitutes alcohol for food, marihuana sharply stimulates the appetite. Chronic alcoholism is associated with various psychotic conditions and diseases such as Korsakoff's psychosis and cirrhosis of the liver. In comparison, the smoking of marihuana produces relatively trivial physical effects, although it does appear that immoderate use of the more concentrated products of the hemp plant may also produce deleterious bodily effects. Such effects, however, are not conspicuous among American reefer smokers, probably because of the relatively small quantities of the essential drug that are ingested from the poor-quality marihuana ordinarily consumed in this country. The American marihuana smoker who inadvertently uses too much when he switches, let us say, to the more potent ganja plant raised in Mexico and the West Indies is likely to experience nothing more alarming than going to sleep and waking up hungry.

Use of Marihuana in Other Countries

Marihuana consists of the dried and crumbled stems, leaves, and seed pods of a plant known as Indian hemp or *Cannabis sativa*. These materials are often mixed with tobacco and in the United States are ordinarily smoked. In many other parts of the world a special type of hemp plant of unusual potency, known commonly as *ganja,* is used in a similar manner or it may be brewed and drunk as ganja tea—a common practice in the West Indies, where this drink is prized for its alleged therapeutic efficacy. In India the uncultivated hemp plant is smoked as marihuana is here and is also drunk. It is known there as *bhang.* The essential drug of the hemp plant is *Cannabis indica* or *cannabinol* and it, of course, can be taken in this form. This essential drug is derived primarily from the resin of the female hemp plant. This concentrated hemp resin is commonly known as *hashish* and is immensely more powerful than either ganja or marihuana. The comparison of hashish and marihuana is like that between pure alcohol and beer. Lurid accounts of the psychological effects and dangers of hemp are often based upon observations made by and upon hashish users. The mixture smoked as marihuana ordinarily contains very small quantities of the drug and its effects are correspondingly less spectacular, less dangerous, and less harmful than those of hashish.

The medical use of *Cannabis indica* has declined in Western medicine, but it is still extensively used in the Ayurvedic and Unani systems of indigenous medicine in India. In various parts of the world folk beliefs attribute great therapeutic and even divine virtues to the drug. In Jamaica it is known to many persons of the lower classes as "the wisdom weed" and it is alleged that it stimulates good qualities in the person who uses it and brings him closer to God. The use of ganja there is supported by references to various Biblical passages which recommend the "herbs of the field." The same passages, incidentally, are taken by the devotees of peyote (a cactus containing mescaline) to refer to that plant. A back-to-Africa protest cult in Jamaica, known as the Ras Tafari, has adopted ganja as a symbol of the movement and its members sometimes refer to themselves as the "herb men." In defiance of the Government, members of this cult, and others who are simply impressed by the fact that ganja is a more profitable crop than any other, grow and harvest the plant and use some of it themselves. Ganja tea is regarded as a prime ameliorative agent in the folk treatment of many diseases, including asthma, tuberculosis, venereal disease, and many others, especially all types of respiratory ailments. Ganja cigarettes are extensively used by the workers in the sugarcane fields and some foremen of the sugar-producing companies state that, were it not for ganja, they would have difficulty finding workingmen to harvest their crops.

On the book jacket of Professor Robert P. Walton's 1938 book, entitled *Marihuana: America's New Drug Problem*, Frederick T. Merrill and Mr. Anslinger are quoted. The latter observed: "It is a new peril—in some ways the worst we have met, and it concerns us all." Merrill was even more emphatic and alarmed: "If the abuse of this narcotic drug is not stamped out at once, the cost in crime waves, wasted human lives, and insanity will be enormous." Quoting Walton, Merrill notes that marihuana often produces "uncontrollable irritability and violent rages, which in most advanced forms cause assault and murder." He continues: "Amnesia often occurs, and the mania is frequently so acute that the heavy smoker becomes temporarily insane. Most authorities agree that permanent insanity can result from continual over-indulgence." Marihuana has had no noticeable effect in increasing the population of our mental institutions, and whatever crimes of violence it may instigate are as nothing when compared with those that are linked with the use of alcohol.

Norman Taylor notes that the hemp plant, called *Cannabis sativa* by Linnaeus in the eighteenth century, probably originated in Central Asia or in China, where it was described in a book on pharmacy written by one Shen Nung nearly three thousand years before the birth of Christ. The euphoric potential of the resinous female plant was known then and troubled Chinese moralists, who called it the "Liberator of Sin." Nung, however, recommended the medicine from this plant for "female weakness, gout, rheumatism, malaria, beri-beri, constipation, and absent-mindedness." From China the use of hemp spread westward to India, to the Middle East, and along both sides of the Mediterranean, and ultimately reached Europe and the Western hemisphere. Nowhere has its use been eradicated, even after thousands of years of effort in some instances. Recent publications of the United Nations comment on the apparent continued spread of the practice.

The evil reputation of hemp was enhanced when, during the eleventh century, it became linked with a cult headed by one Hasan which initiated a new political tactic of secret assassination to cleanse the Moslem world of false prophets. Hasan's full name was Hashishin and he was called the Old Man of the Mountain. The terms *hashish* and *assassin* are linked with the name of *Hasan* and his cult.

Use by Lower Classes

It is possible that the bad reputation of marihuana and other forms of this drug reflects in part the bias of upper classes against an indulgence of the lower strata. Since hemp grows luxuriantly without cultivation in many parts of the world, it is available to many of its devotees at extremely low cost— in India, for example, at about one-twentieth the price of good-quality whiskey in 1894, when the English carried out an extensive inquiry into the subject. Denunciations of the weed come characteristically from persons of those classes which prefer whiskey, rum, gin, and other alcoholic beverages and who do not themselves use marihuana. Such persons, overlooking the well-known effects of alcohol, commonly deplore the effects of hemp upon the lower classes and often believe that it produces murder, rape, violence, and insanity.

Despite the prevalence of these beliefs among the drinkers of rum and whiskey and the upper classes generally, impartial investigations invariably have shown no such results. The moderate use of hemp, according to the Indian Hemp Drug Commission in 1894, does not produce significant mental or moral injuries, does not lead to disease, nor does it necessarily or even usually lead to excess any more than alcohol does. Excess, the Commission said, is confined to the idle and dissipated. Many years later in New York City similar conclusions were stated on the basis of experimental study and from an examination of violent crimes committed in that city over a period of years.

In Jamaica, where the lower classes regard the drug with favor, persons of high social status commonly assert that ganja is a potent cause of much of the personal violence which is relatively frequent there among the working classes. This is staunchly denied by the ganja users, who contend that the effects are usually in the opposite direction but admit that ganja may bring out the evil in some persons who are already evil. Police examination of violent crimes in Jamaica suggests that ganja has little connection with them and that they arise rather from sexual jealousy and the highly informal manner in which sexual matters are arranged on that island among the simpler people of the lower classes.

Marihuana and Alcohol

In general, virtually all of the charges that are made against marihuana tend to shrink or dissolve entirely when they are closely examined by impartial investigators. The present tendency of the rank-and-file policeman, despite the enormous penalties attached to handling marihuana, is to regard it as a minor problem hardly deserving serious attention except for those who handle the weed in large amounts for mercenary purposes or who promote its use among the uninitiated.

Ironically, the accusations that are leveled at marihuana are all applicable to alcohol, as has been demonstrated by innumerable investigations. These studies indicate that much murder, rape, and homicide is committed by persons under the influence. The special psychoses and ailments of alcoholics are numerous and well delineated in countless scientific and literary productions. The menace of the drinking driver of automobiles is well understood by all and is more or less accepted as one of the inevitable hazards of life in the modern world. It is well known, too, that the manufacturers of alcoholic beverages advertise their products and seek to enlarge their markets, and that the use of alcohol spreads from those who already have the practice to those who do not. Why, then, so much excitement about marihuana? It is said that marihuana sometimes causes girls and women to lose their virtue and innocence, but the role of alcohol in this respect is infinitely more important. It seems inconsistent, therefore, that while the decision to drink or not to drink is viewed as a personal moral decision, the use of marihuana should be viewed as a heinous crime subject to long prison sentences.

Among those who have never used hemp or seen it used by others the belief is often found that marihuana acts as a sexual stimulant or aphrodisiac. Actually its effects, like those of opiates, are in exactly the opposite direction, tending to cause the user to lose interest in the opposite sex. Users more frequently than not report the absence of ideas of sex or say that Venus herself could not tempt them when they are under the influence of this drug.

The Effects of Antimarihuana Legislation

In 1937 the Congress passed a Marihuana Tax Act, modeled after the Harrison Act. It was designed to curb the use of marihuana by the use of the federal police power, and like the Harrison Act imposed penalties upon both buyers and sellers. This Act was the result of a publicity campaign staged by the Federal Bureau of Narcotics under Mr. Anslinger's direction and leadership. The bill was passed with little discussion after brief hearings on the ground that marihuana was a highly dangerous drug inciting its users to commit crimes of violence and often leading to insanity.

The beliefs concerning marihuana which led to this legislation may be represented in a pure and extreme form by turning to the writing of a hyperactive reformer and alarmist of the period, Earle Albert Rowell. He claimed in 1939 that he had spent fourteen years campaigning against this weed, delivering more than four thousand lectures in forty states and personally pulling up and destroying many flourishing hemp fields. Mr. Rowell's zealous opposition to marihuana was only slightly less intense than his disapproval of alcohol and tobacco. The use of tobacco, he correctly observed, invariably precedes the smoking of the deadly reefer. Mr. Rowell came into disfavor with the Bureau of Narcotics around 1938 and this agency spent considerable energy and manpower in an attempt to silence and discredit him. This may have been because of Mr. Rowell's view that opiate addiction is a disease, or perhaps because of his repeated allegations that the police were not sufficiently diligent in destroying marihuana.

Mr. Rowell summarized the effects of marihuana as follows:

We know that marihuana—
1. Destroys will power, making a jellyfish of the user. He cannot say no.
2. Eliminates the line between right and wrong, and substitutes one's own warped desires or the base suggestions of others as the standard of right.
3. Above all, causes crime; fills the victim with an irrepressible urge to violence.
4. Incites to revolting immoralities, including rape and murder.
5. Causes many accidents both industrial and automobile.
6. Ruins careers forever.
7. Causes insanity as its specialty.
8. *Either in self-defense or as a means of revenue, users make smokers of others, thus perpetuating evil.* [Italics in original.]

In 1939 when Rowell published his book, marihuana was regarded as a relatively new drug menace in the United States. Mr. Rowell thought that he had already detected an increase of the population of mental hospitals because of it:

Asylums and mental hospitals in this country are beginning to see and feel the influence of marihuana, and are awakening to its deleterious effects on the brain. As we traveled through the various states, superintendents of these institutions told us of cases of insanity resulting from marihuana.

"The baleful mental effects of marihuana," he said, "begin soon after the first reefer is smoked. . . ."

When Mr. Anslinger appeared before the Senate subcommittee which was investigating the illicit drug traffic in 1955 under the guidance of Senator Price Daniel, there were only a few offhand discussions of marihuana. Mr. Anslinger observed that the Bureau in its national survey was "trying to keep away from the marihuana addict, because he is not a true addict." The real problem, he said, was the heroin addict. Senator Daniel thereupon remarked:

> "Now, do I understand it from you that, while we are discussing marihuana, the real danger there is that the use of marihuana leads many people eventually to the use of heroin, and the drugs that do cause complete addiction; is that true?"

Mr. Anslinger agreed:

> "That is the great problem and our great concern about the use of marihuana, that eventually, if used over a long period, it does lead to heroin addiction."

Senators Welker and Daniel pursued the subject, and Mr. Anslinger, when prompted, agreed that marihuana was dangerous. Senator Welker finally asked this question:

> "Is it or is it not a fact that the marihuana user has been responsible for many of our most sadistic, terrible crimes in this nation, such as sex slayings, and matters of that kind?"

Mr. Anslinger hedged:

> "There have been instances of that, Senator. We have had some rather tragic occurrences by users of marihuana. It does not follow that all crime can be traced to marihuana. There have been many brutal crimes traced to marihuana, but I would not say that it is a controlling factor in the commission of crimes."

Eighteen years earlier, in 1937, the year in which the federal antimarihuana law was passed, Mr. Anslinger had presented a very different picture of marihuana. Prior to 1937 Mr. Anslinger and the Bureau of Narcotics had spearheaded a propaganda campaign against marihuana on the ground that it produced an immense amount of violent crime, such as rape, mayhem, and murder, and that many traffic accidents could be attributed to it. During the 1937 hearings before a House subcommittee, Representative John Dingell of Michigan asked Mr. Anslinger: "I am just wondering whether the marihuana addict graduates into a heroin, an opium, or a cocaine user."

Mr. Anslinger replied: "No, sir; I have not heard of a case

of that kind. I think it is an entirely different class. The marihuana addict does not go in that direction."

A few months later in the same year, before a Senate subcommittee that was considering the antimarihuana law, which
the Bureau of Narcotics had asked for, Mr. Anslinger commented: "There is an entirely new class of people using marihuana. The opium user is around 35 to 40 years old. These
users are 20 years old and know nothing of heroin or morphine."

The theme stated by the Commissioner of Narcotics in
1955, that the main threat in marihuana is that it leads to
the use of heroin, is now ordinarily cited as the principal
justification for applying to it the same severe penalties that
are applied in the case of heroin. Reformer Rowell in 1939
was more logical and consistent than either the Senators or
the Commissioner when he emphasized that cigarette smoking
invariably preceded reefer smoking. Mr. Rowell told of a
shrewd gangster whom he engaged in what now appears as a
prophetic discussion of the prospects of the dope industry.

> The gangster remarked: "Marihuana is the coming thing."
> "But," I protested in surprise, "marihuana is not a habit-
> forming drug like morphine or heroin; and, besides, it's too
> cheap to bother with."
> He laughed. "You don't understand. Laws are being passed
> now by various states against it, and soon Uncle Sam will put
> a ban on it. The price will then go up, and that will make it
> profitable for us to handle."

The gangster, according to Mr. Rowell, then commented
on the shrewd manner in which the tobacco companies had
popularized cigarettes among the soldiers of the First World
War and on the enormous increase in cigarette consumption
by young persons. He grew eloquent: "Every cigarette smoker
is a prospect for the dope ring via the marihuana road. Millions of boys and girls now smoke. Think of the unlimited
new market!"

Mr. Rowell got the idea and commented as follows to his
readers:

> Slowly, insidiously, for over three hundred years, Lady Nico-
> tine was setting the stage for a grand climax. The long years
> of tobacco using were but an introduction and training for
> marihuana use. Tobacco, which was first smoked in a pipe,
> then as a cigar, and at last as a cigarette, demanded more and
> more of itself until its supposed pleasures palled, and some

of the tobacco victims looked about for something stronger. Tobacco was no longer potent enough.

Mr. Rowell was not optimistic about the future:

Marihuana will continue to be a problem for both police and educators, because it is so easy to grow, to manufacture, and to peddle, and is such a quick source of easy money. The plant can be grown anywhere; it can be harvested secretly, prepared in twenty-four hours without a penny of investment for equipment; and every cigarette user is a prospect. As our laws are enforced and the weed becomes scarcer, the price will rise, and greater profit accrue to venturesome and successful peddlers. Whereas now it is usually peddled by lone wolves, as soon as the weed becomes scarcer and the price rises, organized crime will step in and establish a monopoly.

While Mr. Rowell, in the manner of reforming alarmists, exaggerated the evil with which he was preoccupied, the above appraisal of the effects of the Marihuana Tax Act has been reasonably well borne out by subsequent events. Certainly it was a more realistic assessment of the law's effects than any that were made by the legislators who passed the bill or by the officials who promoted it. Mr. Rowell was also completely right in pointing out that virtually every marihuana smoker graduated to this practice from cigarette smoking. His gangster informant was correct in his calculation that state and federal laws prohibiting marihuana would make the weed more expensive and more profitable for peddlers to handle, and also correctly foresaw that with the same merchants handling both marihuana and heroin it would become a simpler matter for marihuana users to switch from the less to the more dangerous drug, as they have done.

In the United States during the nineteenth century, and the early decades of the twentieth, addiction to opiates frequently developed from the abuse of alcohol. This still occurs to some extent and is frequently reported from other parts of the world, for morphine provides a potent means of relieving the alcoholic hangover. An American doctor once advocated as a cure of alcoholism that alcohol addicts be deliberately addicted to morphine, arguing with considerable plausibility that of the two habits the latter was obviously the lesser evil. Moreover, he practiced what he preached and recommended his technique with considerable enthusiasm for use by others.

The truth of the matter, of course, is that very few cigarette smokers go on to marihuana, very few marihuana users go on to heroin, and very few alcohol users graduate to the use of heroin. Since some barbiturate and amphetamine users progress to heroin it should be added that it is also only a very small proportion who do. If all of these substances were to be prohibited because they are sometimes involved in the progression toward heroin addiction, there is little doubt that the illicit traffic in marihuana and heroin would be expanded to include the other offending substances and that the movement from less to more serious habits would be greatly facilitated.

No one, of course, recommends the use of marihuana nor does anyone deny that there are evil effects and consequences associated with using it. The fact that the use of marihuana is outlawed, for example, means that it is often obtained through association with unsavory types, often in an underworld environment, and the user takes the risk of criminal prosecution. It is also undeniable that marihuana intoxication may sometimes lead to automobile accidents and to irresponsible or criminal acts. The controversy with respect to marihuana is solely concerning the relative prevalence or frequency of such results in comparison to similar consequences following the use of alcoholic beverages. All empirical investigations indicate that alcohol constitutes a far greater social danger than does marihuana.

Mayor LaGuardia's Committee on Marihuana

Mayor LaGuardia's Committee on Marihuana, on the basis of a close examination of the matter in New York City, stressed the relative triviality of the effects of marihuana use in a report published in 1944. In the July 1943 issue of the *Military Surgeon,* the editor, Colonel J. M. Phalen, commented as follows in an editorial on "The Marihuana Bugaboo":

> The smoking of the leaves, flowers and seeds of *Cannabis sativa* is no more harmful than the smoking of tobacco or mullein or sumac leaves. . . . The legislation in relation to marihuana was ill-advised . . . it branded as a menace and a crime a matter of trivial importance . . . It is hoped that no witch hunt will be instituted in the military service over a problem that does not exist.

Similar statements have been made by many other competent investigators and observers.

On the other hand, as has been pointed out, a sharply divergent view has been presented by law enforcement officials, particularly by the Federal Bureau of Narcotics, and also by many individual writers. The sharp divergence of views among the scientifically oriented evidently depends upon the manner in which the research is done. Investigators who rely on the opinions of high-echelon officials, who have no direct acquaintance with the use of marihuana and who base their opinions on ancedotes rather than on actual statistical data, usually reach the conclusion that marihuana is a highly dangerous drug which produces much violent crime and insanity. These conclusions, as we have suggested, may be a reflection of upper-class hostility toward an unfamiliar lower-class indulgence. More critical and skeptical investigators, who look for basic statistical evidence, invariably fail to find it and end up writing debunking articles for which they are roundly abused by the moralists.

It is often felt that, even if the dangers of marihuana are exaggerated, these exaggerations and misstatements should be allowed to stand so that they may frighten adolescents away from the drug. The implication that adolescents are influenced to any appreciable degree by articles appearing in scientific journals is probably absurd. Those who use marihuana probably come to do so on the basis of personal associations and direct observations of their own.

The deliberate circulation of false information is self-defeating in that the adventurous, experimentally inclined youth can quickly discover for himself, by trying the weed or talking to those who have smoked it, that much of the officially circulated view is false. He is then prepared to believe that everything he has been told about narcotics is equally wrong.

When Mayor LaGuardia's Committee on Marihuana made its report, it was strongly attacked by those committed to a belief in the marihuana menace. The *Journal of the American Medical Association* in 1943 published a letter from Mr. Anslinger in which he criticized an article by Drs. Allentuck and Bowman on findings derived from the New York study in which they had participated. There were rumors that the New York marihuana study was to be suppressed, but after considerable delay, it was ultimately released in 1944. On April 28, 1945, the *Journal of the American Medical Association* editorially assailed the report, using language and arguments of a type not ordinarily found in learned journals:

> For many years medical scientists have considered cannabis a dangerous drug. Nevertheless, a book called *Marihuana Problems* by the New York City Mayor's Committee on Marihuana submits an analysis by seventeen doctors of tests on 77 prisoners and, on this narrow and thoroughly unscientific foundation, draws sweeping and inadequate conclusions which minimize the harmfulness of marihuana. Already the book has done harm. One investigator has described some tearful

parents who brought their 16-year-old son to a physician after he had been detected in the act of smoking marihuana. A noticeable mental deterioration had been evident for some time even to their lay minds. The boy said he had read an account of the LaGuardia Committee report and that this was his justification for using marihuana. He read in *Down Beat*, a musical journal, an analysis of this report under the caption "Light Up, Gates, Report Finds 'Tea' a Good Kick."

A criminal lawyer for marihuana drug peddlers has already used the LaGuardia report as a basis to have defendants set free by the court. . . .

The book states unqualifiedly to the public that the use of this narcotic does not lead to physical, mental, or moral degeneration and that permanent deleterious effects from its continued use were not observed on 77 prisoners. This statement has already done great damage to the cause of law enforcement. Public officials will do well to disregard this unscientific, uncritical study, and continue to regard marihuana as a menace wherever it is purveyed.

Despite the fact that this editorial continues to be cited and reproduced to discredit the New York study, the conclusions of the report enjoy considerable status and are undoubtedly far closer to the realities of the situation than is the view represented by the A.M.A. editorial. Indeed, if one judges the law-enforcement agencies by their actions rather than by their words, it appears that even the police, to a considerable extent, have swung over to the viewpoint of the Mayor's Committee.

Marihuana Arrests

After 1951 the budget and field forces of the Federal Bureau of Narcotics were substantially enlarged. Nevertheless, the number of marihuana arrests has steadily declined and by 1960 it was close to the vanishing point, with only 169 such cases. In previous years the numbers of federal marihuana violations were reported as follows:

1952	1,288
1954	508
1956	403
1958	179

Of the 169 federal marihuana violations reported in 1960, 88 occurred in California, 16 in Maryland, and 13 in Kentucky. No other state had as many as ten, and no violations were reported from 28 states. We have already noted that the

Bureau does not bother to count marihuana users in its national survey of addiction and does not regard marihuana as an addicting drug. The above figures on enforcement suggest that, at the federal level at least, the marihuana laws are being largely ignored since it is not claimed that the use of marihuana is diminishing.

Statistics on marihuana prosecutions as such are extremely difficult to obtain and data that are available are very unreliable and incomplete. The Federal Narcotics Bureau presented to the Daniel Subcommittee a summary of marihuana prosecutions for the year 1954, giving both federal and non-federal cases. It is not claimed that the latter are complete; they are merely figures from some of the main cities in the indicated states.

TABLE 5

Marihuana Arrests—Federal and Local by States—1954

State	ARRESTS Federal	Local	State	ARRESTS Federal	Local
Alabama	2	6	New Hampshire	0	0
Arizona	25	4	New Jersey	5	26
Arkansas	2	0	New Mexico	23	10
California	51	1,101	New York	5	407
Colorado	28	1	North Carolina	0	0
Connecticut	2	6	North Dakota	0	0
Delaware	0	1	Ohio	25	23
District of			Oklahoma	2	13
Columbia	3	17	Oregon	1	8
Florida	4	30	Pennsylvania	3	50
Georgia	4	1	Rhode Island	0	0
Idaho	0	2	South Carolina	4	0
Illinois	13	327	South Dakota	0	0
Indiana	0	14	Tennessee	11	1
Iowa	0	8	Texas	325	612
Kansas	2	0	Utah	4	0
Kentucky	39	8	Vermont	0	0
Louisiana	17	105	Virginia	0	1
Maine	0	0	Washington	22	10
Maryland	2	30	West Virginia	0	0
Massachusetts	5	1	Wisconsin	0	47
Michigan	30	270	Wyoming	4	0
Minnesota	0	5	Alaska	5	0
Mississippi	0	1	Hawaii	14	23
Missouri	9	15		—	
Montana	0	6	Totals	708	3,205
Nebraska	1	13		—	—
Nevada	16	2	Grand Total		3,913

From this table it will be seen that 3,263 of the total of 3,913 arrests were made in the six states of California, Texas, Illinois, Michigan, New York, and Louisiana. These states are, in one way or another, centers of the marihuana traffic. High arrest rates in California, Texas, and Louisiana no doubt arise from the fact that considerable quantities of marihuana are smuggled into the country there from Mexico and the Caribbean area. The rates in Illinois, Michigan, and New York reflect mainly police activity in the three large cities of Detroit, Chicago, and New York, all of them narcotics distribution centers. Heroin arrests are also highest in the states of California, New York, Illinois, and Michigan, while Texas and Louisiana are farther down on the list.

The penalty provisions applicable to marihuana users under state and federal laws are about the same as those applied to heroin users. These penalties are entirely disproportionate to the seriousness of the offending behavior and lead to gross injustice and undesirable social consequences. For example, it is well known that many jazz musicians and other generally inoffensive persons use or have used marihuana. To send these persons to jail is absurd and harmful and serves no conceivable useful purpose. The moderate or occasional marihuana user is not a significant social menace. Jails and prisons, chronically overcrowded, should be used for those who present a genuine threat to life and property. The absurdity is compounded when an occasional judge, ignorant of the nature of marihuana, sends a marihuana user to prison to cure him of his nonexistent addiction. The writer was once in court when a middle-aged Negro defendant appeared before the judge charged with having used and had in his possession one marihuana cigarette during the noon hour at the place where he had worked for a number of years. This man had no previous criminal record and this fact was stated before the court. Nevertheless, a two-year sentence was imposed to "dry up his habit."

The President's Advisory Commission, which reported on narcotic and drug abuse in 1963, took cognizance of the relatively trivial nature of the marihuana evil by suggesting that all mandatory sentences be eliminated for crimes involving it and that judges be granted full discretionary power in dealing with offenders. These suggestions are excessively timid and not entirely logical, for there is no good reason why a mere user of marihuana should be subjected to a jail sentence at all. The marihuana user probably ought to be dealt with by the law along the same lines that are used with persons who drink alcohol.

If it is deemed in the public interest to punish smokers of

marihuana, such punishments should ordinarily consist of fines only, up to some maximum of perhaps $500, depending upon the offense and the defendant's ability to pay. These fines might be scaled down or eliminated entirely for persons who provided information concerning their source of supply. Police efforts should be focused primarily on the traffic rather than on the user. Persons driving automobiles under the influence of the drug might be fined and deprived of their driving licenses for a period of time. Crimes which could be shown to the satisfaction of a court of law to be linked with the use of marihuana ought to be dealt with about the way that crimes arising from the use of alcohol are handled.

Laws such as this, with penalties of a reasonable nature, would probably be more effective than those now in effect because they would be more enforceable and more in accord with the nature of the problem being dealt with. They would have the effect of reducing the discrepancy that now exists between the laws as written and the laws as they are actually enforced. A more matter-of-fact and realistic handling of the marihuana problem would also probably reduce the aura of sensationalism which now surrounds the subject and diminish the illicit glamour which is now attached to the hemp plant.

It is argued by some that the marihuana industry should be brought under control by legalization, taxation, licensing, and other devices like those to control alcohol—and to exploit it as a source of revenue. Advocates of this view might well argue that there should be no unfair discrimination among vices; that if the greater evil of alcohol use is legal, the lesser one of marihuana smoking should be so as well. Since the smoking of marihuana will undoubtedly continue regardless of legislation against it, it can also be argued that it would be better to accept the inevitable than to wage war for a lost cause.

In opposition to this extremely permissive position, the more conservative reformer can call attention to the fact that, outside of a few Asian and African countries, the use of this substance is everywhere disapproved of and subject to legal restrictions. It is possible that legal sanctions exercise some deterrent effect and that without them the use of this drug might spread even more rapidly and assume more virulent forms. Should the use of marihuana become anywhere nearly as widespread as that of alcohol, it might be too late to talk of effective restrictions since the users would command too many votes. A legal marihuana or ganja industry which advertised its product and sought to improve it through research and experimentation would be a distinct embarrassment to the nation as a whole, as well as being a direct economic threat to the alcoholic beverage industries and possibly to the tobacco industry. A final and decisive argument seems to be that public opinion is not likely in the foreseeable future to accept indulgence in marihuana as an equivalent of, or substitute for, indulgence in alcohol.

The long history of the use of marihuana, the spread of the practice throughout the world in the face of determined and sometimes fanatical opposition, and the persistence of the practice once it is established—all suggest that the smoking of marihuana will continue in the United States for some time to come. The practical question seems to be one of minimizing and controlling the practice while avoiding the extreme tactics of prohibitionists. A comprehensive, impartial public inquiry into the matter, based on the assumption that marihuana is *not* the same as heroin, might help to bring about a more sober and rational approach to an indulgence which merits some concern but which is far less serious than is presently suggested by the harsh inflexibility of current laws.

CHAPTER THREE

MARIHUANA:

A Sociological Overview

Dr. Howard S. Becker

Dr. Howard S. Becker, who has taught sociology at Stanford and is now a professor at Northwestern University, is the first American sociologist to explain accurately how and why people learn to use marihuana. His essays Becoming a Marihuana User, Marihuana Use and Social Control, *and* The Marihuana Tax Act *are especially pertinent to this anthology because they contain sound evidence that refutes certain cherished myths about marihuana use and the origins of the laws that have made the use illegal.*

Dr. Becker based his studies on carefully conducted interviews with fifty regular users of marihuana. His own experience as a professional musician—he has performed as a jazz pianist in Chicago and Kansas City—enabled him to gather material that would be denied to most sociologists. Half of the group were musicians; the remainder came from broader social areas and included laborers, machinists, and people in the professions. He concluded that the use of marihuana, by and large, does not *occur because the user wishes to escape from the psychological problems he cannot face. It was mostly used, he found, as a casual and pleasure-giving recreational device.*

. . . marihuana use . . . illustrates the way deviant motives actually develop in the course of experience with the deviant activity. To put a complex argument in a few words: instead of the deviant motives leading to the deviant behavior, it is the other way around; the deviant behavior in time produces the deviant motivation. Vague impulses and desires—in this case, probably most frequently a curiosity about the kind of experience the drug will produce—are transformed into definite patterns of action . . .

. . . What we are trying to understand here is the sequence of changes in attitude and experience which lead to *the use of marihuana for pleasure*. . . . Marihuana does not produce addiction, at least in the sense that alcohol and the opiate drugs do. The user experiences no withdrawal sickness and exhibits no ineradicable craving for the drug. The most frequent pattern of use might be termed "recreational." The drug is occasionally used for the pleasure the user finds in it, a relatively casual kind of behavior in comparison with that connected with the use of addicting drugs. The report of the New York City Mayor's Committee on Marihuana emphasizes this point. . . . In using the phrase "use for pleasure," I mean to emphasize the non-compulsive and casual character of the behavior. (I also mean to eliminate from consideration here those few cases in which marihuana is used for its prestige value only, as a symbol that one is a certain kind of person, with no pleasure at all being derived from its use.)

In discussing the moral entrepreneurs who create and enforce society's rules, Dr. Becker (who is the editor of the journal Social Problems) *has pointed out elsewhere that such rules are established as consequences of moral crusades initiated by reformers for their own ends. The more cynical rule enforcers, he maintains, are frequently motivated by an interest in preserving their jobs and winning the respect of the public and of the superiors for whom they work.*

BECOMING A MARIHUANA USER

An unknown, but probably quite large, number of people in the United States use marihuana. They do this in spite of the fact that it is both illegal and disapproved.

The phenomenon of marihuana use has received much attention, particularly from psychiatrists and law-enforcement officials. The research that has been done, as is often the case with research on behavior that is viewed as deviant, is mainly concerned with the question: why do they do it? Attempts to account for the use of marihuana lean heavily on the premise that the presence of any particular kind of behavior in an individual can best be explained as the result of some trait which predisposes or motivates him to engage in that behavior.

In the case of marihuana use, this trait is usually identified as psychological, as a need for fantasy and escape from psychological problems the individual cannot face.[1]

I do not think such theories can adequately account for marihuana use. In fact, marihuana use is an interesting case for theories of deviance, because it illustrates the way deviant motives actually develop in the course of experience with the deviant activity. To put a complex argument in a few words: instead of the deviant motives leading to the deviant behavior, it is the other way around; the deviant behavior in time produces the deviant motivation. Vague impulses and desires—in this case, probably most frequently a curiosity about the kind of experience the drug will produce—are transformed into definite patterns of action through the social interpretation of a physical experience which is in itself ambiguous. Marihuana use is a function of the individual's conception of marihuana and of the uses to which it can be put, and this conception develops as the individual's experience with the drug increases.[2]

The research reported in this and the next section deals with the career of the marihuana user. In this section, we look at the development of the individual's immediate physical experience with marihuana. In the next, we consider the way he reacts to the various social controls that have grown up around use of the drug. What we are trying to understand here is the sequence of changes in attitude and experience which lead to *the use of marihuana for pleasure*. This way of phrasing the problem requires a little explanation. Marihuana does not produce addiction, at least in the sense that alcohol and the opiate drugs do. The user experiences no withdrawal sickness and exhibits no ineradicable craving for the drug.[3] The most frequent pattern of use might be termed "recreational." The drug is used occasionally for the pleasure the user finds in it, a relatively casual kind of behavior in comparison with that connected with the use of addicting

1 See, as examples of this approach, the following: Eli Marcovitz and Henry J. Myers, "The Marihuana Addict in the Army," *War Medicine*, VI (December, 1944), 382-391; Herbert S. Gaskill, "Marihuana, an Intoxicant," *American Journal of Psychiatry*, CII (September, 1945), 202-204; Sol Charen and Luis Perelman, "Personality Studies of Marihuana Addicts," *American Journal of Psychiatry*, CII (March, 1946), 674-682.

2 This theoretical point of view stems from George Herbert Mead's discussion of objects in *Mind, Self, and Society* (Chicago: University of Chicago Press, 1934), pp. 277-280.

3 Cf. Rogers Adams, "Marihuana," *Bulletin of the New York Academy of Medicine*, XVIII (November, 1942), 705-730.

drugs. The report of the New York City Mayor's Committee on Marihuana emphasizes this point:

> A person may be a confirmed smoker for a prolonged period, and give up the drug voluntarily without experiencing any craving for it or exhibiting withdrawal symptoms. He may, at some time, later on, go back to its use. Others may remain infrequent users of the cigarette, taking one or two a week, or only when the "social setting" calls for participation. From time to time we had one of our investigators associate with a marihuana user. The investigator would bring up the subject of smoking. This would invariably lead to the suggestion that they obtain some marihuana cigarettes. They would seek a "tea-pad," and if it was closed the smoker and our investigator would calmly resume their previous activity, such as the discussion of life in general or the playing of pool. There were apparently no signs indicative of frustration in the smoker at not being able to gratify the desire for the drug. We consider this point highly significant since it is so contrary to the experience of users of other narcotics. A similar situation occurring in one addicted to the use of morphine, cocaine, or heroin would result in a comprehensive attitude on the part of the addict to obtain the drug. If unable to secure it, there would be obvious physical and mental manifestations of frustration. This may be considered presumptive evidence that there is no true addiction in the medical sense associated with the use of marihuana.[4]

In using the phrase "use for pleasure," I mean to emphasize the noncompulsive and casual character of the behavior. (I also mean to eliminate from consideration here those few cases in which marihuana is used for its prestige value only, as a symbol that one is a certain kind of person, with no pleasure at all being derived from its use.)

The research I am about to report was not so designed that it could constitute a crucial test of the theories that relate marihuana use to some psychological trait of the user. However, it does show that the psychological explanations are not in themselves sufficient to account for marihuana use and that they are, perhaps, not even necessary. Researchers attempting to prove such psychological theories have run into two great difficulties, never satisfactorily resolved, which the theory presented here avoids. In the first place, theories based on the existence of some predisposing psychological trait have difficulty in accounting for that group of users, who turn up in

4 The New York City Mayor's Committee on Marihuana, *The Marihuana Problem in the City of New York* (Lancaster, Pennsylvania: Jaques Cattel Press, 1944), pp. 12-13.

numbers in every study,[5] who do not exhibit the trait or traits which are considered to cause the behavior. Second, psychological theories have difficulty in accounting for the great variability over time of a given individual's behavior with reference to the drug. The same person will at one time be unable to use the drug for pleasure, at a later stage be able and willing to do so, and still later again be unable to use it in this way. These changes, difficult to explain from a theory based on the user's needs for "escape," are readily understandable as consequences of changes in his conception of the drug. Similarly, if we think of the marihuana user as someone who has learned to view marihuana as something that can give him pleasure, we have no difficulty in understanding the existence of psychologically "normal" users.

In doing the study, I used the method of analytic induction. I tried to arrive at a general statement of the sequence of changes in individual attitude and experience which always occurred when the individual became willing and able to use marihuana for pleasure, and never occurred or had not been permanently maintained when the person was unwilling to use marihuana for pleasure. The method requires that *every* case collected in the research substantiate the hypothesis. If one case is encountered which does not substantiate it, the researcher is required to change the hypothesis to fit the case which has proven his original idea wrong.[6]

To develop and test my hypothesis about the genesis of marihuana use for pleasure, I conducted fifty interviews with marihuana users. I had been a professional dance musician for some years when I conducted this study and my first interviews were with people I had met in the music business. I asked them to put me in contact with other users who would be willing to discuss their experiences with me. Colleagues working on a study of users of opiate drugs made available to me a few interviews which contained, in addition to material on opiate drugs, sufficient material on the use of marihuana to furnish a test of my hypothesis.[7] Although in the end half of

5 Cf. Lawrence Kolb, "Marihuana," *Federal Probation*, II (July, 1938), 22-25; and Walter Bromberg, "Marihuana: A Psychiatric Study," *Journal of the American Medical Association*, CXIII (July 1, 1939), 11.

6 The method is described in Alfred R. Lindesmith, *Opiate Addiction* (Bloomington, Indiana: Principia Press, 1947), chap. 1. There has been considerable discussion of this method in the literature. See, particularly, Ralph H. Turner, "The Quest for Universals in Sociological Research," *American Sociological Review*, 18 (December, 1953), 604-611, and the literature cited there.

7 I wish to thank Solomon Kobrin and Harold Finestone for making these interviews available to me.

the fifty interviews where conducted with musicians, the other half covered a wide range of people, including laborers, machinists, and people in the professions. The sample is, of course, in no sense "random"; it would not be possible to draw a random sample, since no one knows the nature of the universe from which it would have to be drawn.

In interviewing users, I focused on the history of the person's experience with marihuana, seeking major changes in his attitude toward it and in his actual use of it, and the reasons for these changes. Where it was possible and appropriate, I used the jargon of the user himself.

The theory starts with the person who has arrived at the point of willingness to try marihuana. (I discuss how he got there in the next section.) He knows others use marihuana to "get high," but he does not know what this means in any concrete way. He is curious about the experience, ignorant of what it may turn out to be, and afraid it may be more than he has bargained for. The steps outlined below, if he undergoes them all and maintains the attitudes developed in them, leave him willing and able to use the drug for pleasure when the opportunity presents itself.

Learning the Technique

The novice does not ordinarily get high the first time he smokes marihuana, and several attempts are usually necessary to induce this state. One explanation of this may be that the drug is not smoked "properly," that is, in a way that insures sufficient dosage to produce real symptoms of intoxication. Most users agree that it cannot be smoked like tobacco if one is to get high:

> Take in a lot of air, you know, and . . . I don't know how to describe it, you don't smoke it like a cigarette, you draw in a lot of air and get it deep down in your system and then keep it there. Keep it there as long as you can.

Without the use of some such technique[8] the drug will produce no effects, and the user will be unable to get high:

> The trouble with people like that [who are not able to get high] is that they're just not smoking it right, that's all there is to it.

8   A pharmacologist notes that this ritual is in fact an extremely efficient way of getting the drug into the blood stream. See R. P. Walton, *Marihuana: America's New Drug Problem* (Philadelphia: J. B. Lippincott, 1938), p. 48.

Either they're not holding it down long enough, or they're getting too much air and not enough smoke, or the other way around or something like that. A lot of people just don't smoke it right, so naturally nothing's gonna happen.

If nothing happens, it is manifestly impossible for the user to develop a conception of the drug as an object which can be used for pleasure, and use will therefore not continue. The first step in the sequence of events that must occur if the person is to become a user is that he must learn to use the proper smoking technique so that his use of the drug will produce effects in terms of which his conception of it can change.

Such a change is, as might be expected, a result of the individual's participation in groups in which marihuana is used. In them the individual learns the proper way to smoke the drug. This may occur through direct teaching:

I was smoking like I did an ordinary cigarette. He said, "No, don't do it like that." He said, "Suck it, you know, draw in and hold it in your lungs till you . . . for a period of time."

I said, "Is there any limit of time to hold it?"

He said, "No, just till you feel that you want to let it out, let it out."

So I did that three or four times.

Many new users are ashamed to admit ignorance and, pretending to know already, must learn through the more indirect means of observation and imitation:

I came on like I had turned on [smoked marihuana] many times before, you know. I didn't want to seem like a punk to this cat. See, like I didn't know the first thing about it—how to smoke it, or what was going to happen, or what. I just watched him like a hawk—I didn't take my eyes off him for a second, because I wanted to do everything just as he did it. I watched how he held it, how he smoked it, and everything. Then when he gave it to me I just came on cool, as though I knew exactly what the score was. I held it like he did and took a poke just the way he did.

No one I interviewed continued marihuana use for pleasure without learning a technique that supplied sufficient dosage for the effects of the drug to appear. Only when this was learned was it possible for a conception to emerge of the drug as an object which could be used for pleasure. Without such a conception marihuana use was considered meaningless and did not continue.

Learning to Perceive the Effects

Even after he learns the proper smoking technique, the new user may not get high and thus not form a conception of the drug as something which can be used for pleasure. A remark made by a user suggested the reason for this difficulty in getting high and pointed to the next necessary step on the road to being a user.

> As a matter of fact, I've seen a guy who was high out of his mind and didn't know it.
> [How can that be, man?]
> Well, it's pretty strange, I'll grant you that, but I've seen it. This guy got on me, claiming that he'd never got high, one of those guys, and he got completely stoned. And he kept insisting that he wasn't high. So I had to prove to him that he was.

What does this mean? It suggests that being high consists of two elements: the presence of symptoms caused by marihuana use and the recognition of these symptoms and their connection by the user with his use of the drug. It is not enough, that is, that the effects be present; alone, they do not automatically provide the experience of being high. The user must be able to point them out to himself and consciously connect them with having smoked marihuana before he can have this experience. Otherwise, no matter what actual effects are produced, he considers that the drug has had no effect on him: "I figured it either had no effect on me or other people were exaggerating its effect on them, you know. I thought it was probably psychological, see." Such persons believe the whole thing is an illusion and that the wish to be high leads the user to deceive himself into believing that something is happening when, in fact, nothing is. They do not continue marihuana use, feeling that "it does nothing" for them.

Typically, however, the novice has faith (developed from his observation of users who do get high) that the drug actually will produce some new experience and continues to experiment with it until it does. His failure to get high worries him, and he is likely to ask more experienced users or provoke comments from them about it. In such conversations he is made aware of specific details of his experience which he may not have noticed or may have noticed but failed to identify as symptoms of being high:

I didn't get high the first time. . . . I don't think I held it in long enough. I probably let it out, you know, you're a little afraid. The second time I wasn't sure, and he [smoking companion] told me, like I asked him for some of the symptoms or something, how would I know, you know. . . . So he told me to sit on a stool. I sat on—I think I sat on a bar stool— and he said, "Let your feet hang," and then when I got down my feet were real cold, you know.

And I started feeling it, you know. That was the first time. And then about a week after that, sometime pretty close to it, I really got on. That was the first time I got on a big laughing kick, you know. Then I really knew I was on.

One symptom of being high is an intense hunger. In the next case the novice becomes aware of this and gets high for the first time:

They were just laughing the hell out of me because like I was eating so much. I just scoffed [ate] so much food, and they were just laughing at me, you know. Sometimes I'd be looking at them, you know, wondering why they're laughing, you know, not knowing what I was doing. [Well, did they tell you why they were laughing eventually?] Yeah, yeah, I come back, "Hey, man, what's happening?" Like, you know, like I'd ask, "What's happening?" and all of a sudden I feel weird, you know. "Man, you're on, you know. You're on pot [high on marihuana]." I said, "No, am I?" Like I don't know what's happening.

The learning may occur in more indirect ways:

I heard little remarks that were made by other people. Somebody said, "My legs are rubbery," and I can't remember all the remarks that were made because I was very attentively listening for all these cues for what I was supposed to feel like.

The novice, then, eager to have this feeling, picks up from other users some concrete referents of the term "high" and applies these notions to his own experience. The new concepts make it possible for him to locate these symptoms among his own sensations and to point out to himself a "something different" in his experience that he connects with drug use. It is only when he can do this that he is high. In the next case, the contrast between two successive experiences of a user makes clear the crucial importance of the awareness of the symptoms in being high and re-emphasizes the important role of interaction with other users in acquiring the concepts that make this awareness possible.

[Did you get high the first time you turned on?] Yeah, sure. Although, come to think of it, I guess I really didn't. I mean, like that first time it was more or less of a mild drunk. I was happy, I guess, you know what I mean. But I didn't really know I was high, you know what I mean. It was only after the second time I got high that I realized I was high the first time. Then I knew that something different was happening.

[How did you know that?] How did I know? If what happened to me that night would of happened to you, you would've known, believe me. We played the first tune for almost two hours—one tune! Imagine, man! We got on the stand and played this one tune, we started at nine o'clock. When we got finished I looked at my watch, it's a quarter to eleven. Almost two hours on one tune. And it didn't seem like anything.

I mean, you know, it does that to you. It's like you have much more time or something. Anyway, when I saw that, man, it was too much. I knew I must really be high or something if anything like that could happen. See, and then they explained to me that that's what it did to you, you had a different sense of time and everything. So I realized that that's what it was. I knew then. Like the first time, I probably felt that way, you know, but I didn't know what's happening.

It is only when the novice becomes able to get high in this sense that he will continue to use marihuana for pleasure. In every case in which use continued, the user had acquired the necessary concepts with which to express to himself the fact that he was experiencing new sensations caused by the drug. That is, for use to continue, it is necessary not only to use the drug so as to produce effects but also to learn to perceive these effects when they occur. In this way marihuana acquires meaning for the user as an object which can be used for pleasure.

With increasing experience the user develops a greater appreciation of the drug's effects; he continues to learn to get high. He examines succeeding experiences closely, looking for new effects, making sure the old ones are still there. Out of this there grows a stable set of categories for experiencing the drug's effects whose presence enables the user to get high with ease.

Users, as they acquire this set of categories, become connoisseurs. Like experts in fine wines, they can specify where a particular plant was grown and what time of year it was harvested. Although it is usually not possible to know whether these attributions are correct, it is true that they distinguish between batches of marihuana, not only according to strength, but also with respect to the different kinds of symptoms produced.

The ability to perceive the drug's effects must be maintained if use is to continue; if it is lost, marihuana use ceases. Two kinds of evidence support this statement. First, people who become heavy users of alcohol, barbiturates, or opiates do not continue to smoke marihuana, largely because they lose the ability to distinguish between its effects and those of the other drugs.[9] They no longer know whether the marihuana gets them high. Second, in those few cases in which an individual uses marihuana in such quantities that he is always high, he is apt to feel the drug has no effect on him, since the essential element of a noticeable difference between feeling high and feeling normal is missing. In such a situation, use is likely to be given up completely, but temporarily, in order that the user may once again be able to perceive the difference.

Learning to Enjoy the Effects

One more step is necessary if the user who has now learned to get high is to continue use. He must learn to enjoy the effects he has just learned to experience. Marihuana-produced sensations are not automatically or necessarily pleasurable. The taste for such experience is a socially acquired one, not different in kind from acquired tastes for oysters or dry martinis. The user feels dizzy, thirsty; his scalp tingles; he misjudges time and distances. Are these things pleasurable? He isn't sure. If he is to continue marihuana use, he must decide that they are. Otherwise, getting high, while a real enough experience, will be an unpleasant one he would rather avoid.

The effects of the drug, when first perceived, may be physically unpleasant or at least ambiguous:

> It started taking effect, and I didn't know what was happening, you know, what it was, and I was very sick. I walked around the room, walking around the room trying to get off, you know; it just scared me at first, you know. I wasn't used to that kind of feeling.

In addition, the novice's naïve interpretation of what is happening to him may further confuse and frighten him, particularly if he decides, as many do, that he is going insane:

9 "Smokers have repeatedly stated that the consumption of whiskey while smoking negates the potency of the drug. They find it very difficult to get 'high' while drinking whiskey and because of that smokers will not drink while using the 'weed.'" (New York City Mayor's Committee on Marihuana, *The Marihuana Problem in the City of New York*, op. cit., p. 13.)

I felt I was insane, you know. Everything people done to me just wigged me. I couldn't hold a conversation, and my mind would be wandering, and I was always thinking, oh, I don't know, weird things, like hearing music different. . . . I get the feeling that I can't talk to anyone. I'll goof completely.

Given these typically frightening unpleasant first experiences, the beginner will not continue use unless he learns to redefine the sensations as pleasurable:

It was offered to me, and I tried it. I'll tell you one thing. I never did enjoy it at all. I mean it was just nothing that I could enjoy. [Well, did you get high when you turned on?] Oh, yeah, I got definite feelings from it. But I didn't enjoy them. I mean I got plenty of reactions, but they were mostly reactions of fear. [You were frightened?] Yes. I didn't enjoy it. I couldn't seem to relax with it, you know. If you can't relax with a thing, you can't enjoy it, I don't think.

In other cases the first experiences were also definitely unpleasant, but the person did become a marihuana user. This occurred, however, only after a later experience enabled him to redefine the sensations as pleasurable:

[This man's first experience was extremely unpleasant, involving distortion of spatial relationships and sounds, violent thirst, and panic produced by these symptoms.] After the first time I didn't turn on for about, I'd say, ten months to a year. . . . It wasn't a moral thing; it was because I'd gotten so frightened, bein' so high. An' I didn't want to go through that again, I mean, my reaction was, "Well, if this is what they call bein' high, I don't dig [like] it." . . . So I didn't turn on for a year almost, accounta that. . . .
  Well, my friends started, an' consequently I started again. But I didn't have any more, I didn't have that same initial reaction, after I started turning on again.
  [In interaction with his friends he became able to find pleasure in the effects of the drug and eventually became a regular user.]

In no case will use continue without a redefinition of the effects as enjoyable.
  This redefinition occurs, typically, in interaction with more experienced users who, in a number of ways, teach the novice to find pleasure in this experience which is at first so frightening.[10] They may reassure him as to the temporary character

10   Charen and Perelman, *op. cit.*, p. 679.

of the unpleasant sensations and minimize their seriousness, at the same time calling attention to the more enjoyable aspects. An experienced user describes how he handles newcomers to marihuana use:

> Well, they get pretty high sometimes. The average person isn't ready for that, and it is a little frightening to them sometimes. I mean, they've been high on lush [alcohol], and they get higher that way than they've ever been before, and they don't know what's happening to them. Because they think they're going to keep going up, up, up till they lose their minds or begin doing weird things or something. You have to like reassure them, explain to them that they're not really flipping or anything, that they're gonna be all right. You have to just talk them out of being afraid. Keep talking to them, reassuring, telling them it's all right. And come on with your own story, you know: "The same thing happened to me. You'll get to like that after a while." Keep coming on like that; pretty soon you talk them out of being scared. And besides they see you doing it and nothing horrible is happening to you, so that gives them more confidence.

The more experienced user may also teach the novice to regulate the amount he smokes more carefully, so as to avoid any severely uncomfortable symptoms while retaining the pleasant ones. Finally, he teaches the new user that he can "get to like it after a while." He teaches him to regard those ambiguous experiences formerly defined as unpleasant as enjoyable. The older user in the following incident is a person whose tastes have shifted in this way, and his remarks have the effect of helping others to make a similar redefinition:

> A new user had her first experience of the effects of marihuana and became frightened and hysterical. She "felt like she was half in and half out of the room" and experienced a number of alarming physical symptoms. One of the more experienced users present said, "She's dragged because she's high like that. I'd give anything to get that high myself. I haven't been that high in years."

In short, what was once frightening and distasteful becomes, after a taste for it is built up, pleasant, desired, and sought after. Enjoyment is introduced by the favorable definition of the experience that one acquires from others. Without this, use will not continue, for marihuana will not be for the user an object he can use for pleasure.

In addition to being a necessary step in becoming a user, this represents an important condition for continued use. It is quite common for experienced users suddenly to have an unpleasant or frightening experience, which they cannot define as pleasurable, either because they have used a larger amount of marihuana than usual or because the marihuana they have used turns out to be higher quality than they expected. The user has sensations which go beyond any conception he has of what being high is and is in much the same situation as the novice, uncomfortable and frightened. He may blame it on an overdose and simply be more careful in the future. But he may make this the occasion for a rethinking of his attitude toward the drug and decide that it no longer can give him pleasure. When this occurs and is not followed by a redefinition of the drug as capable of producing pleasure, use will cease.

The likelihood of such a redefinition occurring depends on the degree of the individual's participation with other users. Where this participation is intensive, the individual is quickly talked out of his feeling against marihuana use. In the next case, on the other hand, the experiment was very disturbing, and the aftermath of the incident cut the person's participation with other users to almost zero. Use stopped for three years and began again only when a combination of circumstances, important among which was a resumption of ties with users, made possible a redefinition of the nature of the drug:

It was too much, like I only made about four pokes, and I couldn't even get it out of my mouth, I was so high, and I got real flipped. In the basement, you know, I just couldn't stay in there anymore. My heart was pounding real hard, you know, and I was going out of my mind; I thought I was losing my mind completely. So I cut out of this basement, and this other guy, he's out of his mind, told me, "Don't, don't leave me, man. Stay here." And I couldn't.

I walked outside, and it was five below zero, and I thought I was dying, and I had my coat open; I was sweating, I was perspiring. My whole insides were all . . . , and I walked about two blocks away, and I fainted behind a bush. I don't know how long I laid there. I woke up, and I was feeling the worst, I can't describe it at all, so I made it to a bowling alley, man, and I was trying to act normal, I was trying to shoot pool, you know, trying to act real normal, and I couldn't lay and I couldn't stand up and I couldn't sit down, and I went up and laid down where some guys that spot pins lay down, and that didn't help me, and I went down to a doctor's office. I was going to go in there and tell the doctor to put me out of my misery . . . because my heart was pounding so hard, you know. . . . So then all weekend I started flipping, seeing things there and going through hell, you know, all kinds of abnormal things. . . . I just quit for a long time then.

[He went to a doctor who defined the symptoms for him as those of a nervous breakdown caused by "nerves" and "worries." Although he was no longer using marihauna, he had some recurrences of the symptoms which led him to suspect that "it was all his nerves."] So I just stopped worrying, you know; so it was about thirty-six months later I started making it again. I'd just take a few pokes, you know. [He first resumed use in the company of the same user-friend with whom he had been involved in the original incident.]

A person, then, cannot begin to use marihuana for pleasure, or continue its use for pleasure, unless he learns to define its effects as enjoyable, unless it becomes and remains an object he conceives of as capable of producing pleasure.

In summary, an individual will be able to use marihuana for pleasure only when he goes through a process of learning to conceive of it as an object which can be used in this way. No one becomes a user without (1) learning to smoke the drug in a way which will produce real effects; (2) learning to recognize the effects and connect them with drug use (learning, in other words, to get high); and (3) learning to enjoy the sensations he perceives. In the course of this process he develops a disposition or motivation to use marihuana which was not and could not have been present when he began use, for it involves and depends on conceptions of the drug which could only grow out of the kind of actual experience detailed above. On completion of this process he is willing and able to use marihuana for pleasure.

He has learned, in short, to answer "Yes" to the question: "Is it fun?" The direction his further use of the drug takes depends on his being able to continue to answer "Yes" to this question and, in addition, on his being able to answer "Yes" to other questions which arise as he becomes aware of the implications of the fact that society disapproves of the practice: "Is it expedient?" "Is it moral?" Once he has acquired the ability to get enjoyment by using the drug, use will continue to be possible for him. Considerations of morality and expediency, occasioned by the reactions of society, may interfere and inhibit use, but use continues to be a possibility in terms of his conception of the drug. The act becomes impossible only when the ability to enjoy the experience of being high is lost, through a change in the user's conception of the drug occasioned by certain kinds of experience with it.

MARIHUANA USE AND SOCIAL CONTROL

Learning to enjoy marihuana is a necessary but not a sufficient condition for a person to develop a stable pattern of drug use. He has still to contend with the powerful forces of social control that make the act seem inexpedient, immoral, or both.

When deviant behavior occurs in a society—behavior which flouts its basic values and norms—one element in its coming into being is a breakdown in social controls which ordinarily operate to maintain the valued forms of behavior. In complex societies the process can be quite complicated, since breakdowns in social control are often the consequence of becoming a participant in a group whose own culture and social controls operate at cross-purposes to those of the larger society. Important factors in the genesis of deviant behavior, then, may be sought in the processes by which people are emancipated from the controls of society and become responsive to those of a smaller group.

Social controls affect individual behavior, in the first instance, through the use of power, the application of sanctions. Valued behavior is rewarded and negatively valued behavior is punished. Control would be difficult to maintain if enforcement were always needed, so that more subtle mechanisms performing the same function arise. Among these is the control of behavior achieved by affecting the conceptions persons have of the to-be-controlled activity, and of the possibility or feasibility of engaging in it. These conceptions arise in social situations in which they are communicated by persons regarded as reputable and validated in experience. Such situations may be so ordered that individuals come to conceive of the activity as distasteful, inexpedient, or immoral and therefore do not engage in it.

This perspective invites us to analyze the genesis of deviant behavior in terms of events that render sanctions ineffective and experiences that shift conceptions so that the behavior becomes a conceivable possibility to the person. In this chapter I analyze this process in the instance of marihuana use. My basic question is: What is the sequence of events and experiences by which a person comes to be able to carry on the use of marihuana, in spite of the elaborate social controls functioning to prevent such behavior?

A number of potent forces operate to control the use of marihuana in this country. The act is illegal and punishable by severe penalties. Its illegality makes access to the drug difficult, placing immediate obstacles before anyone who wishes to use it. Actual use can be dangerous, for arrest and imprisonment are always possible consequences. In addition, if a user's family, friends, or employer discover that he uses marihuana, they may impute to him the auxiliary status traits ordinarily assumed to be associated with drug use. Believing him to be irresponsible and powerless to control his own behavior, perhaps even insane, they may punish him with various kinds of informal but highly effective sanctions, such as ostracism or withdrawal of affection. Finally, a set of traditional views has grown up, defining the practice as a violation of basic moral imperatives, as an act leading to loss of self-control, paralysis of the will, and eventual slavery to the drug. Such views are commonplace and are effective forces preventing marihuana use.

The career of the marihuana user may be divided into three stages, each representing a distinct shift in his relation to the social controls of the larger society and to those of the subculture in which marihuana use is found. The first stage is represented by the *beginner,* the person smoking marihuana for the first time; the second, by the *occasional user,* whose use is sporadic and dependent on chance factors; and the third, by the *regular user,* for whom use becomes a systematic, usually daily routine.

First let us consider the processes by which various kinds of social controls becomes progressively less effective as the user moves from level to level of use or, alternatively, the way controls prevent such movement by remaining effective. The major kinds of controls to be considered are: (a) control through limiting of supply and access to the drug; (b) control through the necessity of keeping nonusers from discovering that one is a user; (c) control through definition of the act as immoral. The rendering ineffective of these controls, at the levels and in the combinations to be described, may be taken as an essential condition for continued and increased marihuana use.

Supply

Marihuana use is limited, in the first instance, by laws making possession or sale of the drug punishable by severe penalties. This confines its distribution to illicit sources not easily available to the ordinary person. In order for a person to begin marihuana use, he must begin participation in some group through which these sources of supply become available to him, ordinarily a group organized around values and activities opposing those of the larger conventional society.

In those unconventional circles in which marihuana is already used, it is apparently just a matter of time until a situation arises in which the newcomer is given a chance to smoke it:

> I was with these guys that I knew from school, and one had some, so they went to get high and they just figured that I did too, they never asked me, so I didn't want to be no wallflower or nothin', so I didn't say nothin' and went out in the back of this place with them. They were doing up a couple of cigarettes.

In other groups marihuana is not immediately available, but participation in the group provides connections to others in which it is:

> But the thing was, we didn't know where to get any. None of us knew where to get it or how to find out where to get it. Well, there was this one chick there . . . she had some spade [Negro] girl friends and she had turned on before with them. Maybe once or twice. But she knew a little more about it than any of the rest of us. So she got hold of some, through these spade friends, and one night she brought down a couple of sticks.

In either case, such participation provides the conditions under which marihuana becomes available for first use. It also provides the conditions for the next level of *occasional use*, in which the individual smokes marihuana sporadically and irregularly. When an individual has arrived through earlier experiences at a point where he is able to use marihuana for pleasure, use tends at first to be a function of availability. The person uses the drug when he is with others who have a supply; when this is not the case his use ceases. It tends therefore to fluctuate in terms of the conditions of availability created by his participation with other users; a musician at this stage of use said:

> That's mostly when I get high, is when I play jobs. And I haven't played hardly at all lately . . . See, I'm married twelve years now, and I really haven't done much since then. I had to get a day job, you know, and I haven't been able to play much. I haven't had many gigs [jobs], so I really haven't turned on much, you see.
> Like I say, the only time I really get on is if I'm working with some cats who do, then I will too. Like I say, I haven't been high for maybe six months. I haven't turned on in all that time. Then, since I come on this job, that's three weeks,

I've been high every Friday and Saturday. That's the way it goes with me.

[This man was observed over a period of weeks to be completely dependent on other members of the orchestra in which he worked and on musicians who dropped into the tavern in which he was playing for any marihuana he used.]

If an occasional user begins to move on toward a more regularized and systematic mode of use, he can do it only by finding a more stable source of supply than more or less chance encounters with other users, and this means establishing connections with persons who make a business of dealing in narcotics. Although purchases in large quantities are necessary for regular use, they are not ordinarily made with that intent; but once made, they do render such use possible, as it was not before. Such purchases tend to be made as the user becomes more responsive to the controls of the drug-using group:

I was running around with this whole crowd of people who turned on then. And they were always turning me on, you know, until it got embarrassing. I was really embarrassed that I never had any, that I couldn't reciprocate. . . . So I asked around where I could get some and picked up for the first time.

Also, purchasing from a dealer is more economical, since there are no middlemen and the purchaser of larger quantities receives, as in the ordinary business world, a lower price.

However, in order to make these purchases, the user must have a "connection"—know someone who makes a business of selling drugs. Dealers operate illicitly, and in order to do business with them one must know where to find them and be identified to them in such a way that they will not hesitate to make a sale. This is quite difficult for persons who are casually involved in drug-using groups. But as a person becomes more identified with these groups, and is considered more trustworthy, the necessary knowledge and introductions to dealers become available to him. In becoming defined as a member, one is also defined as a person who can safely be trusted to buy drugs without endangering anyone else.

Even when the opportunity is made available to them, many do not make use of it. The danger of arrest latent in such an act prevents them from attempting it:

If it were freely distributed, I think I would probably keep it on hand all the time. But . . . [You mean if it wasn't

against the law?] Yeah. [Well, so does that mean that you
don't want to get involved . . . ?] Well, I don't want to get
too involved, you know. I don't want to get too close to
the people who traffic in, rather heavily in it. I've never had
any difficulty much in getting any stuff. I just . . . someone
usually has some and you can get it when you want it. Why,
just why, I've never happened to run into those more or less
direct contacts, the pushers, I suppose you'd explain it on
the basis of the fact that I never felt the need for scrounging
or looking up one.

Such fears operate only so long as the attempt is not made,
for once it has been successfully accomplished the individual
is able to use the experience to revise his estimate of the
danger involved; the notion of danger no longer prevents
purchase. Instead, the act is approached with a realistic caution
which recognizes without overemphasizing the possibility of
arrest. The purchaser feels safe so long as he observes elementary, common-sense precautions. Although many of the
interviewees had made purchases, only a few reported any
difficulty of a legal kind and these attributed it to the failure
to take precautions.

For those who do establish connections, regular use is often
interrupted by the arrest or disappearance of the man from
whom they purchase their supply. In such circumstances,
regular use can continue only if the user is able to find a new
source of supply. This young man had to give up use for a
while when:

Well, like Tom went to jail, they put him in jail. Then Cramer,
how did it happen . . . Oh yeah, like I owed him some money
and I didn't see him for quite a while and when I did try to
see him he had moved and I couldn't find out from anyone
where the cat went. So that was that connection . . . [So you
just didn't know where to get it?] No. [So you stopped?] Yeah.

The instability of sources of supply is an important control
over regular use, and reflects indirectly the use of legal sanctions by the community in the arrest of those trafficking in
drugs. Enforcement of the law controls use not by directly
deterring users, but by rendering sources of the drug unde-
pendable and thus making access more difficult.

Each level of use, from beginning to routine, thus has its
typical mode of supply, which must be present for such use
to occur. In this sense, the social mechanisms, which operate
to limit availability of the drug, limit its use. However, participation in groups in which marihuana is used creates the

conditions under which the controls that limit access to it no longer operate. Such participation also involves increased sensitivity to the controls of the drug-using group, so that there are forces pressing toward use of the new sources of supply. Changes in the mode of supply in turn create the conditions for movement to a new level of use. Consequently, it may be said that changes in group participation and membership lead to changes in level of use by affecting the individual's access to marihuana under present conditions in which the drug is available only through illicit outlets.

Secrecy

Marihuana use is limited also to the extent that individuals actually find it inexpedient or believe that they will find it so. This inexpediency, real or presumed, arises from the fact or belief that if nonusers discover that one uses the drug, sanctions of some important kind will be applied. The user's conception of these sanctions is vague, because few users seem ever to have had such an experience or to have known anyone who did; most marihuana users are secret deviants. Although the user does not know what specifically to expect in the way of punishments, the outlines are clear: he fears repudiation by people whose respect and acceptance he requires both practically and emotionally. That is, he expects that his relationships with nonusers will be disturbed and disrupted if they should find out, and limits and controls his behavior to the degree that relationships with outsiders are important to him.

This kind of control breaks down in the course of the user's participation with other users and in the development of his experience with the drug, as he comes to realize that, though it might be true that sanctions would be applied if nonusers found out, they need never find out. At each level of use, there is a growth in this realization, which makes the new level possible.

For the beginner, these considerations are very important and must be overcome if use is to be undertaken at all. His fears are challenged by the sight of others—more experienced users—who apparently feel there is little or no danger and appear to engage in the activity with impunity. If one does "try it once," he may still his fears by observations of this kind. Participation with other users thus furnishes the beginner with the rationalizations with which first to attempt the act.

Further participation in marihuana use allows the novice to draw the further conclusion that the act can be safe no matter how often indulged in, as long as one is careful and makes sure that nonusers are not present or likely to intrude. This kind of perspective is a necessary prerequisite for occasional use in which the drug is used when other users invite one to join them. While it permits this level of use, such a perspective does not allow regular use to occur, for the worlds of user and nonuser, while separate to a degree allowing the occasional use pattern to persist, are not completely segregated. The points where these worlds meet appear dangerous to the occasional user who must, therefore, confine his use to those occasions on which such meeting does not seem likely.

Regular use, on the other hand, implies a systematic and routine use of the drug which does not take into account such possibilities, and plans periods of getting high around them. It is a mode of use which depends on another kind of attitude toward the possibility of nonusers finding out, the attitude that marihuana use can be carried on under the noses of non-users, or, alternatively, on the living of a pattern of social participation which reduces contacts with nonusers almost to the zero point. Without this adjustment in attitude, participation, or both, the user is forced to remain at the level of occasional use. These adjustments take place in terms of two categories of risks involved: first, that nonusers will discover marihuana in one's possession, and second, that one will be unable to hide the effects of the drug when he is high while in the presence of nonusers.

The difficulties of the would-be regular user, in terms of possession, are illustrated in the remarks of a young man who unsuccessfully attempted regular use while living with his parents:

> I never did like to have it around the house, you know. [Why?] Well, I thought maybe my mother might find it or something like that. [What do you think she'd say?] Oh, well, you know, like . . . well, they never do mention it, you know, anything about dope addicts or anything like that, but it would be a really bad thing in my case, I know, because of the big family I come from. And my sisters and brothers, they'd put me down the worst. [And you don't want that to happen?] No, I'm afraid not.

In such cases, envisioning the consequences of such a secret being discovered prevents the person from maintaining the supply essential to regular use. Use remains erratic, since it must depend on encounters with other users and cannot occur whenever the user desires.

Unless he discovers some method of overcoming this difficulty, the person can progress to regular use only when the relationship deterring use is broken. People do not ordinarily leave their homes and families in order to smoke marihuana regularly. But if they do, for whatever reason, regular use, heretofore proscribed, becomes a possibility. Confirmed regular users often take into very serious account the effect on their drug use of forming new social relationships with nonusers:

> I wouldn't marry someone who would be belligerent if I do [smoke marihuana], you know. I mean, I wouldn't marry a woman who would be so untrusting as to think I would do something . . . I mean, you know, like hurt myself or try to hurt someone.

If such attachments are formed, use tends to revert to the occasional level:

> [This man had used marihuana quite extensively but his wife objected to it.] Of course, largely the reason I cut off was my wife. There were a few times when I'd feel like . . . didn't actually crave for it but would just like to have had some. [He was unable to continue using the drug except irregularly, on those occasions when he was away from his wife's presence and control.]

If the person moves almost totally into the user group, the problem ceases in many respects to exist, and it is possible for regular use to occur except when some new connection with the more conventional world is made.

If a person uses marihuana regularly and routinely it is almost inevitable—since even in urban society such roles cannot be kept completely separate—that he one day finds himself high while in the company of nonusers from whom he wishes to keep his marihuana use secret. Given the variety of symptoms the drug may produce, it is natural for the user to fear that he might reveal through his behavior that he is high, that he might be unable to control the symptoms and thus give away his secret. Such phenomena as difficulty in focusing one's attention and in carrying on normal conversation create a fear that everyone will know exactly why one is behaving this way, that the behavior will be interpreted automatically as a sign of drug use.

Those who progress to regular use manage to avoid this dilemma. It may happen, as noted above, that they come to participate almost completely in the subcultural group in which the practice is carried on, so that they simply have a minimal amount of contact with nonusers about whose opinions they care. Since this isolation from conventional society is seldom complete, the user must learn another method of avoiding the dilemma, one that is the most important method for those whose participation is never so completely segregated. This consists in learning to control the drug's effects while in the company of nonusers, so that they can be fooled and the secret successfully kept even though one continues participation with them. If one cannot learn this, there exists some group of situations in which he dare not get high and regular use is not possible:

> Say, I'll tell you something that just kills me, man, I mean it's really terrible. Have you ever got so high and then had to face your family? I really dread that. Like having to talk to my father or mother, or brothers, man, it's just too much. I just can't make it. I just feel like they're sitting there digging [watching] me, and they know I'm high. It's a horrible feeling. I hate it.

Most users have these feelings and move on to regular use, if they do, only if an experience of the following order occurs, changing their conception of the possibilities of detection:

> [Were you making it much then, at first?] No, not too much. Like I said, I was a little afraid of it. But it was finally about 1948 that I really began to make it strong. [What were you afraid of?] Well, I was afraid that I would get high and not be able to op [operate], you dig, I mean, I was afraid to let go and see what would happen. Especially on jobs. I couldn't trust myself when I was high. I was afraid I'd get too high, and pass out completely, or do stupid things. I didn't want to get too wigged.
> [How did you ever get over that?] Well, it's just one of those things, man. One night I turned on and I just suddenly felt real great, relaxed, you know, I was really swinging with it. From then on I've just been able to smoke as much as I want without getting into any trouble with it. I can always control it.

The typical experience is one in which the user finds himself in a position where he must do something while he is high that he is quite sure he cannot do in that condition. To his surprise, he finds he can do it and can hide from others the fact that he is under the drug's influence. One or more occurrences of this kind allow the user to conclude that he can remain a secret deviant, that his caution has been excessive and based on a false premise. If he desires to use the drug regularly he is no longer deterred by this fear, for he can use such an experience to justify the belief that nonusers need never know:

[I suggested that many users find it difficult to perform their work tasks effectively while high. The interviewee, a machinist, replied with the story of how he got over this barrier.]

It doesn't bother me that way. I had an experience once that proved that to me. I was out on a pretty rough party the night before. I got pretty high. On pot [marihuana] and lushing, too. I got so high that I was still out of my mind when I went to work the next day. And I had a very important job to work on. It had to be practically perfect—precision stuff. The boss had been priming me for it for days, explaining how to do it and everything.

[He went to work high and, as far as he could remember, must have done the job, although there was no clear memory of it since he was still quite high.]

About a quarter to four, I finally came down and I thought, "Jesus! What am I doing?" So I just cut out and went home. I didn't sleep all night hardly, worrying about whether I had fucked up on that job or not. I got down the next morning, the boss puts the old "mikes" on the thing, and I had done the fuckin' job perfectly. So after that I just didn't worry any more. I've gone down to work really out of my mind on some mornings. I don't have any trouble at all.

The problem is not equally important for all users, for there are those whose social participation is such that it cannot arise; they are completely integrated into the deviant group. All their associates know they use marihuana and none of them care, while their conventional contacts are few and unimportant. In addition, some persons achieve idiosyncratic solutions which allow them to act high and have it ignored:

They [the boys in his neighborhood] can never tell if I'm high. I usually am, but they don't know it. See, I always had the reputation, all through high school, of being kind of goofy, so no matter what I do, nobody pays much attention. So I can get away with being high practically anyplace.

In short, persons limit their use of marihuana in proportion to the degree of their fear, realistic or otherwise, that nonusers who are important to them will discover they use drugs and react in some punishing way. This kind of control breaks down as the user discovers his fears are excessive and unrealistic, as he comes to conceive the practice as one which can be kept secret with relative ease. Each level of use can occur only when the person has revised his conception of the dangers involved in such a way as to allow it.

Morality

Conventional notions of morality are another means through which marihuana use is controlled. The basic moral imperatives which operate here are those which require the individual to be responsible for his own welfare, and to be able to control his behavior rationally. The stereotype of the dope fiend portrays a person who violates these imperatives. A recent description of the marihuana user illustrates the principal features of this stereotype:[1]

> In the earliest stages of intoxication the will power is destroyed and inhibitions and restraints are released; the moral barricades are broken down and often debauchery and sexuality result. Where mental instability is inherent, the behavior is generally violent. An egotist will enjoy delusions of grandeur, the timid individual will suffer anxiety, and the aggressive one often will resort to acts of violence and crime. Dormant tendencies are released and while the subject may know what is happening, he has become powerless to prevent it. Constant use produces an incapacity for work and a disorientation of purpose.

One must add to this, of course, the notion that the user becomes a slave to the drug, that he voluntarily surrenders himself to a habit from which there is no escape. The person who takes such a stereotype seriously is presented with an obstacle to drug use. He will not begin, maintain, or increase his use of marihuana unless he can neutralize his sensitivity to the stereotype by accepting an alternative view of the practice. Otherwise he will, as would most members of the society, condemn himself as a deviant outsider.

The beginner has at some time shared the conventional view. In the course of his participation in an unconventional segment of society, however, he is likely to acquire a more "emancipated" view of the moral standards implicit in the usual characterization of the drug user, at least to the point that he will not reject activities out of hand simply because they are conventionally condemned. The observation of others

1   H. J. Anslinger and William F. Tompkins, *The Traffic in Narcotics* (New York: Funk and Wagnalls Co., 1953), pp. 21-22.

using the drug may further tempt him to apply his rejection of conventional standards to the specific instance of marihuana use. Such participation, then, tends to provide the conditions under which controls can be circumvented at least sufficiently for first use to be attempted.

In the course of further experience in drug-using groups, the novice acquires a series of rationalizations and justifications with which he may answer objections to occasional use if he decides to engage in it. If he should himself raise the objections of conventional morality he finds ready answers available in the folklore of marihuana-using groups.

One of the most common rationalizations is that conventional persons indulge in much more harmful practices and that a comparatively minor vice like marihuana smoking cannot really be wrong when such things as the use of alcohol are so commonly accepted:

> [You don't dig alcohol then?] No, I don't dig it at all. [Why not?] I don't know. I just don't. Well, see, here's the thing. Before I was at the age where kids start drinking I was already getting on [using marihuana] and I saw the advantages of getting on, you know, I mean there was no sickness and it was much cheaper. That was one of the first things I learned, man. Why do you want to drink? Drinking is dumb, you know. It's so much cheaper to get on and you don't get sick, and it's not sloppy and takes less time. And it grew to be the thing, you know. So I got on before I drank, you know. . . .
> [What do you mean that's one of the first things you learned?] Well, I mean, as I say, I was just first starting to play jobs as a musician when I got on and I was also in a position to drink on the jobs, you know. And these guys just told me it was silly to drink. They didn't drink either.

Additional rationalizations enable the user to suggest to himself that the drug's effects, rather than being harmful, are in fact beneficial:

> I have had some that made me feel like . . . very invigorated and also it gives a very strong appetite. It makes you very hungry. That's probably good, for some people who are underweight.

Finally, the user, at this point, is not using the drug all the time. His use is scheduled; there are times when he considers it appropriate and times when he does not. The existence of this schedule allows him to assure himself that he controls the drug and becomes a symbol of the harmlessness of the practice. He does not consider himself a slave to the drug, because he can and does abide by his schedule, no matter how much use the particular schedule may allow. The fact that there are times when he does not, on principle, use the drug, can be used as proof to himself of his freedom with respect to it.

> I like to get on and mostly do get on when I'm relaxing, doing something I enjoy like listening to a real good classical record or maybe like a movie or something like that or listening to a radio program. Something I enjoy doing, not participating in, like . . . I play golf during the summer, you know, and a couple of guys I play with got on, turned on while they were playing golf and I couldn't see that because, I don't know, when you're participating in something you want your mind to be on that and nothing else, and if you're . . . because I think, I know it makes you relax and . . . I don't think you can make it as well.

Occasional use can occur in an individual who accepts these views, for he has reorganized his moral notions in such a way as to permit it, primarily by acquiring the conception that conventional moral notions about drugs do not apply to this drug and that, in any case, his use of it has not become excessive.

If use progresses to the point of becoming regular and systematic, moral questions may again be raised for the user, for he begins now to look, to himself as well as others, like the uncontrolled "dope fiend" of popular mythology. He must convince himself again, if regular use is to continue, that he has not crossed this line. The problem, and one possible resolution, are presented in a statement by a regular user:

> I know it isn't habit-forming but I was a little worried about how easy it would be to put down, so I tried it. I was smoking it all the time, then I just put it down for a whole week to see what would happen. Nothing happened. So I knew it was cool [all right]. Ever since then I've used it as much as I want to. Of course, I wouldn't dig being a slave to it or anything like that, but I don't think that that would happen unless I was neurotic or something, and I don't think I am, not to that extent.

The earlier rationalization that the drug has beneficial effects remains unchanged and may even undergo a considerable elaboration. But the question raised in the last quotation proves more troublesome. In view of his increased and regularized consumption of the drug, the user is not sure that he is really able to control it, that he has not perhaps become the slave of a vicious habit. Tests are made—use is given up and the consequences awaited—and when nothing untoward occurs, the user is able to draw the conclusion that there is nothing to fear.

The problem is, however, more difficult for some of the more sophisticated users who derive their moral directives not so much from conventional thinking as from popular psychiatric "theory." Their use troubles them, not in conventional terms, but because of what it may indicate about their mental health. Accepting current thinking about the causes of drug use, they reason that no one would use drugs in large amounts unless "something" were "wrong" with him, unless there were some neurotic maladjustment which made drugs necessary. The fact of marihuana smoking becomes a symbol of psychic weakness and, ultimately, moral weakness. This prejudices the person against further regular use and causes a return to occasional use unless a new rationale is discovered.

> Well, I wonder if the best thing is not to get on anything at all. That's what they tell you. Although I've heard psychiatrists say, "Smoke all the pot you want, but leave the horse [heroin] alone."
> [Well, that sounds reasonable.] Yeah, how many people can do it? There aren't very many . . . I think that seventy-five per cent or maybe even a bigger per cent of the people that turn on have a behavior pattern that would lead them to get on more and more pot to get more and more away from things. I think I have it myself. But I think I'm aware of it so I think I can fight it.

The notion that to be aware of the problem is to solve it constitutes a self-justifying rationale in the above instance. Where justifications cannot be discovered, use continues on an occasional basis, the user explaining his reasons in terms of his conception of psychiatric theory:

> Well, I believe that people who indulge in narcotics and alcohol and drinks, any stimulants of that type, on that level, are probably looking for an escape from a more serious condition than the more or less occasional user. I don't feel that I'm escaping from anything. I think that, however, I realize that I have a lot of adjustment to accomplish yet. . . . So I can't say that I have any serious neurotic condition or inefficiency that I'm trying to handle. But in the case of some acquaintances I've made, people who are chronic alcoholics or junkies [opiate addicts] or pretty habitual smokers, I have found ac-

companying that condition some maladjustment in their personality, too.

Certain morally toned conceptions about the nature of drug use and drug users thus influence the marihuana user. If he is unable to explain away or ignore these conceptions, use will not occur at all; and the degree of use appears to be related to the degree to which the conceptions are no longer influential, having been replaced by rationalizations and justifications current among users.

In short, a person will feel free to use marihuana to the degree that he comes to regard conventional conceptions of it as the uninformed views of outsiders and replaces those conceptions with the "inside" view he has acquired through his experience with the drug in the company of other users.

THE MARIHUANA TAX ACT[2]

It is generally assumed that the practice of smoking marihuana was imported into the United States from Mexico, by way of the southwestern states of Arizona, New Mexico, and Texas, all of which had sizable Spanish-speaking populations. People first began to notice marihuana use in the 1920s but, since it was a new phenomenon and one apparently confined to Mexican immigrants, did not express much concern about it. (The medical compound prepared from the marihuana plant had been known for some time, but was not often prescribed by U.S. physicians.) As late as 1930, only sixteen states had passed laws prohibiting the use of marihuana.

In 1937, however, the United States Congress passed the Marihuana Tax Act, designed to stamp out use of the drug. We find in the history of this Act the story of an entrepreneur whose initiative and enterprise overcame public apathy and indifference and culminated in the passage of Federal legislation. Before turning to the history of the Act itself, we should perhaps look at the way similar substances had been treated in American law, in order to understand the context in which the attempt to suppress marihuana use proceeded.

The use of alcohol and opium in the United States had a long history, punctuated by attempts at suppression.[3] Three

2 See Appendix 2.

3 See John Krout, *The Origins of Prohibition* (New York: Columbia University Press, 1928); Charles Terry and Mildred Pellens, *The Opium Problem* (New York: The Committee on Drug Addiction with the Bureau of Social Hygiene, Inc., 1928); and *Drug Addiction: Crime or Disease?* Interim and Final Reports of the Joint Committee of the American Bar Association and the American Medical Association on Narcotic Drugs (Bloomington, Indiana: Indiana University Press, 1961).

values provided legitimacy for attempts to prevent the use of intoxicants and narcotics. One legitimizing value, a component of what has been called the Protest Ethic, holds that the individual should exercise complete responsibility for what he does and what happens to him; he should never do anything that might cause loss of self-control. Alcohol and the opiate drugs, in varying degrees and ways, cause people to lose control of themselves; their use, therefore, is evil. A person intoxicated with alcohol often loses control over his physical activity; the centers of judgment in the brain are also affected. Users of opiates are more likely to be anesthetized and thus less likely to commit rash acts. But they become dependent on the drug to prevent withdrawal symptoms and in this sense have lost control of their actions; insofar as it is difficult to obtain the drug, they must subordinate other interests to its pursuit.

Another American value legitimized attempts to suppress the use of alcohol and opiates: disapproval of action taken solely to achieve states of ecstasy. Perhaps because of our strong cultural emphases on pragmatism and utilitarianism, Americans usually feel uneasy and ambivalent about ecstatic experiences of any kind. But we do not condemn ecstatic experience when it is the by-product or reward of actions we consider proper in their own right, such as hard work or religious fervor. It is only when people pursue ecstasy for its own sake that we condemn their action as a search for "illicit pleasure," an expression that has real meaning to us.

The third value which provided a basis for attempts at suppression was humanitarianism. Reformers believed that people enslaved by the use of alcohol and opium would benefit from laws making it impossible for them to give in to their weaknesses. The families of drunkards and drug addicts would likewise benefit.

These values provided the basis for specific rules. The Eighteenth Amendment and the Volstead Act forbade the importation of alcoholic beverages into the United States and their manufacture within the country. The Harrison Act in effect prohibited the use of opiate drugs for all but medical purposes.

In formulating these laws, care was taken not to interfere with what were regarded as the legitimate interests of other groups in the society. The Harrison Act, for instance, was so drawn as to allow medical personnel to continue using morphine and other opium derivatives for the relief of pain and such other medical purposes as seemed to them appropriate. Furthermore, the law was carefully drawn in order to avoid running afoul of the constitutional provision reserving police powers to the several states. In line with this restriction, the Act was presented as a revenue measure, taxing unlicensed purveyors of opiate drugs at an exorbitant rate while permitting licensed purveyors (primarily physicians, dentists, veterinarians, and pharmacists) to pay a nominal tax. Though it was justified constitutionally as a revenue measure, the Harrison Act was in fact a police measure, and was so interpreted by those to whom its enforcement was entrusted. One consequence of the passage of the Act was the establishment, in the Treasury Department, of the Federal Bureau of Narcotics in 1930.

The same values that led to the banning of the use of alcohol and opiates could, of course, be applied to the case of marihuana and it seems logical that this should have been done. Yet what little I have been told, by people familiar with the period, about the use of marihuana in the late twenties and early thirties leads me to believe that there was relatively lax enforcement of the existing local laws. This, after all, was the era of Prohibition and the police had more pressing matters to attend to. Neither the public nor law enforcement officers, apparently, considered the use of marihuana a serious problem. When they noticed it at all, they probably dismissed it as not warranting major attempts at enforcement. One index of how feebly the laws were enforced is that the price of marihuana is said to have been very much lower prior to the passage of Federal legislation. This indicates that there was little danger in selling it and that enforcement was not seriously undertaken.

Even the Treasury Department, in its report on the year 1931, minimized the importance of the problem:

> A great deal of public interest has been aroused by newspaper articles appearing from time to time on the evils of the abuse of marihuana, or Indian hemp, and more attention has been focused on specific cases reported of the abuse of the drug than would otherwise have been the case. This publicity tends to magnify the extent of the evil and lends color to an inference that there is an alarming spread of the improper use of the drug, whereas the actual increase in such use may not have been inordinately large.[4]

The Treasury Department's Bureau of Narcotics furnished most of the enterprise that produced the Marihuana Tax Act.

4 U.S. Treasury Department, *Traffic in Opium and Other Dangerous Drugs for the Year ended December 31, 1931* (Washington: Government Printing Office, 1932), p. 51.

While it is, of course, difficult to know what the motives of Bureau officials were, we need assume no more than that they perceived an area of wrongdoing that properly belonged in their jurisdiction and moved to put it there. The personal interest they satisfied in pressing for marihuana legislation was one common to many officials: the interest in successfully accomplishing the task one has been assigned and in acquiring the best tools with which to accomplish it. The Bureau's efforts took two forms: cooperating in the development of state legislation affecting the use of marijuana, and providing facts and figures for journalistic accounts of the problem. These are two important modes of action available to all entrepreneurs seeking the adoption of rules: they can enlist the support of other interested organizations and develop, through the use of the press and other communications media, a favorable public attitude toward the proposed rule. If the efforts are successful, the public becomes aware of a definite problem and the appropriate organizations act in concert to produce the desired rule.

The Federal Bureau of Narcotics cooperated actively with the National Conference of Commissioners on Uniform State Laws in developing uniform laws on narcotics, stressing among others matters the need to control marihuana use.[5] In 1932, the Conference approved a draft law. The Bureau commented:

> The present constitutional limitations would seem to require control measures directed against the intrastate traffic in Indian hemp to be adopted by the several State governments rather than by the Federal Government, and the policy has been to urge the State authorities generally to provide the necessary legislation, with supporting enforcement activity, to prohibit the traffic except for bona fide medical purposes. The proposed uniform State narcotic law . . . with optional text applying to the restriction of traffic in Indian hemp, has been recommended as an adequate law to accomplish the desired purposes.[6]

In its report for the year 1936, the Bureau urged its partners in this cooperative effort to exert themselves more strongly and hinted that Federal intervention might perhaps be necessary.

In the absence of additional Federal legislation the Bureau of

5 *Ibid., pp.* 16-17.

6 Bureau of Narcotics, U.S. Treasury Department, *Traffic in Opium and Other Dangerous Drugs for the Year ended December 31, 1932* (Washington: Government Printing Office, 1933), p. 13.

Narcotics can therefore carry on no war of its own against this traffic . . . the drug has come into wide and increasing abuse in many states, and the Bureau of Narcotics has therefore been endeavoring to impress upon the various States the urgent need for vigorous enforcement of local cannabis [marihuana] laws.[7]

The second prong of the Bureau's attack on the marihuana problem consisted of an effort to arouse the public to the danger confronting it by means of "an educational campaign describing the drug, its identification, and evil effects."[8] Apparently hoping that public interest might spur the States and cities to greater efforts, the Bureau said:

In the absence of Federal legislation on the subject, the States and cities should rightfully assume the responsibility for providing vigorous measures for the extinction of this lethal weed, and it is therefore hoped that all public-spirited citizens will earnestly enlist in the movement urged by the Treasury Department to adjure intensified enforcement of marihuana laws.[9]

The Bureau did not confine itself to exhortation in departmental reports. Its methods in pursuing desired legislation are described in a passage dealing with the campaign for a uniform state narcotic law:

Articles were prepared in the Federal Bureau of Narcotics, at the request of a number of organizations dealing with this general subject [uniform state laws] for publication by such organizations in magazines and newspapers. An intelligent and sympathetic public interest, helpful to the administration of the narcotic laws, has been aroused and maintained.[10]

As the campaign for Federal legislation against marihuana drew to a successful close, the Bureau's efforts to communicate its sense of the urgency of the problem to the public bore plentiful fruit. The number of articles about marihuana which

7 Bureau of Narcotics, U.S. Treasury Department, *Traffic in Opium and Other Dangerous Drugs for the Year ended December 31, 1936* (Washington: Government Printing Office, 1937), p. 59.

8 *Ibid.*

9 Bureau of Narcotics, U.S. Treasury Department, *Traffic in Opium and Other Dangerous Drugs for the Year ended December 31, 1935* (Washington: Government Printing Office, 1936), p. 30.

10 Bureau of Narcotics, U.S. Treasury Department, *Traffic in Opium and Other Dangerous Drugs for the Year ended December 31, 1933* (Washington: Government Printing Office, 1934), p. 61.

appeared in popular magazines, indicated by the number indexed in the *Reader's Guide,* reached a record high. Seventeen articles appeared in a two-year period, many more than in any similar period before or after.

Articles on Marihuana Indexed in
The *Reader's Guide to Periodical Literature*

Time Period	Number of Articles
January, 1925-December, 1928	0
January, 1929-June, 1932	0
July, 1932-June, 1935	0
July, 1935-June, 1937	4
July, 1937-June, 1939	17
July, 1939-June, 1941	4
July, 1941-June, 1943	1
July, 1943-April, 1945	4
May, 1945-April, 1947	6
May, 1947-April, 1949	0
May, 1949-March, 1951	1

Of the seventeen, ten either explicitly acknowledged the help of the Bureau in furnishing facts and figures or gave implicit evidence of having received help by using facts and figures that had appeared earlier, either in Bureau publications or in testimony before the Congress on the Marihuana Tax Act. (We will consider the Congressional hearings on the bill in a moment.)

One clear indication of Bureau influence in the preparation of journalistic articles can be found in the recurrence of certain atrocity stories first reported by the Bureau. For instance, in an article published in the *American Magazine,* the Commissioner of Narcotics himself related the following incident:

An entire family was murdered by a youthful [marihuana] addict in Florida. When officers arrived at the home they found the youth staggering about in a human slaughterhouse. With an ax he had killed his father, mother, two brothers, and a sister. He seemed to be in a daze. . . . He had no recollection of having committed the multiple crime. The officers knew him ordinarily as a sane, rather quiet young man; now he was pitifully crazed. They sought the reason. The boy said he had been in the habit of smoking something which youthful friends called "muggles," a childish name for marihuana.[11]

11 H. J. Anslinger, with Courtney Ryley Cooper, "Marihuana: Assassin of Youth," *American Magazine,* CXXIV (July, 1937), 19, 150.

Five of the seventeen articles printed during the period repeated this story, and thus showed the influence of the Bureau.

The articles designed to arouse the public to the dangers of marihuana identified use of the drug as a violation of the value of self-control and the prohibition on search for "illicit pleasure," thus legitimizing the drive against marihuana in the eyes of the public. These, of course, were the same values that had been appealed to in the course of the quest for legislation prohibiting use of alcohol and opiates for illicit purposes.

The Federal Bureau of Narcotics, then, provided most of the enterprise which produced public awareness of the problem and coordinated action by other enforcement organizations. Armed with the results of their enterprise, representatives of the Treasury Department went to Congress with a draft of the Marihuana Tax Act and requested its passage. The hearings of the House Committee on Ways and Means, which considered the bill for five days during April and May of 1937, furnish a clear case of the operation of enterprise and of the way it must accommodate other interests.

The Assistant General Counsel of the Treasury Department introduced the bill to the Congressmen with these words: "The leading newspapers of the United States have recognized the seriousness of this problem and many of them have advocated Federal legislation to control the traffic in marihuana."[12] After explaining the constitutional basis of the bill—like the Harrison Act, it was framed as a revenue measure—he reassured them about its possible effects on legitimate businesses:

> The form of the bill is such, however, as not to interfere materially with any industrial, medical, or scientific uses which the plant may have. Since hemp fiber and articles manufactured therefrom [twine and light cordage] are obtained from the harmless mature stalk of the plant, all such products have been completely eliminated from the purview of the bill by defining the term "marihuana" in the bill so as to exclude from its provisions the mature stalk and its compounds or manufacturers. There are also some dealings in marihuana seeds for planting purposes and for use in the manufacture of oil which is ultimately employed by the paint and varnish industry. As the seeds, unlike the mature stalk, contain the drug, the same complete exemption could not be applied in this instance.[13]

12 *Taxation of Marihuana* (Hearings before the Committee on Ways and Means of the House of Representatives, 75th Congress, 1st Session, on H.R. 6385, April 27–30 and May 4, 1937), p. 7.

13 *Ibid.,* p. 8.

He further assured them that the medical profession rarely used the drug, so that its prohibition would work no hardship on them or on the pharmaceutical industry.

The committee members were ready to do what was necessary and, in fact, queried the Commissioner of Narcotics as to why this legislation had been proposed only now. He explained:

> Ten years ago we only heard about it throughout the Southwest. It is only in the last few years that it has become a national menace. . . . We have been urging uniform State legislation on the several States, and it was only last month that the last State legislature adopted such legislation.[14]

The commissioner reported that many crimes were committed under the influence of marihuana, and gave examples, including the story of the Florida mass-murderer. He pointed out that the present low prices of the drug made it doubly dangerous, because it was available to anyone who had a dime to spare.

Manufacturers of hempseed oil voiced certain objections to the language of the bill, which was quickly changed to meet their specifications. But a more serious objection came from the birdseed industry, which at that time used some four million pounds of hempseed a year. Its representative apologized to the Congressmen for appearing at the last minute, stating that he and his colleagues had not realized until just then that the marihuana plant referred to in the bill was the same plant from which they got an important ingredient of their product. Government witnesses had insisted that the seeds of the plant required prohibition, as well as the flowering tops smokers usually used, because they contained a small amount of the active principle of the drug and might possibly be used for smoking. The birdseed manufacturers contended that inclusion of seed under the provisions of the bill would damage their business.

To justify his request for exemption, the manufacturers' representative pointed to the beneficial effect of hempseed on pigeons:

> [It] is a necessary ingredient in pigeon feed because it contains an oil substance that is a valuable ingredient of pigeon feed, and we have not been able to find any seed that will take its place. If you substitute anything for the hemp, it has a tendency to change the character of the squabs produced.[15]

14 *Ibid.*, p. 20.
15 *Ibid.*, pp. 73-74.

Congressman Robert L. Doughton of North Carolina inquired: "Does that seed have the same effect on pigeons as the drug has on human beings?" The manufacturers' representative said: "I have never noticed it. It has a tendency to bring back the feathers and improve the birds."

Faced with serious opposition, the Government modified its stern insistence on the seed provision, noting that sterilization of the seeds might render them harmless: "It seems to us that the burden of proof is on the Government there, when we might injure a legitimate industry."

Once these difficulties had been ironed out, the bill had easy sailing. Marihuana smokers, powerless, unorganized, and lacking publicly legitimate grounds for attack, sent no representatives to the hearings and their point of view found no place in the record. Unopposed, the bill passed both House and Senate the following July. The enterprise of the Bureau had produced a new rule, whose subsequent enforcement would help create a new class of outsiders—marihuana users.

CHAPTER FOUR

BHANG AND ALCOHOL:

Cultural Factors in the Choice of Intoxicants

George Morris Carstairs,[1] DPM, FRCP

George Morris Carstairs, DPM, is a Fellow of the Royal College of Physicians and Professor of Psychological Medicine at the University of Edinburgh. A world authority on the epidemiology (the incidence, distribution, and control) of psychological illness, he has been a Reith lecturer for the British Broadcasting Corporation.

THE PROBLEM

Throughout the year 1951 the writer of this article was engaged in a field study which involved his living in intimate daily contact with the inhabitants of a large village[2] in the State of Rajasthan, in northern India. In the course of that year, he got to know this community fairly well; and he was struck by one unexpected aspect of the caste system which permeates Hindu society. This was the violent antithesis shown in the community's attitudes toward the two most prevalent forms of intoxication—that caused by drinking *daru*, a potent distilled alcohol derived from the flowers of the mahwa tree *(Bassia latifundia),* and that due to *bhang*, which is the local

1 Psychiatrist, Medical Research Council Unit for Research in Occupational Adaptation, Maudsley Hospital, London.
2 The village had 2,400 inhabitants, of whom 93 were Rajputs and 85 Brahmins.

name for an infusion of the leaves and stems of Indian hemp (*Cannabis indica*), which is readily cultivable in this region. Each had its partisans, and each decried the other faction.

It may be noted, in passing, that these were not the only forms of *nasha*, or intoxication, recognized. Villagers frequently spoke of the *nasha* caused by drinking cups of sickly-sweet tea infused in milk. Some went so far as to blame the breakdown of traditional piety on this modern indulgence in "English tea." They would also describe the *nasha* induced by a few puffs from a communally shared cigarette, and of that brought about by an unaccustomed feast of meat. Instances were cited of men who had become addicted to chewing opium; but in recent years this has become so prohibitively expensive as to have dropped out of the picture. It was remembered by the warrior-caste, the Rajputs, one of whom explained that in the old days they would take opium before a battle in order to steady their nerves and to inhibit untimely bowel movements. Another Rajput, of humbler rank, put it more prosaically: "Yes, they'd issue a lump of opium to every man in those days, and glad to get it. Might as well enjoy it now—may not be here tomorrow."

Here in Rajasthan the Rajput caste held a position of social supremacy. It is they who are the *Rajahs*, the rulers. For centuries their semifeudal authority has governed the State, which was divided into a number of kingdoms, each with a hierarchy of subordinate rulers, down to the village *Thakur*, who is a Rajput squire of a few acres. They traditionally justified their wealth and prestige by their willingness to fight in defense of their land and their religion. On the smallest scale, it was to the Thakur and his kinsmen that the ordinary villagers turned for protection against marauding bands, especially in times of famine or of war.

As fighting men, the Rajputs had certain special prerogatives, notably the right to eat meat and drink alcohol. These privileges, as well as their forefathers' bravery in battle, are commemorated in a rich store of poetry and song. The writer recalls many evenings spent listening to minstrels reciting epics of war and of the hunting field, while drummers played and women's strident voices sang with the refrain: *Pi lo, pi lo manna Raja!* (Drink on, drink on, O King!) His Rajput hosts were careful to point out on such occasions that daru should be taken with circumspection, only in the proper measure (*niyam se*) and with due formality. Yet for all their protestations, "Oaths are but straw to the fire i' the blood," and a typical Rajput party tends to become boisterous, bawdy and unbridled.

Besides the Rajputs, only the *Sudras* (the artisan castes) and the Untouchables—and not all of them—are accustomed to take meat and alcohol. These lower orders also observe a certain formality in their drinking. Usually they go in a group to the village grogshop, and there the daru is passed from hand to hand in a small brass bowl. Each man, before taking his first drink, lets fall a drop or two and says, *"Fai Mataji!"* —invoking the demon-goddess Kali in her local embodiment. In so doing, they fortify themselves with the knowledge that that great goddess, mother and destroyer in one, relishes a diet of blood and alcohol.

In striking contrast, the members of the other top caste-group in the village, the Brahmins, unequivocally denounce the use of daru. It is, they say, utterly inimical to the religious life—and in matters of religion the Brahmins speak with authority. Certainly no Hindu who has tasted or even touched daru will enter one of his temples (not even a goddess temple) without first having a purificatory bath and change of clothes. The first requirement of those who begin to devote themselves seriously to religion is always: "Abhor meat and wine." Priests and holy men insist that a *darulia* (an alcoholic) is beyond the pale of possible salvation. And yet again and again the writer was able to see respectable Brahmins and holy *Saddhus* who were benignly and conspicuously fuddled with bhang. To his eye, they were drunk as lords—drunk as Rajputs—and yet they would have been mortally offended if the comparison had been drawn, because this form of intoxication they believed to be not only no disgrace, but actually an enhancement of the spiritual life.

It might have been thought that if one form of intoxicant were condemned, so would be the other. In time, however, the writer was able to learn not only the subjective characteristics which distinguish these two states, but also the important cultural values which are associated with their use, and a solution to the riddle began to emerge.

Different Effects of Daru and Bhang Intoxication

The physiological and psychological effects of the ingestion of alcohol are sufficiently familiar to require no further elaboration. As Ravi Varma (1) has shown, the stages of inebriation have also been described in ancient Sanskrit texts. He quotes the pre-medieval writer Susruta as distinguishing three phases: first, elation and conviviality with increase in sexual desire; next, a progressive loss of sense of propriety with overactivity and failing coordination; and finally, a comatose, dead-drunk state, "like a felled tree," in which, "though alive, one is as it were dead." As will be shown below, the Rajputs were vividly aware of the "release of sexual and aggressive impulses" which Horton (2) has shown to be the basic role of alcohol in every community which resorts to its use.

The effect of taking *Cannabis indica* in one or other of its preparations is less familiar to occidental readers; and yet it is an intoxicant which is second only to alcohol in the volume of its use, the variety of its recipes, and the profusion of its names.[3] Descriptions of its effect show a number of discrepancies, which may be attributed in part to the varying concentration of the drug in different preparations, and also to the fact that it is often taken in conjunction with other drugs. Thus Porot (3) reports that most North African cannabists are also alcoholics. In the Middle East it is used often in conjunction with an aphrodisiac.

When a cannabis preparation is taken alone and in moderate strength (as is the case with the village bhang drinkers), Porot describes the following sequence of events: *(a)* A transient euphoria, a rich, lively, internal experience, in which ideas rush through the mind and there is an enormous feeling of superiority, of superhuman clarity of insight. *(b)* Sensory hyperesthesia, and coenesthesias: sights and sounds become unusually vivid and meaningful. *(c)* Distortion of sense of time and space. *(d)* Loss of judgment. *(e)* Exaggeration of affects, both of sympathy and of antipathy. *(f)* The phase of excitement is succeeded by one of placid ecstasy, known to Moslems as *el kif*, or "blessed repose." The "will to act" becomes annihilated. *(g)* After some hours of the trancelike state, sleep supervenes.

As a Frenchman, Porot was interested in the cult of cannabism which was created by a circle of writers and painters in Paris during the 1840s: an intellectual vogue which has enriched medical literature with some vivid accounts of the subjective aspects of the intoxication. This reportage was facilitated by the fact that the condition does not interfere with self-awareness, so that the participants had the sensation of being onlookers at the same time as actors in the scene. As Théophile Gautier wrote (4): "Je voyais mes camarades à certains instants, mais défigurés, moitié hommes, moitié

3 These include bhang, charas, ganja (India); kif (Algeria); takrouri (Tunisia); kabak (Turkey); hashish-el-kif (Middle East); djoma (Central Africa); dagga (South Africa); liamba (Brazil); grifa (Mexico); marihuana (South and North America). There are, however, many other names descriptive of particular sweetmeats, cakes, drinks, etc., containing the drug.

plantes, avec des airs pensifs d'ibis debout sur une patte d'autruche."

But Gautier, as Guilly (5) has pointed out in a recent essay on the "Club des Hachischins," was not altogether a reliable witness. His account was frankly embellished, designed to exaggerate the bizarre and the orgiastic elements of the situation; and in so doing he illustrates a finding of his contemporary, Baudelaire, who also was fascinated by the effects of the drug and carried his experiments to extreme lengths. Baudelaire (6) pointed out that cannabis affected people differently according to their degree of intellectual refinement. He distinguished "spiritual" from merely material or brutish intoxication; and to this one can add that the quality of the intoxication can be influenced by the expectations with which the subject enters into it. For example, Tunisian addicts would smoke their *takrouri* in a quiet room, scented and decorated with flowers and with erotic prints calculated to stimulate hallucinations proper to their self-induced anticipation of paradise.

Frivolous though his interest was, Gautier seems to have tasted enough of the drug to have experienced the state of lethargic ecstasy—in Baudelaire's words, "L'apothéose de l'Homme-Dieu"—which he described as follows:

> Je ne sentais plus mon corps; les liens de la matière et de l'esprit étaient déliés; je me mouvais par ma seule volonté dans un milieu qui n'offrait pas de résistance. . . . Rien de matériel ne se mêlait à cette extase; aucun désir terrestre n'en altérait la pureté. . . .

There have been other European experimenters who have described the effects of cannabism but none who have been outspoken in its praise. Walter de la Mare (7) wrote that, "Like opium, it induces an extravagant sense of isolation," and he went on to quote the experience of his friend Redwood Anderson, who reported on the effect of taking small doses of the drug. He was able to describe the euphoria, the rush of ideas, and the intense subjective feelings of awareness and heightened significance of all his perceptions; but he was not seduced by this near-ecstasy, rather struggling to resist the weakening of voluntary control and to repudiate these illusions of godlike intuition.

In this he was at one with Baudelaire, who indulged very profoundly in this as in other forms of intoxication and, in the end, like a true Westerner, protested against any drug which would hamper the exercise of free, individual assertion and volition. He wrote:

Je ne comprends pas pourquoi l'homme rationnel et spirituel
se sert de moyens artificiels pour arriver à la béatitude
poétique, puisque l'enthousiasme et la volonté suffisent pour
l'élever à une existence supra-naturelle. Les grands poètes, les
philosophes, les prophètes sont des êtres qui, par le pur et
libre exercice de leur volonté, parviennent à un état où ils
sont à la fois cause et effet, sujet et objet, magnétiseur et
somnambule.

It is necessary to refer at length to these subjective experiences because, although to the superficial observer the behavior
of the bhang drinker might seem not unlike that of an alcoholic
(except that the progress of intoxication is at first delayed, for
up to 90 minutes, and then proceeds by rapid stages to a profound stupor), the subject's inner experiences are very different. To quote an early medical investigator, Hesnard (8): "Ses
symptomes en sont bien plus riches pour celui qui l'éprouve
que pour l'observateur." This was convincingly demonstrated
to the present writer when he was prevailed upon to share in the
Brahmin group's potations on two occasions. He experienced
the time distortion, the tumbling rush of ideas, the intensified
significance of sights, sounds and tastes and, more strongly
than anything else, the feeling of existing on two planes at
once. His body sat or lay in a state of voluptuous indifference
to its surroundings, while consciousness alternated between
a timeless trancelike state and a painful struggle to keep awake,
to keep on observing and acting (in this case, to keep on writing down notes on his introspective experiences). It became
clear to him, in retrospect, that throughout the intoxication
his bias of personality, and perhaps his less conscious fears of
surrendering to a dreamlike state, resisted the somatic pull of
the drug; and yet he was able to enter sufficiently into the fringe
of the real ecstasy to quicken his future appreciation of what
the experience meant to those who welcomed and valued it.

Hitherto, it will be noted, the state induced by bhang has
been discussed in the terms of reference used by Western observers. The writer's own experience confirmed their clinical
accounts, with emphasis on feelings of detachment, of extreme
introspection, of the loss of volition coupled with a dreamlike
impression of heightened reality. Moreover, the recognition of
his own fear and repudiation of the state opened his eyes to two
possibilities: (a) that other Western observers might have
shared his own reluctance, if not inability, fully to submit to
this intoxication; and (b) that to Hindus, with their different
cultural heritage and personality bias, the experience might
represent something different, at once less frightening and

more congenial. It was with this in mind that he reviewed his notes of some hundreds of conversations with villagers, in order to consider what were their associations to daru and to bhang respectively.

It should be pointed out that this discussion concerns the use rather than the abuse of these intoxicants. There were many habitual drinkers of both, and instances of alcoholic delirium were described by several Rajputs, though not witnessed by the writer. The only Brahmin who could be called an addict to bhang in the strict sense was also an opium eater, and at 75 was one of the oldest men in the village. It is a vexed question as to whether cannabism, when carried to extremes, incites to crimes of violence, as Wolff (9), Dhunjibhoy (10) and Porot (3) assert, or whether, as Bromberg and Rodgers (11) and Wallace (12) have shown in careful statistical studies, this association is not supported by the facts. The present writer's study of the literature supports the view that crime (even the berserk attacks on the Crusaders by the hashish-inspired followers of the Mohammedan Old Man of the Mountains, from which the word *assassin* is said to be derived) is, like the voluptuous daydreams of the Tunisians, merely one of the ends which cannabism can be made to serve during its brief phase of excitement, and not a necessary consequence of taking the drug. In this village, at any rate, there were no instances of crimes attributable to the drinking of bhang, nor was there any evidence to support the suggestion of Dhunjibhoy, among others, that it gives rise to a characteristic psychosis. It remains open to proof whether such cases are not, as Mayer-Gross (13) maintains, simply schizophrenic illnesses occurring in a cannabis-taking population.

Villager's Association to Daru and Bhang

In the following series of quotations from a number of villagers' conversations, it will be helpful to bear in mind that Rajputs are distinguished by the addition of the title *Singh* (lion) to their name; among the Brahmins, a common second name is *Lal* (red, the auspicious color). For the sake of clarity all Brahmin names have been transcribed to conform to this rule.

The first obvious difference to emerge is that while the Brahmins are unanimous in their detestation of daru, the Rajputs do not present a united front in its defense. "Some Rajputs," explained Himat Singh, "those who are worshippers of God, they do not eat meat or drink wine—that is the first thing for them to give up. Wine spoils men's mind; some

swear and give abuse, which is inimical to holiness." Such
Rajputs, however, are few and far between: "The rest, they
eat, drink and remain *must*."[4]

Many Rajputs prided themselves on drinking with discrimination, a fixed measure every day. Thus Nahar Singh: "My
father used to drink a fixed quantity of daru, from a small
measure, every night. It was his niyam, his rule." A young man
called Ragunath Singh was emphatic in asserting the warlike
traditions of his caste, and their need for meat and drink:
"Panthers and tigers don't eat grass—and that's what Rajputs
are like, a carnivorous race." He also, however, stressed that
liquor was a dangerous ally: "If you take it to excess it
destroys your semen, the good stuff, the strength of your body
—but taken in right measure it builds it up."

Gambhir Singh mentioned that his father, a former Inspector of Police, used to allow himself a generous measure
every day: "It helped him in his work, made him fierce and
bold, ready to beat people when that was needed."

This stress on restraint, and on small measures, soon tended
to be forgotten in the course of an evening of Rajput hospi-
tality, when glass after glass was filled and emptied at a
draught. In his cups, Amar Singh used to boast of his un-
governable temper, of men he had killed in the heat of anger,
of his sexual prowess with prostitutes. His friend Gordhan
Singh chipped in with a description of a typical Rajput cele-
bration: "They sit drinking heartily till they are senseless, and
then they talk loudly and make fools of themselves, and spill
their food down the front of their shirts, and shout to the
dancing girls; and some of them pass out altogether—oh, it's
a fine sight to see, it's good fun."

The former Ruler of the village and of the surrounding
principality expressed conflicting views on daru. On the one
hand, he aspired to gain a "spiritual rise" through the practice
of prayers and austerities, and this necessitated a strict ration-
ing of his customary indulgence in alcohol. Quite often, however, something would happen to interrupt his abstemious
intentions, and on such a day his eloquence in praise of wine
was noticeably stimulated:

"Red eyes are thought by us Rajputs to be very beautiful. They
are the sign of lust. Those who have the good fortune to have
red lines in the eyes, they are thought to be very lusty. Rajputs
are very lusty, Sahib. It is because of their meat and drink:
it makes them so that they have to have their lust, poor
fellows."

4 *Must* describes the rage of an elephant which is in heat.

At this point he began to quote verses in praise of wine: "It makes the eyes red, it keeps the pleasure going between the pair, the husband and wife: how shall I praise you enough, oh twice-distilled!" And again: "In time of war, when the drum beats, only opium and daru drive out fear."

On another occasion, the Ruler quoted a ribald couplet to the effect that without meat all food is grass, and without daru even Ganges water has no virtue. But this blasphemy alarmed him into a momentary sobriety. He hastily repudiated the verse, but a few minutes later he was exuberantly describing the scene at a wealthy Rajput's wedding party:

> "They will be sitting drinking far into the night, with dancing girls entertaining them. They will call the dancing girl to sit on their lap, then they will get stirred and take her into a room and bar the doors; and the others will beat upon the door and say, 'Eh, Rao Sahib, we also want to see this girl.' Poor girl, where can she go, all doors are locked! Enjoy till morning, she must do what you want."

The Ruler's younger brother was emphatically not one of those Rajputs who renounced their pleasure in alcohol in the interests of religion: "Sahib, I am not interested in these things. These religious matters, usually one begins to be interested in them after the age of fifty."

And before then?

"Before then, Sahib, eat, drink, and make merry."

Rajputs not infrequently referred to bhang, but never with strong feelings either of approval or condemnation. It is mentioned as a refreshment given to guests who arrive after a long journey. An elderly retainer called Anop Singh said: "We are not in the habit of drinking bhang, though we'll take it if it comes our way. Sometimes holy men come, and they are great ones for bhang, so you have to join them if they invite you, and have some too." On one occasion the writer found a young Rajput landowner called Vijay Singh profoundly fuddled with a large dose of bhang which had been given to him, without his knowledge, in a spiced sweetmeat: "I didn't know I was eating bhang or I wouldn't have taken it—it's not a thing I like. It makes you very sleepy and turns your throat dry . . . I don't like it, it makes you quite useless, unable to do anything. Daru is not like that: you get drunk but you can still carry on."

The Brahmins, on the other hand, were quite unanimous in reviling daru and all those who indulged in it. They de-

scribed it as foul, polluting, carnal, and destructive to the
spark of Godhead which every man carries within him. As
Shankar Lal put it: "The result of eating meat and drinking
liquor is that you get filled with passion, rage—and then what
happens? The spirit of God flies out from you."

The Ruler's own attempt to reconcile religious devotions
with a measure of indulgence in alcohol was rejected with
contumely by Mohan Lal, a scholarly teacher: "He is all
wrong: he is a bogus lecher. Always busy with wine and
women, how can he find his way along this stony and thorny
path?"

In their references to the use of bhang, the Brahmins were
matter-of-fact rather than lyrical. "It gives good *bhakti*," said
Shankar Lal: "You get a very good bhakti with bhang." He
went on to define bhakti as the sort of devotional act which
consists in emptying the mind of all worldly distractions and
thinking only of God. The "arrived" devotee is able to keep
his thoughts from straying off onto trivial or lustful topics; in
his impersonal trance he becomes oblivious to mundane concerns so that you "could hit him in the face with shoes a
hundred times, and he would remain unmoved" (Mohan
Lal).

Brahmin informants made many references to a nearby
pilgrimage center presided over by a very influential priest.
Both he and his predecessors were described, with admiration,
as being mighty drinkers of bhang and heroic in the depth of
their devotional trances. The chief object of worship at this
place was an ancient phallic symbol of black stone, representing the god Shiva; and this god in turn was often cited as both
a bhang drinker and a paragon of the contemplative life. It
is by modeling themselves on this example that religious
ascetics practice severe prolonged austerities, training themselves to withdraw their entire attention from the distractions
of the sensible world until they can exist for hours in an
oblivious, inward-looking state. The ultimate reward of this
asceticism is that the Saddhu is enabled to divest himself
of his body (which becomes imperishable, though apparently
lifeless) and to pass directly into reunion with the spirit of
the universe. (One is reminded of Baudelaire's "l'apothéose de
l'Homme-Dieu.") Bhang is highly regarded as conducing
toward this condition and is taken regularly by most Saddhus.
In the precincts of the great Shiva temple, the writer frequently
encountered holy men, dressed in little more than a coating
of sacred ash, who staggered about in the early stages of
bhang intoxication. If he addressed them, they would reply

only with an elusive smile or with an exclamation like "Hari, Hari, Hari!"—repeating one of the names of God. Ordinary village Brahmins, who did not aspire to such feats of asceticism, made a practice of devoting some minutes or hours every day to sitting in a state of abstraction and prayer, and in this exercise they found a modicum of bhang to be most helpful.

Relevant Themes in Hindu Culture Pattern

Both the Rajput and the Brahmin castes, at least in this large village, belonged to the economically privileged section of the community. Their male members had all received at least enough education to make them literate in Hindi, and in an unsystematic way had been instructed in the fundamentals of their religion and made familiar with the main features of the Ramayana and Mahabharata epics which illustrate those teachings in a variety of dramatic episodes. Hinduism encompasses so wide a range of practical and philosophical beliefs, of myths and ritual ordinances, and contains so many contradictory elements, that one theologian, after 25 years of study, came to the conclusion that there were only two indispensable features in his religion: reverence of the Brahmin, and worship of the cow (14). These features are epitomized in the formal greetings exchanged by Rajput and Brahmin. The former salutes the priestly caste with "I clasp your feet," and the latter replies, "May you live long and protect the Brahmins and the cows." In so doing, they acknowledge each other's caste in its respective status of spiritual and temporal primacy.

The fundamental orthodox Hindu beliefs, as Taylor (15) has pointed out in an analysis drawn from study of a community in an area contiguous with Rajasthan, stem from the concepts of *karma* (predestined lot), of the cycle of rebirth, and of *dharma* (right conduct), observance of which leads to promotion in one's next rebirth and ultimately to the goal of all human endeavor, which is *moksh,* or liberation from the cycle of reincarnation altogether. Socio-economic relationships are accepted as inevitable, as is the hierarchic structure of caste. Indeed, "the individual's security in this society comes from his acceptance of his insignificant part in a vast preordained scheme: he has little anxiety, because he is not confronted with a variety of choice." Rajputs and Brahmins are alike in knowing that virtue consists in performing the duties appropriate to that station in life into which one is born, and in minimizing one's indulgence in sensual and emotional satisfactions of a private nature. Thus Nahar Singh, a Rajput renowned for his religious zeal, said:

> "Those of us who take religion seriously, but have still not wholly renounced the world, we can do it by taking care not to let our affections become too deeply engaged in things of lesser importance. We should do our work, fulfill all our duties, and be affectionate to our families—but all that should be on the surface of our daily lives. Our real souls, deep down, should not be involved in any of these emotional ties . . ."

Mohan Lal expressed similar views: "The religious man lives in the world, but apart. He is like a drop of water on a lotus leaf, which moves over its surface but is not absorbed." His caste-fellow Bhuri Lal described the ideal pattern of "nonattachment," leading in the end to release: "Moksh is obtained by purging the self of all carnal appetites and withdrawing from the illusions of this world. A wise man is cooltempered." Immediately after this, he went on to talk of sexual morality. Sex, he said, should be strictly controlled. It should be regarded as a duty, and used only for the purpose of perpetuating one's male line. He himself had been afflicted with four daughters before his two sons were born, and then, "As soon as my second son was born, I gave up having sex. You say I look young? That's because I have practiced celibacy for years."

This exaltation of asceticism, of self-deprivation, of trying to eliminate one's sensual appetites, is a basic theme. Again and again in Hindu mythology one encounters heroic figures (by no means always virtuous ones) who practice austerities so severe and prolonged that their spiritual power becomes prodigious: the gods themselves beg them to desist and offer to grant anything they ask. Taylor has related this to the absoluteness of paternal authority in the home; the pattern is firmly laid down that one can achieve success and recognition only by self-abnegation and prostration before the all-powerful father figure. A student of Kardiner (16) might be tempted to carry the analogy still farther back, to the Hindu child's wholly indulgent experience at the suckling stage, during which he actually usurps his father's place, because parents are not supposed to sleep together until the child is weaned. In this context, the *tapassya,* which constrains even the gods, can be see as a return to the infant's fantasied omnipotence.

The values discussed thus far are held in common by both castes, with the difference that the Brahmins, being at the pinnacle of the spiritual hierarchy, have a special obligation to lead a pious life. More than ordinary men, they must pay constant attention to the fulfilling of religious duties. Their lives are beset with recurring threats of defilement and their days are punctuated with acts of absolution. Among the many forms of self-denial to which they are accustomed are the avoidance of anger or any other unseemly expression of personal feelings; and abstinence from meat and alcohol is a prime essential. They are rewarded by being regarded, simply by virtue of their birth in this high caste, as already quasi-divine. Ordinary men address them as *Maharaj,* the greeting given to the gods. As one of them put it: "Even now, when people see a man is a Brahmin, they pay much respect in comparison to other castes. He is much more closely related to God."

In this region the Rajputs represent the temporal aristocracy, as the Brahmins do the spiritual. Their caste is one of warriors and landlords. Until the social reforms of 1948, their Rajahs exercised arbitrary and autocratic rule over the innumerable small principalities into which Rajasthan is divided. They owed allegiance in their turn to the Ruler of their State—in the case of this village, to the Maharana of Udaipur. By virtue of their role as warriors, the Rajputs were accorded certain privileged relaxations of the orthodox Hindu rules: in particular, those prohibiting the use of force, the taking of life, the eating of meat and drinking of wine. These all represent violations of basic canons of Hindu dharma, and so they are hedged about with restrictions and formalities in order to minimize their evil effects. Violence is a part of their lives, but they are taught to exercise forbearance, to rebuke an offender twice before chastising him. In warfare they obeyed a code of chivalry not unlike that of the medieval knights. Similarly, the meat of only a few animals is counted fit to eat, and then only the male of the species; and hence, also, the emphasis on restriction and invariable "measure" in drinking daru.

The Rajputs find themselves in a curious position. Their social preeminence is due to their role as defenders of religion, and they are as conservative in belief as they are in politics; and yet their own cherished traditions emphasize their deviation from "right living" in the orthodox Hindu sense. The conflict is heightened by the circumstance that in their case, even more than in all the others, patriarchal authority is stressed. As the writer has pointed out elsewhere (17), both sons and younger brothers in Rajput families have to learn to defer in utter subservience to their fathers and elder brothers. Whereas

in the Brahmin caste this domestic discipline is made tolerable
by the fact that it is impersonal, simply a facet of a general
obedience to propriety which the elders observe in their turn,
among Rajputs it is different. There is a great difference between the status of the head of the family and that of his sub-
ordinates. For example, a younger son inherits an estate only
one-twentieth the size of that which comes to the first-born.
The head of a Rajput family is anything but an impersonal
figure. Coached from infancy by a succession of sycophantic
retainers, he has an inflated idea of his personal importance,
coupled with an often well-founded suspicion that he is surrounded by rivals and enemies. The tensions which arise in such
a setting explode from time to time in violent quarrels. Another
corollary of the peculiar upbringing of the Rajputs is that they
are taught to put great stress on individual bravery and ferocity
in the face of danger. The test of real danger is all too seldom
met with, but every young Rajput lives with the anxiety that
he may not prove adequate to the occasion when it comes. As
a result he tends to be boastful, touchy, and readily inclined to
assuage his anxieties in the convivial relaxation of a drinking
party.

Discussion

In her much-quoted study of patterns of drinking in two
Central American villages, Bunzel (18) remarks, of such sociological appraisals in general: "It should be borne in mind
that each group represents a different problem: it is necessary
in each case to find out what role alcohol plays *in that culture.*"
She was able to demonstrate two widely differing ways of using
alcohol. In Chamula there was little aggression or promiscuity
or severity of discipline; there, heavy drinking was indulged in
from childhood and was attended with no guilt. In Chichicas-
tenango, on the other hand, she saw a strict paternal authority
and an insistence on the repression of aggressive and sexual
impulses, which found release in the course of occasional
drinking sprees; and these were followed by feelings of severe
guilt. The Rajput drinking pattern, obviously, has much in
common with the latter.

A more general frame of reference has been given by Horton
(2) in his survey of alcohol in primitive societies, which led
to his drawing up three basic theorems: (*a*) The drinking of
alcohol tends to be accompanied by release of sexual and aggressive impulses. (*b*) The strength of the drinking response
in any society tends to vary directly with the level of anxiety in

the society. (*c*) The strength of the drinking response tends to vary inversely with the strength of the counteranxiety elicited by painful experiences during and after drinking.

The first of these theorems is abundantly borne out by the behavior of Rajputs in their cups. It is clear also that the presence of socially approved prostitutes and lower-caste servants and dependents enables the carrying out of these impulses in a manner which excites no retribution, and so the third theorem operates in support of their drinking heavily. On the side of restraint is the knowledge that sensual indulgence is an offense against the Hindu code of asceticism; but this code does not weigh heavily on most Rajputs.

On Brahmins, on the other hand, the code weighs very heavily indeed, being associated with their fondest claims to superiority over their fellow men. A Brahmin who gets drunk will be outcasted, condemned to associate with the lowest ranks of society. Consequently the threat of this "counteranxiety" is sufficient to make the drinking of alcohol virtually impossible to Brahmins (at least in the village). There is no reason to suppose, however, that they, any more than the Rajputs, are devoid of anxiety. But the differences in emphasis on individual self-assertion (stressed by Rajput upbringing but constrained by their fiercely authoritarian disciplines) and on the unimportance of personal and sensual experiences (stressed in the Brahmin code) seem to imply that the anxieties of the Rajputs will be more acute, while those of the Brahmins will be more diffuse and more readily sublimated in the religious exercises which play such a large part in their adult lives.

Another consideration is raised by Shalloo's (19) analysis of the way in which Jewish cultural values operate to minimize the incidence of alcoholism in their community. In his view, the Jews develop strong familial and communal ties and stress social conformity and conservatism in mores because they are aware of the critical and often hostile scrutiny of the Gentiles among whom they live. He concludes: "Such an analysis indicates that we are dealing with an 'isolated sacred society' as against a Gentile 'accessible secular society.' "

In our Indian example, the Brahmins represented a "sacred society" but not an isolated one. Far from being alien, they represent the ideal religious aspirations of the masses of ordinary Hindus, those who are obliged to "eat, drink and keep their passions alive," as Shankar Lal once put it. If the Brahmins are abstemious, it is not through an exaggerated fear of the censure of their fellows. On the contrary, their consciousness of their exalted state often makes them high-handed and inconsiderate in ther dealings with those of lower caste; and moreover, they are not abstemious. If Horton's theorems hold good for alcoholism, must a new set be constructed to account for cannabism?

The answer which the present writer would suggest to the problem posed at the outset of this paper would be on the following lines: There are alternative ways of dealing with sexual and aggressive impulses besides repressing them and then "blowing them off" in abreactive drinking bouts in which the superego is temporarily dissolved in alcohol. The way which the Brahmins have selected consists in a playing down of all interpersonal relationships in obedience to a common, impersonal set of rules of Right Behavior. Not only feelings but also appetites are played down, as impediments to the one supreme end of union with God. Significantly, this goal of sublimated effort is often described in terms appropriate to sexual ecstasy, as is the case with the communications of aescetics, and mystics in other parts of the world. Whereas the Rajput in his drinking bout knows that he is taking a holiday from his sober concerns, the Brahmin thinks of his intoxication with bhang as a flight not from but toward a more profound contact with reality.

Westerners, like the Rajputs, are committed to a life of action. They are brought up to regard individual achievement as important, and sensual indulgence to be not wholly wrong if it is enjoyed within socially prescribed limits. In spite of the existence among a sophisticated minority of the cult of nonattachment, the principles of *yoga* are unfamiliar to the West, and the experience of surrendering one's powers of volition is felt to be threatening and distasteful—as European experimenters with hashish (and the writer, with bhang) have found. Wolff (9) is, however, too sweeping in suggesting that cannabism is a peculiarly oriental taste. The Rajputs are far from being the only Easterners who dislike it or feel no need of it. Porot has pointed out that Indian hemp could easily be cultivated in the Far East, and yet it is practically unknown to the peoples of China and Japan. La Barre's (20) account of Chinese personality suggests that that people have little inclination to despise material pleasures of this world; and the Japanese would be the last, one would suppose, to renounce the active life.

On the basis, presumably of his own religious convictions, Wolff has implied that the ecstatic intuitions experienced through cannabism, far from having any validity, represent a flouting of "an inviolable moral law." This is the antithesis of cultural relativism. No one is left in doubt where Wolff takes his stand. Were the present writer to emulate this candor, he would have to say that of the two types of intoxication which he witnessed, and in a measure shared, in this Rajasthan village, he had no doubt that that which was indulged in by the Brahmins was the less socially disruptive, less unseemly, and more in harmony with the highest ideas of their race; and yet so alien to his own personal and cultural pattern of ego defenses, that he much preferred the other. It was a case of *video meliora proboque, deteriora sequor*.

Postscript

Since the above article was written, Aldous Huxley (21) has published an eloquent and perceptive account of the experience of mescalin intoxication, which is shown to resemble that induced by bhang. Huxley was particularly struck by two aspects: in the initial stage, by the primordial vividness of visual impressions, in perceiving ordinarily commonplace objects; and in the later stages, by the feeling of superhuman insight into the nature of things, accompanied by a complete detachment both from his own self and from those of his fellow men. He regards mescalin as a "gratuitous grace" which facilitates the sort of mystical experience which he finds both chastening and rewarding, in much the same way as Brahmins and Saddhus regard bhang as an aid to contemplation. Yet he is unrealistic enough to wish that Americans, and Westerners generally, should take to this drug in preference to alcohol and tobacco. If the thesis of this paper is valid, Westerners have refrained from taking mescalin (which has long been available to them) because its effect does not accord with their desires. Unless there is an unforeseen reversal of their basic values, they are as little likely to follow Huxley's advice as are the Brahmins to abandon bhang in favor of the Rajputs' daru, or vice versa.

Summary

In a village in northern India, members of the two highest caste groups, Rajput and Brahmin, were found to differ in their choice of intoxicant, the one taking alcohol, the other a preparation of *Cannabis indica*. An explanation for this cleavage was sought in their own associations to the two drugs, in the psychological effects of their type of intoxication, and in the different values stressed by each group, both in their personality development and in their ideal patterns of behavior. The cultural uses of alcohol and of cannabis intoxication are discussed in the light of this illustration.

References

1. Ravi Varma, L. A. Alcoholism in Ayurveda. Quart. J. Stud. Alc. 11: 484–491, 1950.

2. Horton, D. The functions of alcohol in primitive societies: a cross-cultural study. Quart. J. Stud. Alc. 4: 199–320, 1943.

3. Porot, A. Le cannabisme (haschich–kif–chira–marihuana). Ann. méd.-psychol. 101¹: 1–24, 1942.

4. Gautier, T. Le club des hachischins, Paris, 1846.

5. Guilly, P. Le club des hachischins. Encéphale 39: 175–185, 1950.

6. Baudelaire, C. P. Les paradis artificiels, opium et haschisch. Paris; 1860.

7. De la Mare, W. J. Desert Islands. London; 1924.

8. Hesnard, A. Note sur les fumeurs de chanvre en Orient. Encéphale 2: 40–46, 1912.

9. Wolff, P. O. Problems of drug addiction in South America. Brit. J. Addiction 46: 66–78, 1949.

10. Dhunjibhoy, J. E. A brief résumé of the types of insanity commonly met with in India, with a full description of "Indian hemp insanity" peculiar to the country. J. ment. Sci. 76: 254–264, 1930.

11. Bromberg, W., and Rodgers, T. C. Marihuana and aggressive crime (in naval service). Amer. J. Psychiat. 102: 825–827, 1946.

12. New York City, Mayor's Committee on Marihuana (Wallace, G. B., Chairman). The Marihuana Problem in the City of New York: Sociological, Medical, Psychological and Pharmacological Studies. New York; Cattell; 1944.

13. Mayer-Gross, W. Die Auslösung durch seelische und körperliche Schädigungen. In: Bumke, O., ed. Handbuch der Geisteskrankheiten; vol. 9, spec. pt. 5, pp. 112–134, 1932.

14. Carstairs, G. The Hindu. Edinburgh; 1926.

15. Taylor, W. S. Basic personality in orthodox Hindu culture patterns. J. abnorm. soc. Psychol. 43: 3–12, 1948.

16. Kardiner, A. The Psychological Frontiers of Society. New York; Columbia Univ. Press; 1945.

17. Carstairs, G. M. The case of Thakur Khuman Singh: a culture-conditioned crime. Brit. J. Delinq. 4: 14–25, 1953.

18. Bunzel, R. Role of alcoholism in two Central American cultures. Psychiatry 3: 361–387, 1940.

19. Shalloo, J. P. Some cultural factors in the etiology of alcoholism. Quart. J. Stud. Alc. 2: 464–478, 1941.

20. La Barre, W. Some observations on character structure in the Orient. *II*. The Chinese. Psychiatry 9: 215–237, 1946.

21. Huxley, A. The Doors of Perception. New York; Harper; 1954.

CHAPTER FIVE

THE POLITICS, ETHICS, AND MEANING OF MARIJUANA

Dr. Timothy Leary

Until the summer of 1963, Timothy Leary, PhD, was a lecturer in clinical psychology at Harvard University. There, with his colleague, psychology professor Richard Alpert, PhD, and others, he conducted extensive original research in the theory and practice of consciousness expansion through the use of psychedelic (literally "mind-manifesting") substances.

Dr. Leary's Harvard studies demonstrated that compounds such as LSD, psilocybin, and mescalin facilitated and accelerated deep and valuable insights into such key value-forming areas as philosophy, ethics, religion, and esthetics. His work indicated the wide applicability of psychedelic materials in the fields of social and personal psychology as well. These discoveries, which seem so valid and worthy of further investigation, were compromised in the eyes of University administrators because of what they considered an alarming excess of undergraduate enthusiasm over the spectacular effects of psychedelics.

Provoked and compromised by a spate of lurid press coverage, the school administration refused to sanction further experiments, which inevitably would have involved newly developed, unorthodox, and therefore controversial psychedelic techniques and theories originated by Dr. Leary and his associates. Drs. Leary, whose contract expired, and Alpert, who was forced to resign, eventually left Harvard amid a storm of student protest.

121

Dr. Leary is the author of forty articles and five books on
the proper use, the effects, and the potentials of psychedelic
materials, to which category marihuana belongs. At present
he directs the Castalia Foundation in Millbrook, New York,
where he is continuing his writing and research. At the time
of this writing he is contesting a sentence of thirty years in
prison and a fine of $30,000 for the possession of less than
one-half ounce of marihuana, arguing that his freedom of
personal conscience, guaranteed by our Constitution, grants
him the right to study and alter his own consciousness with
marihuana. This polemical essay on the rights of human con-
sciousness (the civil rights of the mind) was written for this
volume.

I

I have written these pages about the social, ethical, and
scientific meanings of marijuana under two compelling time-
pressures: first, the gentle prodding of David Solomon, who
was kind enough to hold up publication of this book to include
my hasty comments; and second, the less than gentle insistence
of a Texas judge that I spend the next thirty years in prison.

I am concerned more about my promise to David Solomon
than about the threat of incarceration. If psychedelic drugs
tell us anything, it is that the prisons exist only in man's mind.
Any ground is sacred ground if you are open enough to realize
it. Including Leavenworth.

By legal and social standards, the sentence of thirty years'
imprisonment and a $30,000 fine for the possession of half
an ounce of marijuana might seem severe. But the basic issue
here is internal freedom. The basic charge is heresy. At other
stages in this long struggle for freedom of consciousness such
penalties would be considered light. I protest but not complain.

My crime is the ancient and familiar one of corrupting the
minds of the youth. This charge is a valid one. I have written
some forty articles and five books about the effects of psychedelic drugs. I have addressed these messages to all who can
read, but I have been keenly aware that it has been the young
who have attended and acted on these messages.

The March 11, 1966, issue of *Time* magazine announces
that at least 10,000 students at the University of California
have taken LSD. The number of students who smoke marijuana is considered to be considerably higher.

I am repeatedly asked to deplore this use of psychedelic
drugs by the young. Is not this a dangerous and reckless misuse? And I repeatedly refuse to generally condemn this psy-

chedelic revolt of the young. Cite me an individual case and I may be able to speculate about this specific recklessness or wisdom. But, in general, I say that it is a good thing that more and more Americans are expanding their awareness, pulling back the veil of symbolic platitude, and confronting the many other levels of energy that are available to man. It is a tragedy that more older people aren't joining the young. To parents who are worried about their children "turning on," I would say, "Don't fight your kids; join them in this adventure of exploration. If you are tolerant of your children's use of alcohol (which numbs their vision), why are you intolerant of their wish to expand their vision?" In the gamble of life my wager goes down on the side of the young. The current generation is the brightest, holiest, bravest, and most curious of any generation in human history. And, by God, they better be.

None of us knows how to handle the power and promise-threat of mind-expanding chemicals. But if I am confronted with a fifteen-year-old who does not know what he is doing and a fifty-year-old who does not know what he is doing, I'll take the fifteen-year-old every time. In using a new form of energy, whatever mistakes the teenager makes will be in the direction of sensation, love-making, curiosity, desire for growth. The fifty-year-old has abandoned sensation, lost the impulse to make love, killed his curiosity, and dissipated his lust for growth. You know how he uses new forms of energy: for control and power and war-making.

Support the kids. Listen to them. Learn from them if they will let you. They are closer to their nervous systems, closer to cellular and seed wisdom, closer to the Divine Energy than we parents. The human species, let's face it, is an adolescent, as yet unformed, confused, evolutionary form. Stand in the way of the energy process as it slowly, relentlessly begins to uncoil, and it will crush you and your symbolic illusions. Cherish it, nurture it, let it grow, let it blossom, and you will be reborn in and with your children.

II

Marijuana alters consciousness.

LSD alters consciousness.

On that they all agree. Policeman. Priest. Pusher. Politician. Prophet. Pharmacologist. Psychologist.

They all agree that marijuana and LSD alter consciousness. But how? And to what end—evil or beneficial? To these questions there is no agreement.

Sincere, well-intentioned men are led to extreme positions. On the one hand, punitive laws, repressive crusades, police action, the arming of agents of Health, Education and Welfare, the lengthy imprisonment of citizens for no crime other than the altering of their own consciousness:

> One of the stiffest and most inflexible sets of laws ever put to the Federal books, the Boggs–Daniel Act (1956) represents the high-water mark of punitive legislation against the use, sale, and handling of drugs. It imposed severe mandatory sentences for sale or possession of narcotics—permitting in most cases neither probation nor parole. . . .
> In some states, such as New York, sentencing is fairly lenient. Mere possession (25 or more marijuana cigarettes . . .) carries sentence of only (sic) three to ten years.[1]
> In today's affluent society the use of marijuana is no longer confined to the "dregs" of society. It is becoming increasingly fashionable for middle- and upper-class youth. California jails now hold close to 6,000 people for breaking marijuana laws. Sixty-four percent of all Californians arrested on marijuana charges are under 25 years of age. Arrests for breaking marijuana laws . . . since 1962 . . . have increased nearly 500%.[2]

On the other hand, passive resistance, poetic and artistic and scientific appeals to reason, futile protests, flights into exile, cynicism:

> . . . Dr. S. J. Holmes, director of the narcotic addiction unit of the Alcoholism and Drug Addiction Research Foundation in Toronto . . . believes it is "fantastic and ridiculous" that a person caught with one marijuana cigaret can be sent to prison.
> It is particularly ridiculous, he said, when compared with the use and effect of alcohol. "This situation is really a disgrace to our civilization and merits much consideration."[3]
> The preliminary estimates of a foundation-financed study on drug use at San Francisco State show that 60% of the students will at some time use an illegal drug . . .
> Marijuana is sold on the campus, smoked on the campus, and used by professors.
> A Berkeley sorority girl said, "When you drink you lose control and sensitivity, generally feeling and acting like a slobbering idiot. This never happens with pot."
> Most spoke of the legal problems as did this girl: "It doesn't

1 *The Drug Takers,* TIME-LIFE Books, 1965, pp. 53–54.
2 *San Francisco* Magazine, February 1966, p. 16.
3 Toronto *Globe and Mail,* Feb. 17, 1966, p. 5.

bother me to break the law. How many times do you break
it jaywalking and so on? The main thing is that I just don't
think of using marijuana in these terms. It's pure hypocrisy
and stupidity that it's not legal. The law is wrong for both
practical and moral reasons."[4]

There are many dimensions to the psychedelic drug controversy and no simple answers. I wish to consider in this essay
three issues: the political, the moral, and the scientific.

THE POLITICAL ISSUE

The Politics of Consciousness Expansion

To understand the psychedelic controversy it is necessary
to study the sociology of psychedelic drugs. Who wants to
smoke marijuana? To eat peyote? To ingest LSD? What people
are involved in this new drug menace? The young. The racially
and nationally alienated. The creative. Most users of psychedelic plants and drugs fall into at least one of these three
categories.

The Young

Over 50 percent of the American population is under the
age of 25. Ominous, isn't it? From 50 to 70 percent of the
use of marijuana and LSD is by the high school and college
age group. From 50 to 70 percent of the arrests and imprison-
ments for possession of psychedelic substances fall on the
shoulders of those under the age of 30. Whisky-drinking
middle age imprisons pot-smoking youth. Think about this.

The Racially and Nationally Alienated

Negroes, Puerto Ricans, American Indians. The use of
psychedelic plants in these noble minority groups of the American society is high. The whisky-drinking, white middle-class
imprisons those with different cultural and religious preferences. Think about this.

The Creative

I would estimate that over 70 percent of nonacademic creative artists have used psychedelic substances in their work.
Painters. Poets. Musicians. Dancers. Actors. Directors. The

whisky-drinking middle brow imprisons the growing edge. Think about this.

The Criminal and Psychedelic Drugs

The stereotyped picture of the marijuana smoker is that of a criminal type. The statistics do not support this myth. Marijuana is used by groups that are socially alienated from middle-class values—youth, Negroes, Indians, creative artists, but few criminals. Alcohol is the drug of the nonyouthful, noncreative, white criminal. The economics of heroin leads the addict to commit crime. Few criminals smoke pot. Few pot smokers are criminals (except for the offense of changing their own consciousness).

The Psychedelic Minority Group

A United Nations report on worldwide use of drugs estimated that in 1951 there were 200 million cannabis users. This is an awesome statistic. Worldwide, there are more marijuana users than members of the Protestant and Jewish religions combined.

The number of pot smokers worldwide is larger than the population of the United States of America. It is safe to say that there are more pot smokers than there are members of the middle class throughout the world. Indeed, we have the astonishing spectacle of a middle-class minority, tolerant to alcohol and addicted to bureaucracy, passing laws against and interfering with the social-religious rituals of a statistically larger group! Think about that one.

It has been estimated that as many as ten million people in America today have used marijuana, peyote, and LSD. Remember the Indians, the Negroes, the young, the creative. We deal here with one of the largest persecuted minority groups in the country. This group is nonvocal, effectively prevented from presenting its case, essentially stripped of its constitutional rights.

Another crucial sociological issue that is easily overlooked: psychedelic people tend to be socially passive. The psychedelic experience is by nature private, sensual, spiritual, internal, introspective. Whereas alcohol and amphetamines stimulate the afferent nervous system—inciting furious game activities— the psychedelics stimulate the afferent nervous centers. Contemplation . . . meditation . . . sensual openness . . . artistic and religious preoccupation.

Excesses of passive contemplation are no better than excesses of action—but certainly no worse. God and the DNA code designed man to have interoceptive and exteroceptive neurological systems, and any harmonious view of man should allow for judicious and thoughtful balancing of both.

Throughout world history psychedelic people have not tended to form commissions to stamp out nonpsychedelic people. Nor do they pass laws against or imprison nonpsychedelicists.

THE ETHICAL ISSUE

The Molecular Revolution

Politically oriented activists have throughout history left the psychedelic minority pretty much alone. The power-holders have been too busy fighting each other to worry about those who prefer to live in quiet harmony and creative quietude.

It is harder work to contact and control your nervous system than the external symbol structure. Yogins, meditators, monks, hashish mystics have been too busy decoding and appreciating their afferent (sensory) and cellular communication systems to busy themselves with political struggles.

But now comes the molecular revolution. The work of James McConnell demonstrates that learning is molecular. Dumb flatworms eat smart flatworms and become smart. Holger Hyden discovers that the brain cells of educated rats contain a third more RNA than do the brain cells of uneducated rats. University of California psychologists pass on learning from one rat to another by injecting RNA from trained rats. Neurologists are "wiring-up" the brains of animals and men and altering consciousness by pressing buttons. Press a button: make him hungry. Press a button: make him erotic. Press a button: make him angry. Press a button: make him feel good.

The psychedelic chemicals flood out of the laboratories—into the hands of the two familiar groups: those who want to do something to others and those who want to do something to themselves.

U.S. Army psychologists secretly drop LSD into the coffee of an infantry platoon. The surprised soldiers giggle, break ranks, and wander off looking at the trees. Psychiatrists secretly drop LSD into the water glasses of psychotic patients and report that LSD enhances insanity. And on the college campuses and in the art centers of the country hundreds of thousands of the creative young take LSD and millions smoke marijuana to explore their own consciousness. The new cult of visionaries. They turn on, tune in, and often drop out of the academic, professional and other games-playing roles they have been assigned. They do not drop out of life, but probe more deeply into it, toward personal and social realignments characterized by loving detachment from materialist goals.

Laws are passed encouraging the administration of LSD to the unsuspecting (patients, soldiers, research subjects) and preventing self-administration!

The Two Commandments of the Molecular Age

Of the many powerful energies now suddenly available to man, the most challenging and sobering are those that alter the fabric of thought and judgment—the very core of meaning and being.

Learning, memory, mood, judgment, identity, consciousness can now be transformed instantaneously by electrical and chemical stimuli. In the long-short diary of our species, no issue has posed such a promise-peril.

The history of human evolution (not unlike that of every other species of life on our planet) is the record of new forms of energy—physical, mechanical, chemical—discovered, slowly understood (and misunderstood), painfully debated, eventually adapted to.

Today the human race is confronted with new energies that tax our wisdom, confuse our judgment, terrorize our emotional securities, excite our highest aspirations, and threaten to alter our central notions of man and his place on this planet. Never has man faced ethical and political issues so complex, so delicate, so demanding, so frightening. Never has man been in greater need of ethical guidance. And where is it?

Our scientists plunge enthusiastically into the process of mind-changing, consciousness alteration, with little apparent regard for the moral, political complications.

One of the few men who have recognized the high stakes of this new game of cerebral roulette is David Krech, psychologist at Berkeley. Dr. Krech is quoted as saying:

> Until recently, these substances were considered science-fiction, but real science has been moving forward so rapidly in this area that science-fiction is hard put to keep up with it. About 15 years ago, I doubt whether I could have found more than a half-dozen laboratories in the entire world which were concerned with basic research in behavior, brain, and biochemistry. Today there hardly exists a major laboratory where such research is not being given high priority.
>
> If we should find effective mind-control agents, we must consider whether the manufacture and dispensing of such agents should be left to private enterprise or to military control or to political control. And how should this be done, and when and by whom? It is not too early for us to ponder

very seriously the awesome implications of what brain research may discover.[5]

The time has come for a new ethical code to deal with issues unforeseen (or were they, really?) by our earliest prophets and moralists. Although the social-political implications are hopelessly complicated, the moral issues are clear-cut, precisely pure. And if the moral center of gravity is maintained, the endless chain of political and administrative decisions can be dealt with confidently and serenely.

Two new ethical Commandments are necessary as man moves into the Molecular Age. Compared with these imperatives the codes of earlier prophets seem like game rules— codes for social harmony. The new Commandments are neurological and biochemical in essence, and therefore, I suspect, in closer harmony with the laws of cellular wisdom, the law of the DNA code.

I did not invent these Commandments; they are the result of some 250 psychedelic sessions. They are revealed to me by my nervous system, by ancient, cellular counsel. I give them to you as revelation, but ask you not to take them on faith; check them out with your own nervous system. Ask your DNA code. I urge you to memorize these two Commandments. Meditate on them. You might take 300 gamma of LSD and present these Commandments to your symbol-free nervous system. Nothing less than the future of our species depends upon our understanding of and obedience to these two natural laws.

THE TWO COMMANDMENTS FOR THE MOLECULAR AGE

I. Thou Shalt Not Alter the Consciousness of thy fellow man.

II. Thou Shalt Not Prevent thy fellow man from Altering his own Consciousness.

Commentary on the Two Commandments

Thousands of theological, philosophical, and legal texts will be written in the next few decades interpreting, qualifying, and specifying these two Commandments. I happily leave this chore to those who face the implementation of this code. But a few general comments may be helpful.

1. These Commandments are not new. They are specifications of the first Mosaic Law—that man shall not act as God to others. Be God yourself, if you can, but do not impose your divinity on others. They are also specifications of the two Christian Commandments—Thou shalt love God and thy fellow man.

2. There are several obvious qualifications of the first Commandment. Do not alter the consciousness of your fellow man by symbolic, electrical, chemical, or molecular means. If he wants you to? Yes. You may help him alter his own consciousness. Or you may get his conscious, alerted permission to alter his consciousness for him. In the direction he wants.

3. There are several obvious qualifications of the second Commandment. Do not prevent your fellow man from altering his consciousness by means of symbols. This is the familiar "Freedom of expression" issue. But also you must not prevent your fellow man from altering his own consciousness by chemical, electrical, or molecular means. These are new freedoms which the wise men who wrote the Constitution and the Bill of Rights did not anticipate, but which they might have included had they known.

4. May you prevent your fellow man from altering his consciousness if he thereby poses a threat to others or to the harmonious development of society? Yes. But be careful. You walk a precarious precipice. Whenever society restricts the freedom of the human being to alter his own consciousness (by means of symbols or chemicals), the burden of proof as to danger to others must be on society. We may prevent others from doing things that restrict our consciousness—but the justification must be clear.

THE SCIENTIFIC ISSUE

The Scientific Meaning of Marijuana

The political and ethical controversies over psychedelic plants are caused by our basic ignorance about what these substances do.

They alter consciousness. But how, where, why, what for? Questions about psychedelic drugs remain unanswered because our basic questions about consciousness remain unanswered. As we learn more about the biochemistry and physiology of consciousness then we will understand the specific effects and uses of consciousness-altering plants.

External, look-at-it-from-the-outside science is not enough. Biochemistry and neurology will soon unravel some of the riddles of molecular learning and RNA[6] education. Blessings on James McConnell and David Krech and Holger Hyden. But then what? Who shall use the new magic molecules? Who shall control them? The routine scientoid solutions are: Inject them in the stupid, inject them in the crazy, inject them into army privates, inject them in the senile—and eventually, when they are safe enough to prevent law suits, sell them to the docile middle class.

But wait a minute. We can't do that any more—remember? We are not dealing with molecules that blow up the enemy or eradicate insects or cure headaches or produce the mild stupor of alcohol or tranquilize the active. We are dealing with agents that change consciousness. And we have a new Commandment to obey—remember? "Thou Shalt Not Alter the Consciousness of thy fellow man."

And if you try to control the new molecules, then we have the black-market problem all over again. You remember the LSD situation? The scientoid plan was to research LSD quietly in mental hospitals and army bases—double-blindly drugging the unsuspecting. But the word got out: "LSD produces ecstasy. LSD helps you see through the game veil." And the revolution began. The upper-middle-class underground. the white-collar black-market.

And then the laws and the penalties and the arming of agents of the Department of Health, Education and Welfare, to hunt down psychedelics.

Any officer or employee of the Department . . . may
1. carry firearms
2. execute and serve search warrants . . .

6 Within the nucleus of every living cell lies a tiny, complex chain of nucleic acid molecules called the DNA code. DNA is the brain of the cell: the timeless blueprinting code that designs every aspect of life. DNA executes its plans by means of RNA molecules. RNA is the communication system, the language, the senses and hands of the DNA. The language of RNA can be passed from one organism to another. The discovery of this fact is revolutionizing our theories of memory, learning, consciousness, and education. The basic unit of learning is molecular. The basic unit of consciousness is molecular.

3. execute seizure . . .
4. make arrests without warrants . . .[7]

And next come the Smart-pills. Will the same cycle of dreary platitudes and bureaucratic hysteria make the rounds again?

WASHINGTON, D.C., JANUARY 1, 1969.—HEALTH, EDUCATION AND WELFARE OFFICIALS ANNOUNCED TODAY REGULATIONS CONTROLLING ILLICIT USE OF AMINO ACIDS.

ACCORDING TO THE NEW LAWS, DNA AND RNA MOLECULES CAN BE ADMINISTERED ONLY BY GOVERNMENT-APPROVED PHYSICIANS IN A GOVERNMENT-SUPPORTED HOSPITAL.

HARVARD BLACK MARKET BARED IN RNA.

SMART PILL FAD NEW CAMPUS KICK.
"Hey! Did you hear? There's a new shipment of black-market Einstein A.A. in the village!"
"I'm giving my wife some Elizabeth Taylor acid for Christmas. Smuggled in from Mexico. We can all afford to learn new methods, right?"
"I know it's against the law, but Willy is five years old and can't work quantum-theory equations. So, in despair, I've connected with some Max Planck RNA."

NEW YORK, APRIL 1, 1969, A.P.—The newly organized microbiological unit of the Health, Education and Welfare Department armed with paralysis spray guns and electron microscopes raided an RNA den last night. Over one hundred millionth of a gram of amino acid was seized. Agents estimated that the haul was worth close to $800,000. Held on charges of being present in premises where illegal drugs were seized were a poet, a philosopher, and two college-age girls. H.E.W. agents tentatively labeled the contraband molecules as Shakespeare RNA, Socrates RNA, and Helen of Troy RNA.
R. Wilheim Phlympton, President of the American Psychiatric Association—Amino Acid Division, when notified of the raid, said: "Amino acids RNA and DNA are dangerous substances causing illegitimacy, suicide and irresponsible sexuality. They should only be administered by psychiatrists in government hospitals or army research stations."

7 Drug Abuse Control Amendments of 1965.

The four alleged drug-cultists who were held in $25,000 bail smiled enigmatically, but made no comment.

These headlines won't happen, will they? They can't happen, because now we have the two commandments for the Molecular Age.

Remember: "Thou Shalt Not Alter the Consciousness of thy fellow man."

Remember, congressmen, policemen, judges. And agents of the Department of Health, Education and Welfare, lay down your arms. Remember the second Commandment: "Thou Shalt Not Prevent thy fellow man from Altering his own Consciousness."

Now that chemists have produced psychedelic chemicals, now that biochemists are isolating the powers of RNA, it is time to face the real scientific issue.

The meaning and use of consciousness-changing methods cannot be understood from the standpoint of external science, from the standpoint of look-at-it-from-the-outside science. Not only does this violate the first Commandment, it just doesn't work.

The meaning and use of psychedelic chemicals—LSD, RNA, marijuana—depends on the scientists taking the molecules himself, opening up his own consciousness, altering his own nervous system. Only in this way will we develop the maps, models, languages, techniques for utilizing the new mind-changing procedures.

You can't use the microscope by clapping it over the eyes of unsuspecting mental patients and army privates.

The mind-altering chemicals—marijuana, lysergic acid, amino acid—have to be studied from within. *You* have to take them. You can observe their effects from outside, but this tells you very little. You can "sacrifice" the animals and discover brain changes. You can drug mental defectives and seniles and observe gross behavior changes, but these are the irrelevant husks. Consciousness must be studied from within. Molecular learning is communication at the cellular and molecular level. The mental defectives can't decipher these languages. The molecular psychologist must decipher these languages.

This is not a new idea. This is the core idea of all Eastern psychology. Buddhism, for example, is not a religion; it is a complex system of psychology, a series of languages and methods for decoding levels of consciousness.

And this is the original method of Western scientific psychology—the trained introspection of Wundt, Weber, Fechner, Titchner. The scientist must learn the language of the neuron and cell and teach it to others. It's a tough assignment, isn't it? No more dosing the passive subjects. *You* inhale, swallow, and inject the magic molecule *yourself*. You train others to do the same.

Frightening? Yes, it is frightening. And this defines the first criterion of the scientist of consciousness. He must have courage. He must embark on a course of methodically and deliberately going out of his mind. This is no field for the faint of heart. You are venturing out (like the Portuguese sailors, like the astronauts) on the uncharted margins. But be reassured; it's an old human custom. It's an old living-organism custom. We're here today because certain adventurous proteins, certain far-out, experimenting cells, certain beatnik amphibia, certain brave men, pushed out and exposed themselves to new forms of energy.

Where do you get this courage?

It isn't taught in graduate school or medical school or law school. It doesn't come by arming government agents. It comes from faith. Faith in your nervous system. Faith in your body. Faith in your cells. Faith in the life process. Faith in the molecular energies released by psychedelic molecules.

Not blind faith. Not faith in human social forms, but conscious faith in the harmony and wisdom of nature. Faith easily checked out empirically. Trust your equipment and its reaction to the molecular messages of the psychedelic drugs.

To do this we need a method and a map. The method tells us how to use consciousness-altering substances—marijuana, LSD, RNA. The map is the language of the different levels of consciousness triggered by the psychedelic molecules.

The two Commandments tell you that—politically and ethically—you may not drug others but have to do it to yourself. And the scientific nature of the problem—consciousness—tells you again that you may not drug others but have to do it to yourself.

You cannot understand the use and meaning of such psychedelic substances as marijuana, LSD and RNA until you have models, maps of the different levels of consciousness contacted by these substances.

Maps implement and make possible the two Commandments. These moral imperatives insist that only the carrier of the nervous system can alter the function of that nervous system. Only you should decide where your consciousness should locate. To make such decisions—which levels of consciousness to contact and how to reach them—you need information. To understand how marijuana affects consciousness you must understand the dimensions of consciousness and the specific level which cannabis triggers.

This brief essay does not allow a detailed description of the maps and methods of consciousness expansion and of the exquisitely detailed implications for using psychedelic substances. Here I can list only the major levels of consciousness, indicate which plants and drugs get you to each level, and, in particular, attempt to suggest the meaning of marijuana.

Consciousness is energy received and decoded by a structure. There are as many levels of consciousness available to the human being as there are anatomical structures in the human body for receiving and decoding energy. There are as many levels of reality as there are anatomical structures for decoding energy. The anatomy of consciousness is the anatomy of neural and cellular structures.

There are six levels of consciousness, and each of these levels is reached and triggered by means of chemicals—produced naturally by the body or ingested in the form of drugs.

1. *The Level of Minimal Consciousness:* sleep, coma, stupor. This state occurs naturally by means of internal body chemistry or can be induced by drugs such as barbiturates, somnambulants, alcohol, and opiates. External stimuli are disregarded.

2. *The Level of Symbolic Consciousness* (usually and erroneously called "normal consciousness"). This level of consciousness is exclusively focused on external perceptions or mentalisms (thoughts) about external conditioned symbols. This state occurs through the process of imprinting—a chemical fixing of the nervous system which "hooks" attention to externals. The chemical process is at present unknown. Serotonin may be the chemical secreted by the body that addicts the nervous system to symbolic externals. Note that narcotic-type drugs (including alcohol) release man from the addictive hook to symbols in the direction of "escape" whereas the psychedelic chemicals release man from the external-symbolic in the direction of expanded consciousness.

3. *The Level of Sensory Awarenesss—External.* Here, consciousness is focused on the sensory nerve endings that receive energy from the outside. The retina of the eye, the eardrum and the Organ of Corti, the olfactory (smell) bulbs, the taste buds, the naked endings which receive impulses of touch, temperature, pain. In routine consciousness we are aware only of symbols—"things" seen, heard, touched, tasted. At the Neural or Sensory Level we are aware of direct energy exploding on our sense endings—light waves hurtling into the

retina at the speed of 186,000 miles a second, pressure exploding the naked grenades of sensation in our touch receptors, and so forth. Drugs that trigger direct sensation are marijuana, small doses of LSD (25–50 gamma), of mescaline (50–150 mg), psilocybin (6–16 mg).

Certain yoga exercises can attain the Sensory Level of Consciousness. [Yoga is the royal road to the Divine through the senses. The strategy of the Yogin is to eliminate all external stimuli except those that trigger the sense organ he wishes to "turn on." Meditation is a technique for eliminating extraneous stimuli and zeroing-in on the eye (mandala), ear (mantra), taste-touch-smell (tantra).]

Marijuana is the mildest of the psychedelic drugs. It activates the external sensory system and tones down the symbolic game addiction. Experienced marijuana users know how easy it is "to hang someone up" on the gustatory sense by talking about food during a session. Pot-smoking musicians let themselves get hung-up on sound waves hitting the tympanic membrane. Pot-smoking artists turn off visual symbols and register light pounding against their retinas. The aphrodisiac, touch amplification of cannabis is a well-known, well-guarded secret among marijuana adepts.

4. *The Level of Sensory Awareness—Interoceptive.* Here, consciousness is focused on the billions of nerve endings that are buried within the body and clustered in centers that receive impulses from visceral organs. For thousands of years it has been known that existing in the body is a chain of neural centers that collect messages from internal-organ systems. These centers are called *cakras.* Sexual, digestive, eliminative, cardiac, respiratory, cerebellar, cortical—the seven sense organs of the internal environment: structures for decoding energy as complex and varied as the eye, ear, tongue, nose. Chemical alteration of the nervous system is required to contact these inner sense organs. Marijuana can do it only if you turn off external stimuli. Smoke pot in a completely dark, silent room, and if you are well trained, you can contact your *cakras.* Moderate or large doses of LSD propel consciousness into the kaleidoscopic Niagara of internal-body sensation, but when this happens the unprepared voyager either gets confused or lets this internal flood of electric energy flow by unrecognized.

5. *The Cellular Level of Consciousness.* Every cell in your body is playing out a game that has been played out millions of times before. Within the nucleus of each cell in your body is a strand of nucleic acid molecules, possessing a timeless wisdom, which creates bodies (like yours and mine) exactly the

way General Motors designers plan each year's crop of automobiles. (An accurate irony. And designed for quick obsolescence, too.)

Now it is possible for man's nervous system to get in touch with cellular consciousness. This statement may sound far-out and mystical, but it is not. I am talking about the transmission of information in electro-molecular form from within the cell to nerve endings outside the cell. The brain can be "taught" by molecules such as RNA. Tribal educational processes employ symbols given social meaning through conditioned associations. Recently scientists have discovered another form of education: learning by means of cellular molecules which pass on ancient energy-wisdom in the language of chemistry. Molecular learning, cellular consciousness, can be stimulated by plants and drugs. Moderate doses of LSD (100–250 gamma), of mescaline (150–500 mg), of psilocybin (16–50 mg) can put the nervous system in contact with cellular messages—if external stimulation is temporarily blocked off. These experiences often described in the language of "reincarnation" are routine phenomena in LSD sessions. Marihuana and mild doses of psychedelic drugs cannot produce this level of consciousness.

6. *The Pre-Cellular (Atomic) Level of Consciousness.* For thousands of years psychedelic philosophers have reported the ultimate state of transcendental consciousness in terms of pure energy: "void," "white light," "the core flame," "the light within." Though metaphors vary, there is agreement on the elemental, pre-life nature of this energy. Many LSD subjects also report similar experiences—after ingesting large doses (250–1500 gamma). Here our maps of consciousness fade into obscurity. Here our symbols become poetic, mystical. The empirical question is: Can the human nervous system contact, pick up, chemical energies of a molecular or atomic level? Can such experiences be mapped and made available for subsequent observations? I do not know. I present this sixth level of consciousness hesitantly, knowing that I risk losing even the least skeptical of my readers. We must keep an open mind. We must provide in our symbolic mappings categories for events that, at the moment, go beyond our observations.

This list of six levels of consciousness may be thought of within the metaphor of expanding optical lenses—which are familiar external techniques for expanding man's visual consciousness.

Narcotic drugs—including alcohol—shut off vision, dull perception, provide escape from the glare of reality.

"Normal" symbolic consciousness is normal, uncorrected vision.

Marijuana is the weakest, the mildest of the expanding lenses. It and other stimulants of sensory awareness are like corrective lenses; they bring vision into sharper focus. Moderate doses of LSD, mescaline, psilocybin are powerful microscopes that bring cellular structures into focus. Heavy doses of LSD are like the electron microscope. They magnify to such a power that cellular structure is reduced to a whirring flux of molecular particles.

You can no more generalize about psychedelic drugs than you can about optic magnification. Before making a statement about the psychedelic experience or about a psychedelic substance you must define the type and the dosage. Expanding lenses run from the corrective lens through the range of magnification to the millionth-power amplifiers.

A final comment about the disciplined yoga of psychedelic drugs. They are not shortcuts; they do not simplify. They answer no questions; they solve no problems. Indeed, the psychedelic drugs complicate knowing and understanding because they show each issue in multidimensional complexity.

My first adult psychedelic experience came in Mexico in 1960 after eating seven of the Sacred Mushrooms of Mexico. I have often said of this experience that I learned more in five hours than I did in the previous sixteen years as a psychological researcher. But this learning must be specified. It was revelatory rather than intellectual. For example, suppose that I had been living three hundred years ago and had spent sixteen years in medical research, poking, examining, and thumping sick bodies to determine the cause of disease. Then one day someone puts a microscope to my eye and I look at the blood cells of a healthy person and the blood cells of a sick person. In one split second I would have understood more about the cause of disease than I had learned in the previous sixteen years. I would have understood that there exists a level of energy and invisible meaning, hitherto undreamed of, that was crucial to my profession. I would realize that the rest of my professional life would be dedicated to the laborious, disciplined looking through the lenses at the new data suddenly made available.

The understanding and application of the psychedelic drugs require brutal diligence on the part of the researcher or the searcher. There is no instant mysticism, no instant psychoanalysis available here. Only the challenge and the promise of long, dedicated, systematic work, of observation and replication.

Even the benign and gentle amplification of marijuana requires study and discipline. It takes time to use marijuana. It is a subtle and fleeting experience. One who is used to the crudity and jolting paralysis of alcohol smokes cannabis and says nothing happens. He fails to notice the soft, sensitive unfolding of his sense endings. The wise use of cannabis requires a precise knowledge of its effects and exquisite skill in arranging the external stimuli so that they gratify and talk directly to the exposed sensory nerve endings rather than inundate and jumble. For some reason my countrymen are reluctant to realize that psychedelic drugs pose a linguistic problem. That one must painstakingly learn the new dialects of sensual and cellular energy.

From the earliest days of our search-research project at Harvard, in Mexico, and later in Millbrook, New York, we have stressed training. In lecturing about the effects of psychedelic drugs I repeat this point over and over again: training . . . specialized training. After four years of college, if you want to specialize in science it takes four years to get a doctorate. Four postgraduate years to get a PhD. To specialize in medicine, it requires eight years after college. Eight postgraduate years to get the MD. Dear friends, to specialize in the use of your own nervous system, to learn to use your head, and to use the wisdom in your cells, it requires many more years. Count on fifty years of postgraduate work to get your LSD.

CHAPTER SIX

HISTORICAL NOTES

W. Reininger

These notes, which originally appeared in Ciba Symposia *with essays by Dr. Victor Robinson (See Book Two, Chapter 8), are of particular interest because of the anthropological evidence they offer regarding the use of a consciousness-expanding herb —hemp—as the central ritualistic communion device in the establishment of a new primitive religion.*

The Use of Hashish in a Cult

The explorer Hermann von Wissmann (1853–1905) visited the Baloubas, a Bantu tribe of the Belgian Congo, as well as the tribes subject to them. He relates that in 1888 Kalamba-Moukenge, the Balouba chief, in order to strengthen the kingdom that he had founded by conquest, and to link together in one cult the diverse subjugated tribes, had the ancient fetishes burned publicly, and replaced the worship of these idols with a new ritual which consisted essentially in the smoking of hashish.

On all important occasions, such as holidays or the conclusion of a treaty or alliance, the Balouba smoke hemp in gourds which may be as much as one meter in circumference. In addition, the men gather each evening in the main square where they solemnly smoke hemp together. But hemp is also used for punishment. The delinquent is compelled to smoke a particularly strong portion until he loses consciousness. The subjects of Kalamba began to smoke hemp with such passion that they ended by calling themselves "bena-Riamba" (sons of hemp), after the name which this plant has in their language. Remnants of hemp dating from prehistoric times were discovered in 1896 in northern Europe when the German archaeologist Hermann Busse opened a tomb containing a funerary urn at Wilmersdorf (Brandenberg). The vessel in question contained sand in which were mixed remnants of plants. It dated from the 5th century B.C. The botanist Ludwig Wittmaack (1839–1929) was able to find among this plant débris fragments of the seed and pericarp of *Cannabis sativa L.* At the session of the Berlin Society for Anthropology, Ethnology and Prehistory on May 15, 1897, Busse presented a report on his discovery and drew the conclusion that hemp had already been known in northern Europe in prehistoric times. But Rudolf Virchow (1821–1902) threw doubt on this interpretation that hemp had already been known in northern Europe at such an early time. He expressed the hypothesis that the hemp in question might have been introduced into the vase much later. The close examination of the place where the urn was found, and of its position, which Busse undertook at the time of discovery showed that this conjecture could be discarded. Furthermore, one must agree with C. Hartwich that hemp was already employed in northern Europe at the same time that it was by the Chinese and the Scythians for food and pleasure. All that remains is to determine whether hemp was imported from the Orient or whether it was already cultivated in the country.

The use of hemp in the manufacture of ropes and fabrics seems to have been introduced rather late. Not a single passage is to be found in the writings and mural inscriptions of the ancient Egyptians and Hebrews which makes any allusion to such usage. Herodotus, on the other hand, reports that the inhabitants of Thrace made clothes from hemp fibers. It is related that Hiero (3rd century B.C.), tyrant of Syracuse, had hemp brought from Rhodanus (the country of the Rhône?) in order to equip a ship. Pausanias (2nd century B.C.) mentions that hemp and other textile plants were cultivated in Elide; and Pliny the Elder (A.D. 23–79) relates that the sails and cordage of the Roman galleys were made of hemp. Until the end of the 19th century, hemp played an important role because of the industrial exploitation of its fibers. Today hemp is cultivated on a large scale, chiefly in Russia, Italy, and Yugoslavia.

Formerly, besides the fibers, use was made of the seed, from which as much as 20% to 30% oil was extracted. This was utilized chiefly for illumination and the manufacture of soap. The residue, or bagasse, was used as fishbait and as fertilizer.

BOOK TWO

Literary and
Imaginative Papers

CHAPTER ONE

THE HERB PANTAGRUELION

François Rabelais
Translated by Samuel Putnam

The herb "pantagruelion," which occupies the profound botanical and mystical attention of the French Renaissance physician and master satarist François Rabelais in Chapters 49 through 52 of the Third Book of Pantagruel, *is none other than marihuana. M. Leon Faye, in his monograph* Rabelais, botaniste *(Angers, 1854), verified this, pointing out that Rabelais' description of "pantagruelion" is not only botanically accurate, but as full of life and earthiness as the herb itself.*

Rabelais obviously knew many of the valuable attributes of marihuana: birdfood manufacturers would heartily agree that the seeds are "mantled with . . . delicious taste and savour to all shrill and sweetly singing birds." Moreover, Yugoslav and Hungarian scientists who over four hundred years later reported to the United Nations that, according to their experiments, marihuana possesses remarkable antibiotic properties, would in no way be surprised to learn from Dr. Rabelais that the plant's sap

killeth every kind of vermin that by any manner of putrefaction cometh to be bred and engendered there, and destroyeth also any whatsoever any other animal that shall have entered in thereat. If, likewise, you put a little of the said juice within a pail or bucket full of water, you shall see the water instantly turn and grow thick therewith, as if it were milk curds, whereof the virtue is so great, that the water thus curded is a present remedy for horses subject to the cholic, and such as strike at their own flanks. The root thereof well boiled mollifieth the joints, softeneth the hardness of shrunk-in sinews, is every way comfortable to the nerves, and good against all cramps and convulsions, as likewise all cold and knotty gouts.

Finally, both ancient Greeks and 20th-century hedonists would emphatically agree with the canny savant that

of old amongst the Greeks there was certain kind of fritters, and pancakes, buns and tarts, made thereof, which commonly for a liquorish daintiness were presented on the table after supper, to delight the palate and make the wine relish the better.

How Pantagruel Prepared to Embark; and Something about the Plant Called Pantagruelion[1]

A few days later, Pantagruel, after he had taken leave of the good Gargantua, and after the latter had wished his son Godspeed, arrived at the port of Thalasse, near Saint-Malo, accompanied by Panurge, Epistemon, Friar John Hackem, Abbott of Thélème, and others of his household. Among these others was Xenomanes, the great traveler and hero of perilous crossings, who had joined them upon Panurge's summons, since he held some arriere fee or other of the castellany of Salmagundi.

When they had reached the port, Pantagruel drew up a fleet of ships, to the number of those which Ajax of Salamina had mustered in convoying the Greeks to Troy, loading and equipping them with all the sailors, pilots, towers, interpreters, workmen, men-of-war, victuals, artillery, munitions, clothing, money and other supplies necessary for a long and hazardous voyage. Among other things, I observed that he took on a big cargo of his plant, the Pantagruelion, in the green and raw, as well as in the prepared state.

Now, this plant, the Pantagruelion, has a rather small, rather hard and rather round root, ending in an obtuse point; it is white, with few filaments, and does not grow deeper down than a foot and a half in the earth. From the root springs a solitary stock, round and ferulaceous,[2] green on the outside and whitish within, and concave, like the stock of the smyrnium,[3] the olus

---

1 On the significance of this plant, see end-of-chapter note. The plant referred to is generally supposed to be hemp.

2 Like the *ferrula*. Urquhart: *"cane-like."*

3 Myrrh.

atrium,[4] beans and the gentian. It is ligneous, straight, crisp and notched a little, in the form of lightly streaked columns. It is full of fibers, which are the distinguishing feature of the plant, especially as regards the variety known as *Mesa,* or "middling," and that which is known as *Mylasia.*[5]

In height, it grows, commonly, from five to six feet. Sometimes, it exceeds the length of a lance, which happens when it encounters a light, soft, marshy soil, warm and damp, like that of Olonne,[6] and like that of Rosa, near Praeneste, in Sabinia,[7] or when there happens to be plenty of rain about the time of the Fishermen's Holidays, and the summer solstice. Sometimes, it even exceeds the trees in height, and you might then, on the authority of Theophrastus,[8] refer to it as *Dendromalache.*[9] The plant, however, perishes each year, being perennial neither in root, trunk, bark nor boughs. For from the stock spring large strong boughs.

Its leaves are three times longer than they are wide, always green, rather rough, like the alkanet, rather hard and circularly incised like a sickle, or like the betony, and ending in a Macedonian pike-point, somewhat resembling a surgeon's lancet. The leaf, in appearance, is little different from those of the ash and agrimony, and so very like the eupatorium that a number of botanists, classifying this plant as domestic, have called the eupatorium the wild Pantagruelion. The leaves are arranged in rows around the stock, at equal distances apart, with five or seven in a row; for Nature so cherishes the Pantagruelion that she has endowed its leaves with those two odd numbers, which are so divine and mysterious. Its odor is strong, and none too pleasant to delicate nostrils.

The seeds are to be found near, and a little under, the head of the plant. They are as plentiful as those of any plant there is, being spherical, oblong or rhomboid in shape, of a light black, almost tan color, rather hard, and with a fragile coating. All singing birds, such as linnets, goldfinch, larks, canaries, tarins and others, are extremely fond of it. But in the human being,

4 Black cabbage.

5 Or Mylasea; a variety of hemp, in Pliny. For this and *mesa,* see Pliny, XIX., 9, 56.

6 "Town of Poitou, surrounded with swamps and salt-beds." (Des Marets-Rathery.)

7 See Pliny, XIX., 9.

8 *History of Plants,* I, 5.—"It is from this author and from Pliny that Rabelais gets the greater part of what he has to say, in this chapter and those following." (Marty-Laveaux.)

9 Greek for *tree-mallow.*

who eats much or often of this seed, it tends to exterminate the germinative principle; and while the Greeks used to employ it in making certain kinds of fricassees, tarts and fritters, which they ate after supper, along with their wine, as a dessert, it is, nevertheless, difficult to digest, hard on the stomach, begets bad blood and, on account of its excessive heat, goes to the brain and fills the head with painful and annoying fumes.[10]

And just as, in the case of a number of plants, such as the laurel, palm, oak, holly, asphodel, mandragora, fern, agaric, birthwort, cypress, turpentine-tree, penny-royal, peony and others, there are to be found two sexes, the male and the female, so in this plant, there is a male, which bears no flower but abounds in seeds, and a female which is rich in little whitish useless flowers, and which does not bear any seed worth speaking of. And just as in the case of other similar flowers, the female has a leaf wider and not quite so hard as that of the male, and does not grow to an equal height. And this Pantagruelion is planted when the swallows come again, and is taken from the earth at the time when the grasshoppers commence to be a little hoarse.

TRANSLATOR'S NOTE

These last botanical, and highly mystical, chapters of Book Third appear to cry aloud for some sort of "explanation" or comment.

"The Pantagruelion *plant, so called for the reason that 'Pantagruel was the discoverer of it,' is none other than the hemp, the* cannabis sativa *of Linnaeus," says M. Marty-Laveaux. And M. Johanneau gives as some historic data:*

"In addition to the essential part which hemp plays in shipping, in the making of ropes and sails, history shows us that never in France had the use of the hangman's rope been more frequent than under Francis I, when it was employed against the Lutherans and the Calvinists. . . . It was under Francis I that the hempen rope came to be used, in place of the halter, in hanging criminals."

And this appears to be about the only none too illuminating light that is to be thrown upon the subject. In any event, we have to admire Rabelais' botanical erudition; and it has been very much admired by his compatriots.

Among the eulogists of Rabelais as a botanist is Antoine

10   "It is well known that it is from a species of hemp that the peoples of the Orient prepare their hashish." (Des Marets-Rathery.)

*Leroy; and others, specialists in their field, have followed him.
De Candolle, in a note to his* Théorie élémentaire, *remarks that
Rabelais has distanced all other writers in his dissertation on the
origin of the names of plants; and M. Léon Faye contrasts with
the coldly exact description of the hemp given by De Candolle
in his* Flore française *the emotional description given us by
Rabelais. (See* Rabelais botaniste, Léon Faye, Angers, 1854.)*

*In an address delivered at Montpellier, on the eighth of June,
1856, before the members of the Société botanique de France,
M. le comte Jaubert paid a high tribute to Rabelais, both as
botanist and as philologist. Rabelais' remarks, he pointed out,
are "seasoned with a witty irony on the subject of the credulity
of the ancients regarding the properties of plants."*

*"Let any one compare these passages with the older works on
botany which were printed about the same time, with the* De
Plinii erroribus *of Leonisenus, in 1532, or the work of Otto
Brunfels, in 1533 . . . and one will see in how far Rabelais
was their superior."*

*There is, also, a story that is not without its interest, concern-
ing Rabelais as a botanist. The scene is the University of Montpellier; and in the Faculty room, the learned professors are
listening to a thesis* De herbis et plantis medicinalibus *(on
medical plants and herbs). Rabelais becomes impatient at listening to so much bad science, and shows his impatience, unmis-
takably. The dean perceives this, and invites Dr. François to
take a share in the argument. Rabelais, at first, modestly declines, but is unable, eventually, to keep out of it. The battle
is on, and Rabelais speaks so forcefully and to the point that
the enthusiasm of the auditors waxes high. The end of it is, our
friend Rabelais walks off with the honors of the day.*

*As to Rabelais' injection of his botanical learning at this par-
ticular point, M. Moland, perhaps, gives as likely an explanation as any.*

*"Rabelais makes it (the Pantagruelion)," says M. Moland,
"the symbol of social discipline and human industrial activity,
a sort of active talisman of Holy Grail calibre, and one which
he sets over against the myths contained in the old romances."*

*Rabelais is here improvising on a theme from Pliny (cf. the
first six chapters of the latter's nineteenth book; cf, also Pliny's
Chapter LVI.) The variation was probably suggested by the
sails of Pantagruel's ships.*

*Our author's distinction with regard to the sex of plants has
been remarked, but this knowledge was common property with
the ancients. He, however, confuses the sexes—a confusion
common in country districts.*

See Sainéan's L'Histoire naturelle . . . dans . . . Rabelais; *also,* La Lengue de Rabelais. Vol. I., pp. 24ff.

How the Celebrated Pantagruelion Should Be Prepared and Employed

The Pantagruelion is prepared at the time of the autumnal
equinox, in a number of different manners, according to popular fancy and differences in national custom.

According to Pantagruel's instructions, the first thing to do
was to divest the stock of its leaves and seeds, and then to
macerate it in still, not running, water—for five days, if the
weather was dry and the water warm; for nine or twelve, if the
weather was cloudy or the water cold—then to dry it in the
sun; and afterwards, in the shade, the bark was to be peeled
from the fibers, in which, as has been said, the whole character
and value of the plant lies, and these fibers were to be separated
from the ligneous part, which is of no use, except for making
a luminous flame, for kindling fires and for the amusement of
little children, who employ it to put in pigs' bladders.[11]

Under-cover topers sometimes use it as a syphon for suck-
ing and drawing up the new wine through the bunghole. Some
modern Pantagruelists, desirous of avoiding the manual labor
involved in thus peeling the plant, make use of certain cata-
ractie[12] instruments, constructed in the form in which the
spiteful Juno held her hands to prevent the birth of Alcmene,
Hercules' mother.[13] By means of this instrument, they crush
and break the ligneous part and render it useless, in order to
save the fibers.

This preparation is an all-sufficient one for those who, contrary to popular opinion, and in a manner which all philosophers would term paradoxical, earn their living backwards.[14]
Those who put a higher value on it do something which reminds one of what we are told concerning the pastime of the
three sister Parcae, concerning the nocturnal sports of the
noble Circe, and concerning the long apology which Penelope
made to her lovelorn lilies, during the absence of her husband,
Ulysses. In this manner are its inestimable virtues brought out,

11   To "make them rattle." (Urquhart.)
12   The meaning is: *for bruising* (Greek *Kataraktikos*).
13   Pliny, XXVIII, 6.—Juno held her hands with fingers joined in the
form of a comb.
14   "He means the rope-makers (*cordiers*), who earn their living by
working *à reculons.*" (*Variorum.*)

which I would, in part, expound to you, since to expound to you the whole is an impossible task for me. What I shall endeavor to do is to explain its name for you.

I find that plants get their names in different ways. Some take the name of the one who first discovered and came to know them, who pointed them out, cultivated, tanned and domesticated them. Thus, the mercurialis takes its name from Mercury; the panacea[15] from Aesculapius' daughter; the artemisia from Artemis, or Diana; the eupatorium from King Eupator,[16] the telephium[17] from Telephus,[18] the euphorbia from Euphorbus, physician to King Juba;[19] the clymenus[20] from King Clymenus;[21] the alcibiadion,[22] from Alcibiades; the gentian from Gentius, King of Slavonia.

And so highly, in the old days, was this privilege of giving one's name to a newly discovered plant, esteemed that, just as there sprang up a quarrel between Neptune and Pallas as to whose name the land they had discovered together should take,—the district which later was called Athens, from Athene, or Minerva,—so, in a like manner, Lyncus, King of Scythia, endeavored to betray and kill the young Triptolemus, who had been sent by Ceres to make men acquainted with wheat, which up to that time had been unknown. Lyncus desired, through the death of Triptolemus, to have his own name given to the find, in order that the immortal honor and glory of being the discoverer of this grain, which is so useful and necessary to human life, might be his; and for this reason, he was transformed by Ceres into a lynx. So, too, great and long wars were formerly waged between certain kings, with nothing better to do, in Cappadocia, the only question in dispute being as to whose name a certain plant should bear; and for this reason, the plant was called polemonia,[23] or the warlike flower.

Others have retained the names of regions to which they

15 "Sort of plant, remedy for all afflictions." (Moland.)—Probably, ginseng. The name is applied in Pliny to the *ligusticum silvestre* and to the *cunila bubula* (species of origanum).

16 Of Pontus; see the English dictionary, under *eupatorium*.

17 The *telephion* of Pliny, herb resembling purslain.

18 Son of Hercules and the nymph Auge, and King of Mysia.

19 King of Numidia.

20 Unknown plant in Pliny.

21 King of Orchomenus in Boetia.

22 Variety of anchusa, employed as an antidote for the bite of serpents.

23 From the Greek *polemos,* war. Greek valerian, otherwise called *philaeteria*. See Pliny.

were transported. Thus Median apples[24] take their name from
Media where they were first found; Punic apples,[25] or pome-
granates, were brought from Phoenicia,[26] or Carthage; the
ligusticum[27] was brought from Liguria, or the Genoese coast;
the rhubarb came from a river in Barbary called the Rha,[28]
as Ammianus[29] tells us. We have other examples in the san-
tonica,[30] in Greek fennel, in chestnuts (*castanes*),[31] in
persica,[32] in the sabina,[33] in the stoechas, which takes its name
from my Hyerean Islands, formerly called the Stoechades,[34]
in the spica celtica,[35] etc.

Others get their names by way of anthiphrasis. Absinth, for
example, is the opposite of *pinthe*,[36] so called because it is
unpleasant to drink; while holosteon[37] means "all bone,"
whereas, contrary to its name, there is not a more fragile or
a more tender plant in all nature.

Others derive their names from their virtues or the manner
in which they work, like the aristolochia,[38] which aids women
in childbirth; the lichen, which cures maladies of its name;[39]
the mallow, which mollifies; and the callithrichum, which
makes beautiful hair. Other examples are to be found in the

24   *Mala medica.*

25   *Mala punica.*

26   Rabelais writes *Punicia.*

27   The plant known as lovage.

28   This etymology is doubtful. *Rhubarb* (French: *rhubarbe*) comes
from the late Latin *rheubarbarum*, for *rheum barbarum* (Greek: *rheon*).

29   Book XXII.

30   The lavender (from the land of the *Santoni*, or people of Gaul, the
present Saintonge).

31   From Castana, city of Pontus.

32   The *persicum pomum* or *persicum* was a variety of peach.

33   The savin, or variety of juniper.

34   On these Islands, see the *Translator's Note* to Book Third.—The
stoechas was French lavender.

35   The large lavender.

36   Or *pint;* that is, the opposite of *drinking.*—As De Marsy remarks,
Rabelais is apparently deriving the word absinth from the Greek *pineo*,
drink, looking upon the Greek *apsinthion* as equivalent to *apinthion*—
composed, that is, of the privative prepositional particle *apo* and *pin-
thios.* This same fanciful etymology is reproduced by Scapula in his
Lexicon graeco-latinum of 1580.—Urquhart: "because it is contrary to
psintos."

37   A whitish plantain.

38   Or birthwort.—Greek: *aristos*, best; *locheia*, childbirth.

39   Blotches, the Latin signification of *lichen.*

alyssum,[40] the ephemerum,[41] the bechium,[42] the nasturtium[43] or Orléans cress,[44] the hyoscyamus,[45] the henbane, etc.

Others are named from the extraordinary qualities which have been discovered in them, as, for example, the heliotrope, or marigold, which is so called for the reason that it *follows the sun;* for when the sun rises, it expands; when the sun climbs upward, it climbs upward, too; when the sun sinks, it, too, droops; when the sun hides itself, it closes its petals. There is the adiantum,[46] so called because it never retains humidity, even though it grows near the water, and even though it be submerged in water for a very long time. There are, also, the hieracium,[47] the eryngium[48] and others.

Others get their names from metamorphoses which men or women of like name are supposed to have undergone. The daphne, or laurel, is so called from Daphne; the myrtle from Myrrhine; the Pitys[49] from Pitys. In addition, there is the cinara, or artichoke, the narcissus, the saffron,[50] the smilax[51] and others.

Others get their names from a fancied resemblance. For example, the hippuris, so called because it resembles a horse's tail; the alopecurus, which is like a fox's tail; the psyllium, which is like a flea; the delphinium, which is like a dolphin; the bugloss, which is like a beef's tongue; the iris, which in its flowers is like a rainbow; the myosota, which is like a mouse's ear; the coronopus, which is like a crow's foot, etc.

On the other hand, the members of the Fabian family have left their name with the beans,[52] the Piso's with the peas,[53] the Lentuli with the lentils,[54] and the Cicero's with the chick-

---

40 The mad-wort, used against the bite of mad dogs; also as a remedy for hiccups. Greek *alysso,* be uneasy.

41 An unknown plant.

42 Colt's foot.—A cough-remedy; Greek *bechia,* hoarseness.

43 See the English dictionary.

44 We find in the *Crieries* de Paris of G. de la Villeneuve: *"Vez ci bon cresson Orlenois."*

45 Henbane. Literally: *hog's bean.*

46 The maiden's hair (*capillus veneris*).

47 The mouse-ear (*hieracium pilosella*).—"Hawk-ear."

48 Variety of thistle.

49 Greek name for pine. The nymph, Pitys, was changed into a pine.

50 Or crocus.

51 After a young girl who was changed into one.

52 *Fabae.*

53 *Pisa.*

54 *Lenticulae.* (As a matter of fact, this word is a diminutive of the Latin *lens.*)

peas.[55] We have, also, going a little higher up in the scale, Venus' navel, Venus' locks, Venus' tub, Jupiter's beard, Jupiter's eye,[56] Mars' blood, Mercury's fingers or the hermodactyls, etc.

Others are named from their forms, as the trefoil, which has three leaves; the pentaphyllon, which has five leaves; and the *serpolet* (wild thyme), which creeps (*qui herpe*) along the ground. There are, also, the helxine, [57] the pestasites,[58] and the myrobalans, to which the Arabs gave the name *Been*,[59] since this fruit is like an acorn in shape and very oily.

Where the Pantagruelion Gets Its Name; the Admirable Virtues of This Plant

In all of these manners, except the fabulous—since God forbid that we should make use of fable in so veracious a narrative as this—the plant Pantagruelion gets its name.

For Pantagruel was the discoverer,[60] I will not say of the plant itself, but of a certain use to which it may be put, a use that is more hated and abhorred by robbers, and more inimical to their welfare, than is the moth or the dodder to flax, reeds to the fern, the horsetail to reapers, tares to chick-peas, the darnel to barley, the wolf-bean to lentils, the antranium to beans, rye-grass to wheat or ivy to walls; more inimical than the pond-lily, or nymphea heraclia, is to bawdy monks,[61] than the birch and rod are to the pupils of Navarre, than cabbage is to the vine, garlic to the magnet, the onion to the sight, fern-seed to pregnant women, willow-seed to vicious nuns, the yew-tree's shade to those sleeping under it, wolf's bane to wolves and leopards, the smell of the fig-tree to enraged bulls, hemlock to goslings, purslain to the teeth, or oil to trees.

For many of them, as a result of such an employment of this plant, have seen their lives end high and short, after the manner of Phyllis,[62] Queen of Thrace, of Bonosus, Emperor

---

55   *Cicer*, a chick-pea. These are the traditional etymologies.

56   "The name which the Latins give to the *Sempervivum majus.*" (Variorum.)

57   The parietary.—Greek: *helko*, trail.

58   Plant with a broad leaf like a hat (petasus); kind of colt's foot.

59   "That is, *acorn.*" (Variorum.)—Le Duchat refers to Avicenna, Canon II, Chapter LXXXV.

60   "It was, as a matter of fact, Francis I who substituted the rope and the strappado for the halter." (Variorum.)

61   "It is especially prescribed for monks against temptations of the flesh." (Le Duchat.)

62   Daughter of Sithon, King of Thrace, who hanged herself out of despair over her lover, Demophoön, Theseus' son.

of Rome,[63] of Amata, wife of the Latin king, of Iphis, of Autolyca,[64] of Lycambes,[65] of Arachne, of Phaedra, of Leda, of Achaeus, King of Lydia,[66] and others. They were greatly put out by the fact that, without their being otherwise ill, the passage by which their gab left and their grub entered was, through the use of the Pantagruelion, suddenly shut off, in a nastier fashion than if they had had the sore throat or the quinsy.

We have heard others, at the moment when Atropos was snipping their life-thread, moaning and lamenting because, as they said, Pantagruel had them by the throat. But alas! It was not Pantagruel. He was never yet a hangman. It was merely Pantagruel turned into a halter and providing them with a nice little necktie.[67] And so, they were speaking out of turn and incorrectly: unless, possibly, one may excuse them under the figure known as synecdoche, assuming that they were taking the discovery for the discoverer, as Ceres is commonly taken for bread, Bacchus for wine. I swear to you, by the nice line of gab that's in the bottle, cooling in that bucket over there, that our friend Pantagruel never held any one by the throat, unless it was those who had neglected to ward off an imminent thirst.

This plant is also called Pantagruelion out of resemblance. For when Pantagruel was born into the world, he was as big as this plant I am telling you of; and it was a very easy matter to take his measurements, in view of the fact that he was born in a period of drought, at a time when this plant was being gathered, and when Icarus' dog,[68] by his barkings at the sun, was turning the whole world Troglodyte and forcing every one to live in caves and subterranean retreats.

It is, in addition, called Pantagruelion on account of its singular virtues. For just as Pantagruel is the embodiment of all jovial perfection—a fact of which none of you drinkers, I

63 Favorite of Probus, who had himself proclaimed emperor by the army of the Rhine, but who was conquered and put to death. One story is that he hanged himself.

64 Daughter of Autolycus and mother of Ulysses. She hanged herself when the false news of the death of her son was brought her.

65 Having promised his daughter to the poet Archilochus, he failed to deliver her, was punished by a plague of worms and hanged himself, along with his daughter, in despair.

66 Hanged by his revolting subjects because he desired to levy new taxes.

67 *leurs servant de cornette.*—We speak of a hanging as a "necktie party."

68 The dog-star.

take it, is in doubt—so in the Pantagruelion, I recognize so
many virtues, so much energy, so high a degree of perfection,
and so many admirable qualities that if it and its qualities
had been known at the time when the trees, according to the
Prophet's narrative, were engaged in electing a king of the
forest to rule them, it would, undoubtedly, have carried off a
majority of the votes. Shall I go further and say more? If
Oxylus, son of Ares, had begotten this plant by his sister,
Hamadryad, he would have taken more delight in its fair
worth than in all his eight children of immortal memory,
about whom our mythologists make such a fuss. (The eldest
daughter's name, by the way, was Vine; the son who came
next was named Fig-tree, the next Walnut, the next Oak, the
next Sorbapple, the next Service-tree, while the last-born bore
the name of Elm, and was a great surgeon in his day.)

I shall not stop to tell you how the juice of this plant,
squeezed out and dropped into the ears, kills all kinds of
vermin bred by putrefaction, as well as any other form of
animal life which may have found its way in. If you put some
of this juice into a pail of water, you will at once see the
water turn, as though it had been curdled, so great is the
strength of the plant. And water so curdled is a very good
remedy for colicky horses and those who bite at their flanks.[69]
The root of the plant, boiled in water, slackens taut nerves
and contracted joints, and loosens up scirrhous and knotty
cases of gout. If you wish promptly to heal a burn, a burn from
either water or fire, apply the Pantagruelion raw, that is, in
the form in which it comes from the earth, without any other
application of any sort; but be careful to change it, as soon
as you see it drying upon the wound.

Without this plant, kitchens would be disgraceful and tables
unbearable, even though the latter might be laden with all
sorts of exquisite dishes. There would be no pleasure in beds,
even though they might be rich in gold, silver, amber, ivory
and porphyry. Without it, millers would not carry corn to the
mill nor bring back flour. Without it, how would the lawyers'
speeches be carried to the courtroom? How, without it, would
the plaster be carried to the workshop? Without it, how would
water be drawn from the wells? Without it, what would the
notaries, copyists, scribes and secretaries do? Would not all
records and documents perish? Would not the noble art of
printing be lost forever? Of what would they make printer's
chases? How would they ring the bells?

69 See Pliny, Book XX, next to last chapter. This remedy, according
to Le Duchat, was employed in Alsace, in the year 1705, to cure a
species of colic among the horses of the French army.

With it, in addition, the priests of Isis are adorned and Egyptian Image-bearers clad; it is the primal covering of all humankind. All the wool-bearing trees of the Seres,[70] all the cotton-trees of Tylus in the Persian Sea, all the cyni[71] of the Arabians and the vines of Malta never clothed so many persons as does this one plant alone. It shelters armies, now, much more effectively than they were formerly sheltered with skins; it shades theatres and amphitheatres against the heat, and surrounds woods and thickets for the pleasure of hunters; it descends into waters, either fresh or salt, for the benefit of fishermen. By it, boots, shoes, slippers, pumps, kicks, brogans and clogs are shaped for use. By it, bows are stretched, crossbows tightened and slings set. And, as though it were a sacred plant, vervain-like and revered by the manes and the spirits of darkness, no human corpses are interred without it.

I will go further. By means of this plant, invisible substances are visibly halted, captured, detained and, as it were, put into prison. Thanks to this achievement, big, heavy mills are skillfully turned, to the great advantage of human life. And I am greatly astonished by the fact that this use of the plant was, for so many centuries, an unrevealed secret to the old philosophers, considering the intolerable labor which, without it, they had to endure in manipulating their mills.

By means of this plant, through its retention of aerial currents, the big ships and commodious luxury-crafts,[72] the mighty galleons and the hundred-men and thousand-men boats are launched and propelled, at the will of their helmsmen. Thanks to it, those nations which Nature would appear to have hidden away, with the object of leaving them unknown and inaccessible—these nations have come to us, and we have gone to them, something which the birds could not do, however light of wing they might be, and whatever ability to swim upon the air might have been conferred upon them by Nature. Ceylon has seen Lapland; Java has seen the Hyperborean Mountains; Phebol shall see Thélème, and the Icelanders and Greenlanders shall drink from the Euphrates. Thanks to it, Boreas has visited the house of Auster, and Eurus has called upon Zephyrus.

As a result of all this, the celestial Intelligences, the gods of

70 "Ancient people of Asia, who have been believed to be Chinese." (Des Marets-Rathery.)

71 Arabian trees, from the product of which the natives, according to Pliny, made clothing. Pliny gives this tree the name of *cynus*.

72 *thalameges*. These were large and luxurious boats, furnished with beds.

the sea as well as those of the earth, have become thoroughly frightened, as they beheld, through the employment of this blessed Pantagruelion, the Arctic peoples crossing the Atlantic in full view of those in the Antarctic region, crossing the two Tropics, taking a turn through the Torrid Zone, taking the measure of the entire Zodiac, and disporting themselves under the Equinoctial, with each Pole in sight, on a level with their horizon.

The Olympian gods, spurred by a similar terror, have said to one another:

"Pantagruel, through the use of this marvelous plant, is putting us to a lot more bother and worry than the Aloïdae[73] ever did. He will be married before long, and will have children by his wife. This destiny we cannot forestall, since it is one which has passed through the hands and spindles of the fatal sisters, the daughters of Necessity. By his children, it may be, there will be invented, a plant of like energy, by means of which human beings will be enabled to visit the sources of the hailstorms, the lands from which the rains come, and the factory of thunder-bolts; they will be able to invade the regions of the moon, to enter the district of the heavenly signs, and to find a lodging, some on the Golden Eagle, others on the Sheep, others on the Crown, others on the Harp and others on the Silver Lion. They will sit at table with us, and will take our goddesses for wives, since that will be their one means of becoming gods like us."

The short of it was, they decided to hold a council and discuss a possible means of preventing all this.

How a Certain Species of Pantagruelion Cannot Be Consumed by Fire

The properties which I have been describing for you are great and marvelous, but if you will venture to believe me, I will tell you of yet another divine quality of this sacred Pantagruelion. You may believe it or not, it is all one to me; it is enough for me to have told the truth. And the truth I mean to tell you. But before we go on, for the road leading up is rather rough and difficult, I would ask you a question:

If I had put into that bottle two measures of wine and one of water, and then had mixed them well together, how would you set about it to unmix them? How would you separate them, in such a manner as to be able to give me the water without the wine, and the wine without the water, in the same quantities?

73　The giants, Othus and Ephialtes, sons of Aloeus, who fought Heaven.

Or to put it differently, if the teamsters and sailors, in bringing, to stock your houses, a certain number of barrels and
hogsheads of the wine of Grave, of Orléans, of Beaune and
of Mirevaux, had lapped and drunk them half up and filled
the rest up with water, as the Limousins do by the shoeful, in
carting the wines of Argenton and Saint-Gaultier, how would
you set about it to remove the water entirely? How would you
purify the wine?

I can hear you very well: you are telling me about an ivy
funnel. You will find that device, it is true, mentioned in literature, and it has been tested by a thousand experiences, as
you very well know; yet those who had never known about
it, or who had never seen the thing done, would not believe
it possible. But let us pass on.

Suppose we were living in the age of Sulla, Marius, Caesar
and the other Roman emperors, or in the time of the old
Druids, who burned the dead bodies of their lords and rela-
tives, and supposing that you wished to drink the ashes of
your wives or fathers, in an infusion of good white wine, as
Artemisia did the ashes of her husband, Mausolus, or supposing that you merely wished to keep them intact in some
urn or reliquary, how would you set about to save the ashes,
by separating them from those of the funeral pyre? Now, tell
me that.

Faith, but you're up a stump. I will let you go this time, simply informing you that, having taken enough of the heavenly
Pantagruelion to cover the body of the dead, and having
wrapped and bound the body well in this, sewing it in with the
same material, you may then cast it upon as ardent a fire as you
like; and the fire, through the Pantagruelion, will burn the
body and reduce body and bones to ashes, and not only will
the Pantagruelion not be consumed or burned, but not a single
atom of the ashes enclosed in it will be lost, nor will the
Pantagruelion take up a single atom of the incinerary ashes;
but it will come forth from the fire, in the end, whiter and
cleaner than when you put it in. For this reason it is called
Asbestine.[74] You will find an abundance of it, very cheap, at
Carpasia and in the region about Syene.

Oh, what a great and marvelous thing! To think that the
fire, which devours, ruins and consumes everything, should,
alone, clean, purge and whiten the Carpasian Pantagruelion,
the asbestine flax. If you are inclined to doubt this, and to

74 Rabelais writes *Asbeston.* "*Asbestinum* is the Latin name of the
amianthus, a sort of incombustible flax." (Des Marets-Rathery.)

demand the usual proofs, like the Jews and other incredulous persons, then, take a fresh egg and bind it around with this divine Pantagruelion. Thus bound, it may be placed upon a bed of coals, as big and as hot as you like; leave it there as long as you like, and in the end, you will take out the egg hard boiled, without any change of any sort in the sacred Pantagruelion, and without the latter's being even heated. For less than fifty thousand Bordelais crowns, minus the twelfth part of a quarter-denier,[75] you can put this to a test and find out for yourselves. And don't quote me the example of the salamander, for that is bunk. I am quite willing to admit that a little straw bonfire is good for the salamander, but in a great furnace, it would, I assure you, like every other animal, be suffocated and consumed. We know this by experience; Galen proved it, a long time ago, *lib. 3. De temperamentis,* and he is supported by Dioscorides, lib. 2.

And please don't mention, either, plume-alum nor the wooden tower in the Piraeus, which L. Sulla never succeeded in burning, for the reason that Archelaüs, governor of the city for King Mithridates, had wholly covered it with alum. And don't bring up, by way of comparison, that tree which Alexander Cornelius named *Eon,* remarking that it was like the oak in that it bore mistletoe, and in that it could not be consumed or damaged by fire or water any more than the oak tree's mistletoe, adding that from its wood had been built the ship *Argos,* which is so famous. Go look for it, if you believe him; but please excuse me.

And please don't try to compare, however miraculous it may be, that species of trees which you find on the mountains near Briançon and Embrun, which from its roots supplies us with the edible agaric and from its body furnishes us with a resin so excellent that Galen even goes so far as to compare it with turpentine, while its delicate leaves secrete a fine, heavenly honey, a veritable manna. However gummy and oily it may be, this tree is, yet, indestructible by fire.[76] You call it *Larix* in Greek and Latin; the Alpine folk call it the Larch, and the Antenorides and Venetians the *Larega,* from which comes the name *Larignum* given to that castle in the Piedmont which stood out against Julius Caesar upon the latter's march into Gaul.

Julius Caesar had expressly commanded all the inhabitants of the Alps and the Piedmont region to bring food-supplies and munitions to those stations which he had established along

75   This is about one 1/204th of a cent in our currency.
76   This, needless to say, is a slight exaggeration.

his line of march, in order to provide for his advancing army. All obeyed these orders, except those in the stronghold of Larigno, who, confident in the natural strength of their position, refused to make the contributions demanded. With the object of chastising them for this refusal, the emperor marched his army straight to the spot. In front of the castle-gate, a tower had been erected, composed of great rafters of larch-wood, laid alternately one upon another, like a pile of logs. This tower was so high that, from its machicolations, the defenders, by means of stones and handspikes, could readily repel any invaders.

When Caesar learned that those inside had no weapons of defense except spikes and stones, and that these could hardly be thrown as far as the approaches to the place, he commanded his soldiers to pile fagots around the tower and to set fire to it. This was at once done. When the fagots had been kindled, the flames leaped up higher than the castle; and so, they naturally thought that, in very short order, the tower would be burned to the ground. But when the flames died down, and the fagots had been burned, the tower still stood there whole, without being damaged in the slightest. When Caesar perceived this, he commanded that a network of ditches and trenches should be constructed about the place, out of stone's throw.

Then it was that the people of Larigno began to sue for peace, and it was through them that Caesar learned of the marvelous character of this wood, which of itself produced neither fire, flame nor coal, and was, therefore, worthy of being compared to the true Pantagruelion,—all the more so, from the fact that, out of it, Pantagruel commanded all the doors, gates, windows, gutter-spouts, copings and roofings of Thélème should be made. He, likewise, employed it in covering the poops, prows, cabins, decks, passageways and railings of his freighters, ships, galleys, galleons, brigs, rowing craft and the other vessels in his navy-yard at Thalasse. The only thing was that larch, in a great furnace, with an intense fire provided by other varieties of wood, is at last destroyed, like stones in a lime-kiln. But the asbestine Pantagruelion is, by such a test, freshened up and given a new lease on life, rather than disintegrated and destroyed. For this reason,

> *Indians, Arabs, Sabaeans, cease*
> *To vaunt your ebony, incense, myrrh;*
> *Come here and see our blessings, please,*
> *And take a little seed from her;*

Then, bless the heavens, if they concur,
And this plant with you grows;
And bless our France, each traveler,
Where the Pantagruelion blows.

END OF THE THIRD BOOK OF THE HEROIC DEEDS AND SAYINGS
OF THE WORTHY PANTAGRUEL

CHAPTER TWO

THE HASHISH CLUB

Théophile Gautier
Translated by Ralph J. Gladstone

*It should be remembered by the reader that the fantastic hal-
lucinatory episodes Gautier claims to have experienced in
this colorful account of his initiation into* Le Club des Hachichins *may be attributed to several factors: the first concerns
literary style—Gautier was habituated to a rococo form of
prose that was frequently excessive in its rhetorical flourishes
—a style which was, however, characteristic of much French
writing in the middle of the 19th century; moreover Gautier's
"set and setting" (the "set" being his general psychological
make-up as modified by his mood and expectations, and the
"setting" being the atmosphere of the physical surroundings
and the interpersonal vibrations of the people present) were,
as the essay demonstrates, enormously stimulating and melodramatic per se. Much of the grotesque, incredible flavor of
this account, then, may be attributed to the interacting influences of the Hotel Pimodan's haunted neo-Gothic interiors,
the mystery-laden, ritualistic inclinations of Gautier's fellow
hashish eaters, and an acutely inflamed and uninhibited literary
imagination. Finally, the quantity of Dawamesc—a confection
whose main ingredient is hashish—which was eaten by
Gautier (administered presumably by Dr. Jacques Joseph
Moreau de Tours, a psychiatrist who pioneered in the therapeutic use of hashish in the treatment of emotional and mental
disorders) was "about the size of one's thumb," rather an*

163

excessive amount to be initially subtracted from the author's "share in Paradise."

I PIMODAN HOUSE

One December evening, in answer to a mysterious summons drawn up in enigmatic terms understood only by the knowing and unintelligible to others, I arrived in a remote section, a sort of oasis of solitude in the midst of Paris, which the river, surrounding it with both its arms, seems to defend against the encroachments of civilization: an old mansion on the Isle Saint-Louis, Pimodan House built by Lauzun, was where the bizarre club of which I was a recent member held its monthly sessions, which I was attending for the first time.

Although it was barely six o'clock, the night was black.

A mist, thickened by the proximity of the Seine, dimmed all objects with its ragged cotton wadding, torn, here and there, by the reddish haloes of lanterns and ribbons of brightness escaping from lighted windows.

The pavement, flooded with rain, glistened beneath the street lamps like water mirroring harbor lights, while a sharp wind, laden with frozen particles, whipped my face, and guttural whistling sounds provided the treble to a symphony having the breaking of the swollen waves against the bridges' arches as its bass: the evening lacked none of the rough poetry of winter.

It was difficult, along the deserted quay and in the mass of dark buildings, to distinguish the house I was seeking. However, my coachman, by rising on his seat, was able to make out, on a marble plaque with the gilt half worn off, the name of the former mansion where the adepts met.

I raised the ornate knocker, as the use of brass-buttoned bells had not yet penetrated into these out-of-the-way regions, and several times I heard the cord scrape unsuccessfully, finally it gave way to a stronger pull; the old, rusted bolt was drawn aside and the massively timbered door turned on its hinges.

Behind a yellowish, transparent pane there appeared, as I entered, the head of an old female gatekeeper, outlined by a trembling candle, a ready-made painting by Skalken. The head grimaced at me curiously, and a thin finger, extending from the gate-house, pointed the way.

As far as I could distinguish in the pale glow which always falls even from the darkest sky, the courtyard I was crossing was surrounded by buildings of ancient architecture with steep-pitched roofs; my feet felt as wet as if I had walked through a meadow, for the cracks between the paving stones were filled with grass.

The high, narrow-paned windows of the flamboyant staircase against the somber façade served as my guide and kept me
from straying.

Once across the porch, I found myself at the foot of one of
those immense staircases built in the days of Louis XIV, in
which a modern house could dance with ease. An Egyptian
chimera in the style of Lebrun, bestraddled by a Cupid,
stretched forth its paws upon a pedestal, holding a candle in its
upturned claws.

The slope of the stairs was gentle; rests and landings were
well distributed and bore witness to the genius of the old
architect and the grandiose life of centuries gone by. Ascending this admirable incline, clothed in my thin, black evening
coat, I felt as though I were a blot on the surroundings, usurp-
ing a right to which I had no title; the service staircase would
have served for me.

Paintings, most of them unframed, copies of masterpieces of
the Italian and Spanish schools, lined the walls; in the shadows
overhead were the vague outlines of a large mythological
ceiling painted in fresco.

I reached the indicated floor.

A Utrecht velvet drum, crushed and stained, whose yellowed
braid and dented nails told of its long service, marked the
proper door.

I rang, and was admitted with the usual precautions. I found
myself in a large room, lighted at the far end by a few lamps.
To enter was to step two centuries back; time, which passes so
fast, seemed not to have elapsed in this house, and like a clock
negligently left unwound, its hands showed the same date
always.

The walls, paneled in white-painted wood, were half-covered
with darkened canvases that bore the stamp of the period. On
a gigantic mantelpiece rose a statue that one might suppose to
have been pilfered from the Versailles gardens.

On the ceiling, which arched into a dome, writhed a sprawl-
ing allegory painted with broad strokes, in the manner of
Lemoine, which might have been by that painter.

I advanced toward the luminous part of the room, where
several human shapes bustled about a table; and as soon as the
light reached me and revealed who I was, a hearty hurrah
shook the sonorous depths of the old structure.

"Here he is! Here he is!" several voices cried out together.
"Give him his portion!"

The doctor stood near a sideboard whereon rested a tray
laden with small Japanese porcelain saucers. A piece of greenish paste or jam, about the size of one's thumb, was drawn by

him by means of a spatula from a crystal jar, and placed, beside a vermilion spoon, on each saucer.

The doctor's face beamed with enthusiasm, his eyes sparkled, his cheeks reddened, the veins in his temples stood out and his dilated nostrils drew in the air with force.

"This will be subtracted from your share in Paradise," said he, handing me my allotted dose.

When each had eaten his portion, coffee was served in the Arab manner, that is, with the grounds and without sugar.

Then we sat down to the table.

This inversion of culinary habits has doubtless surprised the reader; indeed, it is scarcely usual to take coffee before the soup, and it is generally only at the dessert that jams are eaten. The matter surely warrants explanation.

II PARENTHESIS

Long ago, in the Orient, there existed a dreaded order of devotees commanded by a shiekh who styled himself the Old Man of the Mountain, or prince of the Assassins.

This Old Man of the Mountain was obeyed without question; the Assassins, his subjects, would act with absolute devotion in performance of his orders, whatever they might be; no danger staved them, not even the most certain death. At a sign from their leader, they would leap from a tower, or go to stab a sovereign in his palace, amidst his guards.

By what artifice did the Old Man of the Mountain instill such thorough abnegation?

By means of a wonderful drug whereof he had the formula, which had the property of inducing dazzling hallucinations.

Those taking it, on awaking from their intoxication, found real life so sad and colorless that they joyfully sacrificed it to re-enter the paradise of their dreams, for every man killed while accomplishing the orders of the sheikh went straight into heaven, while those who escaped were again permitted to enjoy the felicities of the mysterious concoction.

Now, the green paste that the doctor had just passed out among us was precisely that which the Old Man of the Mountain used to administer to his fanatics without their knowledge, making believe that he held access to Mohammed's heaven and the three classes of houris—that is, hashish, whence comes hashisheen or hashish-eater, the root of the word "assassin," whose ferocious meaning is readily explicable by the bloodthirsty habits of the votaries of the Old Man of the Mountain.

Surely, those who saw me leave my home at the hour when ordinary mortals take their nourishment had no notion that I

was on my way to the Isle Saint-Louis, a virtuous and patriarchal spot if ever one was, to consume a strange dish, which,
several centuries ago, served an impostor sheikh as an induce-
ment to drive his zealots to assassination. Nothing in my
perfectly ordinary appearance could have drawn suspicion to
such an excess of orientalism; I rather seemed some nephew on
his way to dine at his aunt's, than a believer about to taste the
joys of Mohammed's heaven in company with twelve exceedingly French Arabs.

Before this revelation, had you been told that in Paris, in
1845, that period of stock-trading and railroads, there existed
an order of hashisheen, you would not have believed it, but
nonetheless nothing would have been more true—as is customary with unlikely things.

III AGAPE

The meal was served in a bizarre manner, with every sort
of extravagant and picturesque ware.

Large Venetian glasses crisscrossed with milky spirals, his-
torically emblazoned German seidels, Flemish stoneware mugs,
slender-necked flasks still wrapped in reeds, took the place of
glasses, bottles, and pitchers.

Louis Leboeuf opaque porcelain and English flowered
faience, the adornments of middle-class tables, shone by their
absence; no two plates were alike, yet each had its own merit;
China, Japan, and Saxony contributed samples of their finest
clays and richest colors; all a bit chipped, a bit cracked, but
all in exquisite taste.

The plates, for the most part, were Bernard de Palissy
enamels or Limoges faiences, and at times the carver's knife,
under a real dish, would come across a reptile, frog, or bird
in relief. The edible eel mingled its coils with those of the
moulded snake.

An honest Philistine would have felt some dismay at the
sight of these long-haired, bearded, moustached or singularly
shorn guests, brandishing sixteenth-century daggers, Malayan
krisses or navajas, and bending over food to which the gleams
of the flickering lamps imported a dubious appearance.

The dinner was drawing to its close, and some of the more
fervent adepts were already feeling the effects of the green
paste. I, myself, had undergone a complete transposition of
my taste. The water I was drinking seemed to savor like the
most delicate wine, the meat turned to raspberries in my
mouth, and conversely. I could not have told a cutlet from a
peach.

My neighbors began to seem a little peculiar; they were opening wide, owl's eyes; their noses were lengthening into probosces; their mouths were widening like the openings in sleighbells. Their faces took on supernatural tints.

One, with a pale face in a black beard, was in peals of laughter before some unseen spectacle; another made unbelievable efforts to carry his glass to his lips, while his contortions to achieve his purpose produced a roar of jeers.

Another, in nervous agitation, twiddled his thumbs with incredible agility; yet another, thrown back in his chair, with dreamy eyes and lifeless arms, voluptuously let himself glide into the bottomless sea of oblivion.

Resting my elbows on the table, I considered everything in the gleaming of a remnant of reason which went and returned by instants like a candle ready to gutter. Vague warmths traveled over my limbs, and madness, like a wave foaming against a rock, which withdraws to hurl itself anew, entered and departed my brain, at length altogether invading it.

Hallucination, that strange guest, had set up his dwelling place in me.

"To the drawing room! to the drawing room!" cried one of those present. "Do you not hear the celestial choirs? The musicians have long been at their stands."

A delightful harmony was reaching us through the tumult of the conversation.

IV AN UNINVITED GENTLEMAN

The drawing room was an enormous chamber with molded and gilded woodwork, a painted ceiling, and friezes adorned with satyrs pursuing nymphs among rushes; it held a vast, colored marble mantelpiece, and ample brocade draperies that breathed forth the opulence of times gone by.

Upholstered furniture, settees, armchairs, and cushioned seats wide enough for the skirts of duchesses or marquises to be spread out with ease, received the hashisheen in their soft, ever-open arms.

A low seat by the chimney corner beckoned to me. I installed myself in it, surrendering unresistingly to the effects of the fantastic drug.

After several minutes, my companions had vanished, one after another, leaving no trace other than their shadows on the walls, which were soon absorbed like the brown stains that water makes on sand, fading as they dry.

As I was no longer conscious, from that time on, of what

others were doing, you now must be content with a relation of my simple personal impressions.

Solitude reigned in the drawing room, which was studded with only a few dubious gleams; all of a sudden, a red flash passed beneath my eyelids, innumerable candles burst into light and I felt bathed in a warm, clear glow. I was indeed in the same place, but it was as different as a sketch is from a painting: everything was larger, richer, more gorgeous. Reality served as a point of departure for the splendors of the hallucination.

I could still see no one, but I divined the presence of a multitude.

I heard the rustling of fabrics, the creaking of shoes, voices that whispered, murmured, and lisped, stifled bursts of laughter, the scraping of chair and table legs. Dishes were roughly handled, doors were opened and closed; something unaccustomed was going on.

An enigmatic character suddenly appeared before me. How had he come in? I cannot say; yet the sight of him caused me no alarm. His nose was curved like a bird's beak; his green eyes, which he frequently wiped with an immense handkerchief, were encircled with three brown rings; a high, heavy white cravat—in its knot a visiting card containing the words: *Daucas-Carota, of the Golden Pot*—strangled his thin collar, causing the skin of his cheeks to overflow in ruddy folds; a black, square-cut coat, whence dangled loops of watch chains and fobs, imprisoned his body, which was thrust out like the breast of a capon. His legs, I must confess, were made of a bifurcated mandrake root—black, rough, full of knots and bulges—which seemed to have been freshly picked, for clods of earth still clung to its filaments. These legs thrummed and twisted with extraordinary activity, and, when the small torso that they upheld stood entirely facing me, the strange character burst into sobs, wiped his eyes with a sweeping gesture, and said in the most mournful tones:

"It is today that we must die laughing."

Tears as large as peas rolled across the wings of his nose.

"Laughing . . . laughing . . ." repeated a choir of echolike, discordant nasal voices.

V FANTASIA

I then looked at the ceiling and perceived a host of bodiless heads like cherubims', with such comical expressions, such jovial physiognomies, and so profoundly happy a look that I could not but share in their hilarity. Their eyes were wrinkled about, their mouths widened, and their nostrils flared; their grimaces would have brought joy to spleen personified. These farcical masks turned in areas of opposite movement, producing a dazzling and dizzying effect.

Little by little, the drawing room became filled with extraordinary figures such as one finds only in the etchings of Callot and the aquatints of Goya: characteristic hodgepodges of spangles and rags of human and bestial figures; at another time, I would perhaps have been apprehensive about such company, but there was nothing menacing in these monstrosities. It was slyness, not ferocity, that sparkled in their pupils. Good humor alone uncovered their jagged fangs and sharp incisors.

As though I were the lord of the feast, each shape came in turn into the luminous circle whereof I occupied the center, with an air of grotesque deference, to mutter in my ear banter, none of which I now remember, but which, at the time, I found prodigiously witty, and which excited me to the maddest gaiety.

With each new apparition, a Homeric, Olympian, immense, dumbfounding laugh, which seemed to resound through infinity, burst about me with a thunderous roar.

Voices, now whining, now cavernous, screamed:

"No, it's too funny; no more! My God, my God, what fun! Funnier and funnier!"

"Enough! I can bear no more . . . Ha, ha! Ho, ho! He, he! What a fine farce! What a good pun!"

"Stop! I'm stifling! I'm choking! Don't look at me so . . . or place hoops about me, I'm going to burst . . ."

Despite these half-jesting, half-entreating protestations, the awesome hilarity went ever increasing, the din grew in intensity, the floors and walls of the house heaved and palpitated like a human diaphragm, shaken by the frenetic, irresistible, implacable laughter.

Soon, instead of coming before me one by one, the grotesque phantoms assaulted me in a body, swaying their long jesters' sleeves, tripping over the folds of their magicians' gowns, flattening their cardboard noses in ridiculous collisions, making the powder of their wigs fly off in clouds, and singing extravagant songs, with impossible rhymes, off key.

All the types ever invented by the mocking verve of nations and artists were gathered there, but multiplied tenfold, a hundredfold, in strength. It was a curious throng: the Neapolitan Punchinello familiarly tapping England's Punch on his hunched shoulder; the Harlequin of Pergamum thrusting his black snout into the floury mask of the Paillasse of France, who uttered fearful cries; the Bolognese Doctor throwing snuff into Father Cassandra's eyes; Tartaglia galloping his horse over a clown; Giles kicking Don Spavento's behind; and Karagheuz, armed with his obscene stick, fighting a duel with a buffoon Osco.

Beyond, fantasies of droll dreams confusedly danced about: hybrid creations, formless mixtures of men, beasts, and utensils; monks with wheels for feet and cauldrons for bellies; warriors, in armor of dishes, brandishing wooden swords in birds' claws; statesmen moved by turnspit gears; kings plunged to the waist in saltcellar turrets; alchemists with their heads arranged as bellows, their limbs twisted into alambics; bawds made up of bizarrely knobbed squashes—everything which, with a feverishly heated pencil, a cynic might trace when intoxication guides his hand.

Everything writhed, crawled, skipped, grunted, whistled, as Goethe says in his Walpurgis Night.

In order to escape the excessive bustle of these baroque characters, I sought refuge in a dark corner, whence I could see them giving themselves up to dances such as the Renaissance never knew in Chicard's time, nor the opera under the reign of Musard, the king of the disheveled quadrille. These dancers, with an entrechat or a balancé, wrote comedies a thousand times better than Molière, Rabelais, Swift, or Voltaire, comedies so profoundly philosophical, satires of such high reach and mordant wit, that I was obliged to hold my sides in my corner.

Daucas-Carota, wiping his eyes, was performing inconceivable pirouettes and leaps, especially for a man with legs of mandrake root, repeating in farcically piteous tones, "Today is when we must die laughing!"

You who think you know what is a comic masque, had you attended this ball induced by hashish you would agree that the most mirth-provoking farceurs of our small theaters are worthy of being sculptured at the corners of a pall, or on a tomb!

What bizarrely contorted faces! What eyes, winking and sparkling with sarcasm beneath their birdlike membranes! What piggybank smiles! What hacked-out mouths! What facetiously twelve-sided noses! What abdomens, huge with Pantagruelion mockeries!

Through all the movement of this unterrifying nightmare, there flashed sudden images of countenances of irresistible effect, caricatures that would have produced jealousy in Daumier, fantasies that would have delighted the marvelous artists of China, the Phidiases of the rickshaw.

Not all these visions, however, were monstrous or bur-
lesque; gracefulness too showed itself in this carnival of forms.
Near the fireplace, a small head with peachlike cheeks, showing, in an endless fit of mirth, thirty-two small teeth the size
of grains of rice, uttered a high-pitched, vibrant, silvery, prolonged burst of laughter embroidered with trills and organ-
bursts which penetrated my eardrums and, by a nervous mag-
netism, compelled me to commit a host of extravagances.

The joyous frenzy was at its peak; nothing now could be
heard save convulsive sighs, inarticulate cluckings. The laughter lost its timbre and turned into grunts, while spasms followed after pleasure: Daucas-Carota's words were about to
come true.

Already, a few annihilated hashisheen had rolled to the
ground with that lax heaviness of intoxication that reduces
the danger in falling; exclamations such as "My God, how
happy I am!" "What felicity!" "I am swimming in ecstasy!"
"I am in Paradise!" "I am diving into abysses of delight!"
crossed, merged, and covered one another.

Hoarse cries burst from oppressed chests; arms writhed
with desire toward some fleeting vision; heels and the backs
of heads drummed against the floor. It was time to throw a
drop of cold water on this seething vapor, lest the boiler burst.

Man's bodily envelope, which has so little strength for
pleasure and so much for pain, could not have endured happiness at too high a pressure.

One of the club's members, who had not partaken of the
voluptuous intoxicant in order to watch over the fantasia
and prevent those of us who might think we had wings from
going through the windows, rose, opened the lid of the piano
and sat down. His hands, falling together, sank into the ivory
of the keyboard, and a glorious chord resounded with force,
stilling all murmurs and changing the direction of the intoxication.

VI AL-KIEF

The theme he struck up was, I believe, Agatha's aria in
Die Freyschütz; the celestial melody, like a breath sweeping
misshapen clouds away, soon dissipated the ridiculous visions
that had obsessed me. The grimacing ghosts withdrew, crawling beneath armchairs or hiding between the folds of the
draperies, heaving small, stifled sighs, and again I seemed
to be alone in the drawing room.

The colossal organ of Fribourg assuredly does not produce
a greater mass of sonority than the piano played by the *seer*

(as the sober adept is called). The notes quivered with such power that they entered my breast like luminous arrows; soon, the air played seemed to come from myself; my fingers moved over an absent keyboard; sounds sprang forth, blue and red, in electric sparks; Weber's soul had become incarnated in me.

The piece concluded, my inner improvisations in the style of the German master continued, causing me ineffable ecstasy. What a pity that a magical stenographer could not have transcribed those inspired melodies, heard by me alone, and which, modestly enough, I do not hesitate to place above the masterworks of Rossini, Meyerbeer, and Félicien David!

After the somewhat convulsive gaiety of the beginning, an indefinable feeling of well-being, a boundless calm, took over.

I was in that blessed state induced by hashish which the Orientals call *al-kief*. I could no longer feel my body; the bonds of matter and spirit were severed; I moved by sheer willpower in an unresisting medium.

Thus I imagine the movement of souls in the world of fragrances to which we shall go after death. A bluish haze, an Elysian light, the reflections of an azure grotto, formed an atmosphere in the room through which I vaguely saw the tremblings of hesitant outlines; an atmosphere at once cool and warm, moist and perfumed, enveloping me like bath water in a sort of enervating sweetness. When I tried to move away, the caressing air made a thousand voluptuous waves about me; a delightful languor gripped my senses and threw me back upon the sofa, where I hung, limp as a discarded garment.

Then I understood the pleasure experienced by the spirits and angels, according to their degree of perfection, when they traverse the ethers and the skies, and how eternity might occupy one in Paradise.

Nothing material was mingled with this ecstasy; no terrestrial desire marred its purity. Love itself, in fact, could not have increased it. Romeo as a hashisheen would have forgotten his Juliet. The poor child, bending over her jasmines, would have stretched her alabaster arms across the balcony and through the night in vain. Romeo would have stayed at the foot of the silken ladder, and although I madly love the angel of youth and beauty created by Shakespeare, I must agree that the prettiest girl in Verona, to a hashisheen, is not worth the bother of stirring.

So, with a peaceful though fascinated eye, I watched a garland of ideally beautifully women, who diademed a frieze with their divine nudity; I saw the gleam of their satin shoulders, the sparkle of their silvery breasts, the overhead tripping of small pink feet, the undulation of opulent hips, without feeling the least temptation. The charming spectres that disturbed Saint Anthony would have had no power over me.

By some bizarre prodigy, after several minutes of contemplation I would melt into the object looked at, and I myself would become that object. Thus I turned into a nymph Syrinx, since the fresco represented Leda's daughter pursued by Pan. I felt all the terrors of the poor fugitive, and sought to hide behind the fantastic reeds to avoid the ram-footed monster.

VII AL-KIEF TURNS TO A NIGHTMARE

During my ecstasy, Daucas-Carota had come in. Seated like a tailor or a pasha on his appropriately twisted roots, he fixed blazing eyes upon me; his beak clapped so sardonically, so mocking an air of triumph burst through his small, distorted person, that I shuddered in spite of myself.

Guessing my alarm, he redoubled his contortions and grimaces, coming near with little jumps like a wounded daddy-longlegs or a legless cripple in his basket.

Then I felt a cold breath at my ear, and a voice told me in familiar tones, although I could not determine whose, "That wretched Daucas-Carota, who sold his legs for drink, has purloined your head and replaced it, not with an ass' head as Puck did to Bottom, but with an elephant's head!"

Singularly intrigued, I went straight to the mirror, and saw that the admonition was not unfounded.

I would have been taken for a Hindu or Javanese idol: my forehead had risen; my nose, lengthened into a trunk, curled on my chest, my ears swept my shoulders, and to compound the grievance, I was indigo in color, like the blue god Shiva.

Exasperated with fury, I began to pursue Daucas-Carota, who jumped about and whimpered, giving every sign of abject terror; I managed to seize him, and knocked him so violently against the edge of the table that at length he gave me back my head, which he had wrapped in his handkerchief.

Satisfied with this victory, I was about to resume my place on the couch when the same small, unknown voice said:

"Beware, you are surrounded by enemies; the invisible forces are seeking to attract you and hold you. You are a prisoner here: try to leave, and you will see."

A veil was rent asunder in my mind, and it became clear to me that the members of the club were nothing other than cabalists and magicians who wanted to drag me down to my perdition.

VIII THE TREADMILL

I rose with a great deal of trouble and headed toward the door of the drawing room, which I reached only after a considerable time, for some unknown force compelled me to take one step backward out of every three. According to my reckoning, it took me ten years to cover the distance.

Daucas-Carota followed me, cackling with laughter, and mumbling in mock commiseration: "If that's how fast he walks, when he arrives, he'll be an old man."

I nevertheless managed to reach the next room, which seemed to be of strange, unrecognizable dimensions. It lengthened out, lengthened out . . . indefinitely. The light that twinkled at the far end seemed as distant as a fixed star.

Discouragement took hold of me, and I was going to stop when the small voice, nearly brushing against my ear, said:

"Courage! *She* expects you at eleven o'clock."

Calling desperately upon the forces of my spirit, I succeeded, by an enormous projection of will, in raising my feet, which gripped the ground and which I was compelled to uproot like tree trunks. The monster with the mandrake legs escorted me, parodying my exertions, and chanting in dirge-like tones: "The marble is gaining ground! The marble is gaining ground!"

To be sure, I could feel my limbs petrifying, and the marble enveloping me to the waist like the Tuileries' Daphne; I was a statue halfway up, like the enchanted princes in the *Arabian Nights*. My hardened heels rang out formidably against the floor; I could have played the Commander in *Don Giovanni*.

By this time I had reached the head of the stairs, which I undertook to descend; they were half-lit, and through my dream they took on Cyclopean, gigantic proportions. Their two ends, bathed in shadow, seemed to plunge into heaven and hell, both of them abysses; raising my head, I indistinctly discerned, in a prodigious perspective, countless superposed landings, ramps leading up as to the top of the tower of Lylacq; looking down, I felt the presence of abysses of steps, whorls of spirals, dazzling circumvolutions.

This staircase must pierce the earth through and through, said I to myself as I continued my mechanical walking. I shall reach the bottom the day after Judgment Day.

The figures in the paintings were looking at me with a pitying air; some moved with halting contortions, like dumb folk wanting to impart important news on a supreme occasion. One would have thought they wanted to warn me about some trap to avoid, but an inert, dull force led me on. The steps were soft and sank beneath me, like the mysterious ladders in Free-masonic initiations. The sticking, yielding stairs gave way like the bellies of toads; new landings, new stairs appeared unceasingly before my resigned steps, while those that I had passed resumed their place in front of me. These proceedings took a thousand years, as I calculate it. At length I reached the vestibule, where another, no less terrible persecution awaited me.

The chimera holding a candle in its paws, which I had noted when I came in, was barring my way with clearly hostile intent; its greenish eyes sparkled with mockery, its malicious mouth laughed evilly; it was coming toward me nearly crawling on its stomach, dragging its bronze caparison through the dust, although not in submission; ferocious quivers shook its lion's haunches, and Daucas-Carota was urging it on like a dog that one wants to make fight.

"Bite him! Bite him! Marble meat for a brazen gullet, there's a savory treat!"

Without letting myself be alarmed by the horrible beast, I stepped by. A gust of cold air struck me in the face, and the night sky, cleansed of its clouds, suddenly appeared. A scattering of stars powdered the veins of the vast block of lapis-lazuli with flecks of gold.

I was in the courtyard.

To convey the effect produced on me by the somber architecture, I would need the burin used by Piranesi to scratch the black varnish of his marvelous copperplates: the courtyard had taken on the proportions of the Champs-de-Mars, and in a few hours had become bordered with giant buildings set out against the horizon in a tracery of steeples, domes, towers, gables, and pyramids worthy of Rome and Babylon.

My surprise was extreme. I had never suspected the Isle Saint-Louis of containing so many monumental splendors, which, moreover, would have covered twenty times its true area; and I thought, not without apprehension, of the power of the magicians who could, in an evening, erect such structures.

"You are the plaything of idle illusions; this courtyard is very small," murmured the voice. "It is twenty-seven paces long by twenty-five across."

"Yes, yes," grumbled the bifurcated freak, "paces with seven-league boots. Never will you arrive at eleven; it is fifteen hundred years since you left. Half your hair has turned gray. Go back upstairs, it is the wisest course."

As I did not obey, the odious monster entangled me in the meshes of his legs, and, aided by his clutching hands, took

me in tow despite my resistance, making me return up the
stairs where I had undergone such anguish, and, to my great
despair, reinstalling me in the drawing room from which I
had with such pains escaped. Then the dizziness quite overwhelmed me; I became insane, delirious.

Daucas-Carota was cavorting, leaping up to the ceiling,
saying, "Imbecile! I gave you back your head, but first I took
out the brains with a spoon!"

I felt a fearful sadness as, raising my hand to my cranium,
I found the top missing; then I lost consciousness.

IX PLACE NO FAITH IN CHRONOMETERS

When I came to, I saw the room full of people dressed in
black, coming together with sad looks and shaking hands with
a melancholy cordiality, like persons afflicted with a common
sorrow.

They were saying: "Time is dead. Henceforth there will be
no years, no months, no hours; time is dead, and we are going
to its funeral."

"True, it was old enough, but I did not anticipate this
development."

"It was in excellent health for its years," added one of the
mourners whom I recognized as a painter friend of mine.

"Eternity was worn out; there had to be an end," resumed
another.

"Great God!" I cried, struck by a sudden notion. "If there
is no more time, when will it be eleven o'clock?"

"Nevermore," cried Daucas-Carota in thunderous tones,
flinging his nose before my face and showing himself to me
in his true guise . . . "Nevermore . . . it will always be a
quarter past nine . . . the hands will remain on the minute
when time ceased to be, and your punishment will be to come,
look at the motionless hands, and sit down once more only
to begin again, until you are walking on the bones of your
heels."

A superior force impelled me, and I made the journey four
or five hundred times to interrogate the clock face with a
horrible anxiety.

Daucas-Carota had seated himself astride the clock, and
made fearsome faces at me.

The hands did not move.

"Wretch! You have stopped the pendulum," I cried, drunken
with rage.

"I have not, it is going back and forth as usual . . . but suns will crumble into dust before yon steel arrow advances a millionth of one millimeter."

"Come, come, I see we must conjure the evil spirits, things are turning distasteful," said the *seer;* "let's make a little music. David's harp will be replaced this time by an Erard piano."

And sitting on the stool, he played melodies with joyous strains . . .

This seemed greatly to annoy the mandrake-man, who diminished, grew flat, lost his color, and uttered inarticulate moans; at last he lost all human semblance, and rolled on the floor in the shape of a double-rooted salsify.

The spell was broken.

"Hallelujah! Time has risen from the dead," shouted happy, childish voices. "Now go see the clock!"

The hands pointed to eleven o'clock.

"Sir, your carriage is downstairs," said a servant.

The dream was at an end.

The hashisheen went off, each in his own direction, like the officers in *Marlbrough Goes to War.*

With light steps, I went down the stairs that had caused me so much anguish, and a few moments later I was in my room, in full reality; the last vapors raised by the hashish had vanished.

My reason had returned, or at least what I call such for want of another term. My lucidity could even have enabled me to review a pantomime or comic play, or to write three-lettered rhyming verses.

La Revue des Deux Mondes, Feb. 1, 1846.

CHAPTER THREE

AN EXCERPT FROM
THE SERAPHIC THEATRE

Charles Baudelaire
Translated by Norman Cannon

*The morbid, neurotic, but consummately gifted Charles Baude-
laire became a member of the famous* Club des Hachichins
*in 1844, eventually taking lodgings (as Théophile Gautier had)
in the attic of the Hotel Pimodan on the Left Bank, where
the club convened. In 1858 he wrote a long article on his
hashish experiences, which first appeared in the* Revue Con-
temporaine *under the title "De l'Ideal artificiel" (On the Artificial Ideal). The poet republished this monograph two years
later in his masterpiece* Les Paradis Artificiels *(Artificial Para-
dises) and called it "Le Poème du hachich." It is from this
work that "The Seraphic Theatre" has been excerpted. Aside
from the sheer beauty of the prose, impressive even in translation, the value of the following essay lies in its superbly sensitive evocation of the psychological reactions of the hashish
eater.*
*In a later segment of "Le Poème du hachich" Baudelaire de-
plored what he considered hemp's undermining effect on man's
moral structure. Scholars have pointed out that the "Poème"
was written over a decade after the experiences described
actually occurred, and that Baudelaire's remarks concerning
the spiritually detrimental effects of hashish were probably
rooted in his depression-inducing, long-standing opiate and
alcohol addictions, misfortunes which pre-dated his experiments with hashish and undoubtedly colored them.*

179

"What does one experience? What does one see? Wonderful things, eh? Amazing sights? It is very beautiful? Very terrible? Very dangerous?"

Such are the questions put, with a mixture of curiosity and fear, by the ignorant to the initiated. The questioners seem to have a childish impatience for knowledge, such as might be felt by somebody who has never left his fireside, on meeting a man returning from distant and unknown lands. They think of the intoxication caused by hashish as a land of miracles, a huge conjuror's theatre where everything is marvellous and unexpected.

This is an ill-informed notion, a complete misunderstanding. Since, for the common run of readers and questioners, the word hashish conveys an idea of strange, topsy-turvy worlds, an expectation of miraculous dreams (a more accurate word would be hallucinations—which, in any case, are less frequent than is generally supposed), I shall at once point out an important difference between the effects of hashish and the phenomena of sleep.

In sleep, that nightly journey of adventure, there positively is something miraculous, although the miracle's mystery has been staled by its punctual regularity. Men's dreams are of two kinds. Those of the first kind are full of his ordinary life, his preoccupations, desires, and faults, mingled in a more or less bizarre fashion with things seen during the day that have indiscriminately attached themselves to the huge canvas of his memory. This is the natural dream—the man himself.

But the other kind of dream—the absurd, unpredictable dream, with no relation to or connection with the character, life, or passions of the dreamer. This, which I shall call the "hieroglyphic" dream, obviously represents the supernatural side of life; and it is just because of its absurdity that the ancients regarded it as divine. Since it cannot be explained as a product of natural causes, they attributed it to a cause external to mankind; and even today, and apart from the oneiromancers, there is a school of philosophy that sees in dreams of this sort sometimes a reproach and sometimes a counsel; a symbolic moral picture, that is to say, engendered actually in the mind of the sleeping person. It is a dictionary that requires study for its comprehension, a language to which wise men can obtain the key.

The intoxication of hashish is utterly different. It will not bring us beyond the bounds of the natural dream. It is true that throughout its whole period the intoxication will be in the nature of a vast dream—by reason of the intensity of its colors and its rapid flow of mental images; but it will always retain the private tonality of the individual. The man wanted the dream, now the dream will govern the man; but this dream will certainly be the son of its father. The sluggard has contrived artificially to introduce the supernatural into his life and thoughts; but he remains, despite the adventitious force of his sensations, merely the same man increased, the same number raised to a very high power. He is subjugated—but, unfortunately for him, only by himself; in other words, by that part of himself that was already previously dominant. *He wished to ape the angel, he has become an animal;* and for a brief while the latter is very powerful—if power is the correct word for an excessive sensibility—because it is subject to no restraining or directing government.

It is right, then, that sophisticated persons, and also ignorant persons who are eager to make acquaintance with unusual delights, should be clearly told that they will find in hashish nothing miraculous, absolutely nothing but an exaggeration of the natural. The brain and organism on which hashish operates will produce only the normal phenomena peculiar to that individual—increased, admittedly, in number and force, but always faithful to their origin. A man will never escape from his destined physical and moral temperament: hashish will be a mirror of his impressions and private thoughts—a magnifying mirror, it is true, but only a mirror.

Have a look at the drug itself: a green sweetmeat, the size of a nut and singularly odorous—so much so that it provokes a certain disgust and velleities of nausea; as, indeed, any odor would do, however pure or even agreeable in itself, if enhanced to its maximum of strength and, so to speak, density. (I may be allowed to remark, in passing, that this last statement has a corollary, that even the most disgusting and revolting scent might perhaps become a pleasure if it were reduced to its minimum of quantity and effluvium.)

Here, then, is happiness! It is large enough to fill a small spoon. Happiness, with all its intoxications, follies and puerilities. You can swallow it without fear—one does not die of it. Your physical organs will be in no way affected. Later on, perhaps, a too frequent consultation of the oracle will diminish your strength of will; perhaps you will be less of a man than you are today. But the retribution is so distant, and the disaster in store for you so difficult to define! What are you risking? A touch of nervous exhaustion tomorrow? Do you not daily risk worse retribution for lesser rewards?

Well, now, your mind is made up. You have even—in order to make the dose stronger and more diffusely effective—melted your rich extract in a cup of black coffee; you have seen to it that your stomach is empty, by postponing your main meal until nine or ten o'clock that evening, in order to give the poison full freedom of action; perhaps in an hour's time you will take, at the most, some thin soup. You now have enough ballast for a long and singular voyage. The steam-whistle has blown, the sails are set, and you have a curious advantage over ordinary travellers—that of not knowing whither you are going. You have made your choice: hurrah for destiny!

I assume that you have chosen your moment for this adventurous expedition. Every perfect debauch calls for perfect leisure. I have told you, moreover, that hashish produces an exaggeration not only of the individual, but also of his circumstances and surroundings. You must, therefore, have no social obligations demanding punctuality or exactitude; no domestic worries; no distressing affair of the heart. This is most important: for any grief or spiritual unrest, any memory of an obligation claiming your attention at a fixed time, would toll like a bell amidst your intoxication and poison your pleasure. The unrest would become an agony, the worry a torture.

If all these indispensible conditions have been observed, so that the moment is propitious; if your surroundings are favorable—a picturesque landscape, for example, or a poetically decorated apartment; and if, in addition, you can look forward to hearing a little music: why, then, all is for the best.

Intoxication with hashish generally falls into three successive phases, quite easy to distinguish. For beginners even the first symptoms of the first phase will be interesting enough. You have heard vague reports of the drug's marvellous effects. Your imagination has preconceived some private notion of them, something in the nature of an ideal form of drunkenness. You are impatient to learn if the reality will match your expectations. This is sufficient to throw you, from the beginning, into a state of anxiety, which to no small extent encourages the infiltration of the victorious and invading poison.

Most novices, of only the first degree of initiation, complain that hashish is slow in taking effect. They wait with childish impatience for it to do so; and then, when the drug does not function quickly enough to suit them, they indulge in a swaggering incredulity, which gives great delight to old initiates, who know just how hashish sets about its work.

The earliest encroachments of the drug, like symptoms of a storm that hovers before it strikes, appear and multiply in the very bosom of this incredulity. The first of them is a sort of irrelevant and irresistible hilarity. Attacks of causeless mirth, of which you are almost ashamed, repeat themselves at frequent intervals, cutting across periods of stupor during which you try in vain to pull yourself together. The simplest words, the most trivial ideas, assume a new and strange guise; you are actually astonished at having hitherto found them so simple. Incongruous and unforeseeable resemblances and comparisons, interminable bouts of punning on words, rough sketches for farces, continually spout from your brain. The demon has you in thrall. It is useless to struggle against this hilarity, which is as painful as a tickle. From time to time you laugh at yourself, at your own silliness and folly; and your companions, if you have such, laugh alike at your condition and at their own. But, since they laugh at you without malice, you laugh back at them without rancor.

This mirth, with its alternating spells of languor and convulsion, this distress in the midst of delight, generally lasts only for a fairly short time. Soon the coherence of your ideas becomes so vague, the conducting filament between your fancies becomes so thin, that only your accomplices can understand you.

And once again, on this question, too, there is no means of ascertaining the truth: perhaps they only think they understand you, and the deception is mutual. This crazy whimsicality, these explosive bursts of laughter, seem like real madness, or at least like a maniac's folly, to anyone who is not in the same state as yourself. Conversely, the self-control, good sense and orderly thoughts of a prudent observer who has abstained from intoxication—these delight and amuse you like a special sort of dementia. Your roles are inverted: his calmness drives you to extremes of ironic disdain.

How mysteriously comical are the feelings of a man who revels in incomprehensible mirth at the expense of anyone not in the same situation as himself! The madman begins to feel sorry for the sane man; and, from this moment on, the notion of his own superiority begins to gleam on the horizon of his intellect. Soon it will grow, swell and burst upon him like a meteor.

I once witnessed a scene of this sort, which was carried to great lengths. Its grotesque absurdity was intelligible only to such of those present as understood, at least from observing others, the effects of the drug and the enormous difference in pitch that it creates between two supposedly equal intellects.

A famous musician, who knew nothing of the properties of hashish, and perhaps had never even heard of the drug, found himself among a company of whom several persons had been taking it. They tried to make him understand its marvellous effects. He smiled graciously at their fabulous accounts, out of sheer politeness, in the manner of a man willing to make himself agreeable for a few minutes. His disdain was quickly felt by the others, whose perceptions had been sharpened by the poison, and their laughter wounded him. Finally their hilarious outbursts, the puns and strangely altered faces, the whole unhealthy atmosphere irritated him to the point of saying— perhaps more hastily than he might have wished: "This is an evil burden for an artist to take upon himself; moreover, it must be very very fatiguing."

To the others, the comicality of this remark seemed dazzling. Their joyful merriment was redoubled.

"This *burden* may suit you," said the musician, "but it would not suit me."

"All that matters is whether it suits us," one of the sick company said egotistically.

Not knowing whether he had to do with real madmen, or with people who were shamming madness, the musician thought it best to leave. But somebody locked the door and hid the key. Another person, going on his knees before the musician, begged his pardon, in the name of the company, and informed him, lachrymosely but insolently, that despite his (the musician's) spiritual inferiority, which perhaps excited a little pity, all present were filled with the deepest affection toward him.

The musician resigned himself to remaining, and, at the company's urgent request, was even so good as to play some music. But the sound of the violin, spreading through the room like a new contagion, laid hands (the expression is not too strong) first on one of the sick men and then on another. There were deep, hoarse sighs, sudden sobs, floods of silent tears. The musician grew alarmed, and stopped playing. Going up to the man whose blissful state was causing the greatest hubbub, he asked him whether he was in great pain, and what he (the musician) could do to help him. One of those present, a "practical man," suggested lemonade and stomach-powders. But the sufferer, his eyes shining with ecstasy, looked at them both with unutterable scorn. To think of wishing to "cure" a man sick with super-abundance of life, a man sick with joy!

As this anecdote shows, one of the most noticeable sensations resulting from the use of hashish is that of benevolence; a flaccid, idle, dumb benevolence, resulting from a softening of the nerves.

In confirmation of this, somebody once told me of an adventure that had befallen him whilst at this stage of intoxication. Since he had retained a very exact memory of his sensations, I could perfectly understand the grotesque embarrassment in which he had been inextricably involved as a result of that difference in pitch and level of which I was speaking.

I cannot remember whether my informant was having his first or second experience of the drug. Did he take rather too strong a dose, or did the hashish produce, without any apparent cause—this often happens—much more vigorous effects than usual? He told me that, in the midst of his delight (that supreme delight of feeling oneself filled with life, and believing oneself filled with genius), he was all at once seized with terror. After having at first been dazzled by the beauty of his sensations, he was suddenly appalled by them. He asked himself what would become of his intellect and physical faculties if this condition, which seemed to him supernatural, were to grow more and more aggravated; if his nerves were to become continually more and more delicate?

Because of the power of enlargement possessed by the inward eye of the victim, such a fear as this can be unspeakable torture. My informant said as follows:

I was like a runaway horse galloping toward a precipice, trying to halt but unable to do so. It was truly a fearsome gallop; and my thoughts, enslaved by circumstances, situation, accident—by everything implied in the word "hazard"—had taken a purely rhapsodic turn. "It is too late!" I kept desperately repeating.

When this mode of sensation ceased—after what appeared to me an infinity of time, lasting, perhaps only a few minutes—and I was expecting to be able at last to sink into that state of beatitude, so dear to Orientals, which follows on the phase of furor, I was overwhelmed by a new "unhappiness." I was stricken with a new disquiet—this time quite trivial and childish. I suddenly remembered that I had been invited to a formal dinner with a party of respectable people. I foresaw myself in the midst of a discreet, well-behaved crowd, where everybody else would be in full control of his faculties, whilst I myself would be obliged carefully to conceal my mental condition—and under brilliant lamplight! I was fairly confident of being able to do this, but almost swooned at the thought of the efforts of will I should have to exert.

By I know not what accident, the words of the Gospel "Woe to him who giveth scandal!" arose in my memory. I tried hard to forget them, but kept ceaselessly repeating them in my mind. My unhappiness (for it was a real unhappiness) assumed grandiose proportions. I resolved, despite my weakness, to pull myself together and consult an apothecary; for I knew nothing of reagents, and proposed to present myself, free and without a care, in the society to which duty called me.

But at the door of the shop a sudden thought struck me,

causing me to stop and consider for a few moments. I had just seen my reflection in a shop window, and the sight of my own face amazed me. My pallor, my receding lips, my bulging eyes! "I shall upset the worthy apothecary," I told myself, "and for what a silly reason!"

Another feeling I had was a fear of meeting people in the shop and appearing ridiculous. But all other feelings were dominated by a sense of benevolence toward the unknown apothecary. I thought of him as a man having the same exaggerated sensibilities as I myself had at that terrible moment. I supposed, therefore, that his ear-drums and soul must quiver, as mine did, at the least noise, and I decided to enter his shop on tiptoe. "I cannot be too careful," I said to myself, "in dealing with a man who, in his goodness of heart, will be alarmed at my plight."

I also assured myself that I would muffle not only the sound of my steps, but also the sound of my voice.

The result was the contrary of what I had hoped. In my resolve to reassure the apothecary, I succeeded in scaring him. He knew nothing of my "illness"; he had never even heard of it. Nevertheless, he looked at me with a curiosity strongly mixed with disgust. Was he taking me for a madman, or for a beggar? Neither the one nor the other, no doubt; but these were the crazy notions that passed through my brain. I felt obliged to explain to him, at great length (and with what weariness!) all about conserve of hemp and the use to which it was put. I continually repeated to him that there was no reason for *him* to be alarmed, and that all I wanted was some palliative or antitoxin. I kept insisting on the sincere regret I felt at my vexatious intrusion.

Finally—and imagine all the humiliation to which the words subjected me!—the man simply asked me "please to leave the shop." This was the reward of my exaggerated charity and benevolence!

I went to my dinner party, and created no scandal. Nobody guessed at the superhuman efforts I had to make to be like everyone else. But I shall never forget the tortures of an ultra-poetical intoxication hampered by the need for decorum and thwarted by a sense of duty!

Although naturally inclined to sympathize with all sufferings that arise from imagination, I could not help laughing at this narrative. The man from whom I had it is not cured. He has continued to demand from the accursed sweetmeat the stimulus that one should find in oneself; but because he is a careful and orderly person, "a man of the world," he has reduced the doses, thus enabling himself to increase their frequency. He will make acquaintance later with the rotten fruits of his dietetic system.

Let me now revert to the normal development of the intoxication. After the first phase of childish mirth comes a sort of momentary lull. But soon new adventures are heralded by a sensation of chilliness in the extremities (for some people this becomes an intense cold), and a great weakness in all the members. In your head, and throughout your being, you feel an embarrassing stupor and stupefaction. Your eyes bulge, as if under the pull, both physical and spiritual, of an implacable ecstasy. Your face is flooded with pallor. Your lips shrink and are sucked back into your mouth by that panting movement that characterizes the ambition of a man who is a prey to great projects, overwhelmed by vast thoughts, or gaining breath for some violent effort. The sides of the gullet cleave together; so to speak. The palate is parched with a thirst that it would be infinitely pleasant to satisfy, if only the delights of idleness were not still more agreeable, and did they not forbid the slightest disarrangement of the body's posture. Hoarse, deep sighs burst forth from your chest, as if your *old* body could not endure the desires and activity of your *new* soul. Now and then a jolt passes through you, making you twitch involuntarily. It is like one of those sharp sensations of falling that you experience at the end of a day's work, or on a stormy night just before finally falling asleep.

Before going any further, I would like to recount, concerning the sensation of chilliness that I mentioned above, yet another anecdote, which will serve to show how greatly the drug's effects, even the purely physical ones, can vary between individuals. This time the speaker is a man of letters, and some passages of his narrative betray, I think, signs of a literary temperament.

I had taken a moderate dose of rich extract, he told me, and all was going well. The attack of morbid merriment had not lasted long, and I was in a state of languor and stupefaction which was almost one of happiness. I was therefore looking forward to a peaceful and carefree evening.

Unfortunately I was by chance constrained to accompany someone to a theater. I bravely faced the task, determined to disguise my immense desire for idleness and immobility. Since all the carriages in my district were engaged, I had to resign myself to a long walk amidst the harsh noises of carriages, the stupid conversations of passers-by, a whole ocean of trivial stupidities.

I had already begun to feel a slight chilliness in the tips of my fingers. This soon turned into an intense cold, as if both my hands were dipped in a pail of icy water. But this was not a hardship; the almost piercing sensation affected me more as a pleasure. Nevertheless, the cold invaded me more with every step I took on this interminable journey.

Two or three times I asked the person accompanying me if the weather was really very cold. He replied that, on the contrary, the temperature was more than warmish.

When I was at last installed in the body of the theater, shut up in the assigned box, with three or four hours of rest in store for me, I felt as if I had arrived in the Promised Land. The feelings that I had been suppressing on the way, with all the poor strength of which I was capable, now burst in upon me, and I abandoned myself to my silent frenzy. The cold became deeper and deeper; yet I saw that other people were lightly clad, or were even wiping their brows.

I was seized by a delightful notion that I was a man uniquely privileged, alone allowed the right to feel cold in a theater in summer. The cold increased until it became alarming; but I was principally dominated by a curiosity to know how far the thermometer would fall. Finally it fell to such a point, the cold was so complete and general, that all my ideas froze, so to speak. I was a block of thinking ice. I felt like a statue hewn from an icy slab. This mad illusion provoked in me a pride, a sense of moral well-being, that I cannot describe to you.

My abominable delight was enhanced by the certain knowledge that none of the spectators was aware of my nature, of my superiority to them. It was gleeful to think that my companion did not for an instant suspect what bizarre sensations had possessed me. I held the reward for my dissimulation: my unique form of pleasure was a real secret.

I should add that, soon after I entered my box, my eyes were assailed by an impression of darkness—which I think is somehow akin to the notion of cold. It was very possible that the two notions mutually strengthen each other.

As you know, hashish always evokes magnificent illuminations, glorious splendors, cascades of liquid gold. Under its influence, all light is good: light that gushes in floods or clings like tinsel to points and rough surfaces; the light of drawing-room candelabra or the tapers of May; the rose-red avalanches of the setting sun. Here in the theater, the light emitted by the wretched chandelier seemed quite inadequate to my insatiable thirst for brightness. I appeared to myself to be entering, as I have said, a world of darkness—a darkness that gradually thickened, whilst I dreamt of polar night and everlasting winter.

The stage itself (the theater habitually shows farces) was the only patch of light, extremely small and far, far away, as if it were at the end of a huge stereoscope. I shall not try to tell you that I listened to the actors, because you know that this would have been impossible. Occasionally my mind caught hold, in passing, a shred of phrase, and like a skilled dancer used it as a springboard from which to leap into remote fantasies.

One might suppose that a play heard in this fashion would lack logic and sequence. Do not make this mistake: I discovered a very subtle meaning in a play created by my errant fancy. Nothing in it took me by surprise: I was like the poet who, on seeing for the first time a performance of "Esther," found it quite natural that Haman should make love to the Queen. (This was the poet's interpretation, as you will have realized, of the scene in which Haman flings himself at Esther's feet to beg forgiveness for his crimes.) If all plays were listened to in this fashion they would gain much new beauty —even the plays of Racine.

The actors seemed to me exceedingly small, and to be clearly and carefully outlined, like figures by Meissonier. I could distinctly see not only the most minute details of their costumes—the patterns of the materials, the needlework, buttons, etc.—but also the dividing line between the make-up and the face, the patches of white, blue, and red on their features. These Lilliputians were invested with a cold, magical brightness, like that of a very clean sheet of glass over a painting in oils.

When I was at last able to emerge from this cave of icy darkness, when my inward fantasmagoria had melted away and I had returned to my proper senses, I felt more exhausted than I have ever been by any spell of intent and pressing work.

As the narrator indicates, it is at this phase of intoxication that a new subtlety or acuity manifests itself in all the senses. This development is common to the senses of smell, sight, hearing and touch. The eyes behold the Infinite. The ear registers almost imperceptible sounds, even in the midst of the greatest din.

This is when hallucinations set in. External objects acquire, gradually and one after another, strange new appearances; they become distorted or transformed. Next occur mistakes in the identities of objects, and transposals of ideas. Sounds clothe themselves in color, and colors contain music.

"There's nothing at all unnatural about that," the reader will say. "Such correspondences between sounds and colors are easily perceived by a poetic brain in its normal healthy state." But I have already warned the reader that there was nothing positively supernatural about the intoxication of hashish. The difference is that the correspondences take on an unusual liveliness; they penetrate and invade the mind, despotically overwhelming it. Notes of music turn into numbers; and, if you are endowed with some aptitude for mathematics, the melody or harmony you hear, whilst retaining its pleasurable and sensuous character, transforms itself into a huge arithmetical process, in which numbers beget numbers, whilst you follow the successive stages of reproduction with inexplicable ease and an agility equal to that of the performer.

It sometimes happens that your personality disappears, and you develop objectivity—that preserve of the pantheistic poets —to such an abnormal degree that the contemplation of outward objects makes you forget your own existence, and you soon melt into them. Your eye rests upon an harmoniously shaped tree bowing beneath the wind. Within a few seconds something that to a poet would merely be a very natural comparison becomes to you a reality. You begin by endowing the tree with your own passions, your desire or melancholy; its groanings and swayings become your own, and soon you *are* the tree. In the same way, a bird soaring beneath a blue sky, at first merely *represents* the immortal yearning to soar above human life; but already you are the bird itself.

Let us suppose that you are sitting and smoking. Your gaze rests a moment too long on the bluish clouds emerging from your pipe. The notion of a slow, steady, eternal evaporation will take hold of your mind, and soon you will apply this notion to your own thoughts and your own thinking substance. By a singular transposition of ideas, or mental play upon words, you will feel that you yourself are evaporating, and that your pipe (in which you are huddled and pressed down like the tobacco) has the strange *power to smoke you.*

Luckily this apparently interminable fancy has lasted only for a single minute—for a lucid interval, gained with a great effort, has enabled you to glance at the clock. But a new stream of ideas carries you away: it will hurl you along in its living vortex for a further minute; and this minute, too, will be an eternity, for the normal relation between time and the individual has been completely upset by the multitude and intensity of sensations and ideas. You seem to live several men's lives in the space of an hour. You resemble, do you not? a fantastic novel that is being lived instead of being written. . . .

CHAPTER FOUR

SELECTIONS FROM THE HASHEESH EATER

Fitzhugh Ludlow

In 1855 Bayard Taylor, a well-known American man of letters and foreign diplomat, wrote a travel book, Land of the Saracens, *in which he included an account of an experience with hashish in the Near East. In a rather bombastic and moralistic chapter which he called "The Vision of Hashish," Taylor stated that the herb "revealed to me deeps of rapture and suffering which my natural faculties never could have sounded. . . ." That account, however exaggerated, may possibly have inspired young Fitzhugh Ludlow, a recent college graduate who lived in the then bucolic Hudson River Valley town of Poughkeepsie, New York, to experiment with hashish. Ludlow, the son of an abolitionist minister, was heavily schooled, as might be suspected, in the Bible, but he was also immersed, in keeping with the customs of the time, in Latin and Greek classical studies. He was a highly imaginative, intelligent youth with a decided taste for philosophical speculation. After teaching school for a short time, he went on to become a widely published journalist and critic of the period, and in the latter role he became a friend and early supporter of Mark Twain.*

The knowledge and experience Ludlow gained from his youthful experiences with hashish (then obtainable under the trade name Tilden's Extract for six cents a dose from his friendly

191

village apothecary) was later distilled in his anonymous auto-biography, The Hasheesh Eater, *from which the following material has been selected. As with Baudelaire, Ludlow finally tempered his enthusiasm for hashish on moral grounds.*

THE NIGHT ENTRANCE

About the shop of my friend Anderson the apothecary there always existed a peculiar fascination, which early marked it out as my favorite lounging place. In the very atmosphere of the establishment, loaded as it was with a composite smell of all things curative and preventive, there was an aromatic invitation to scientific musing, which could not have met with a readier acceptance had it spoken in the breath of frankincense. The very gallipots grew gradually to possess a charm for me as they sat calmly ranged upon their oaken shelves, looking like a convention of unostentatious philanthropists, whose silent bosoms teemed with every variety of renovation for the human race. A little sanctum at the inner end of the shop, walled off with red curtains from the profane gaze of the unsanative, contained two chairs for the doctor and myself, and a library where all the masters of physic were grouped, through their sheep and paper representatives, in more friendliness of contact than has ever been known to characterize a consultation of like spirits under any other circumstances. Within the limits of four square feet, Pereira and Christison condensed all their stores of wisdom and research, and Dunglison and Brathwaite sat cheek by jowl beside them. There stood the Dispensary, with the air of a business-like office, wherein all the specifics of the materia medica had been brought together for a scientific conversazione, but, becoming enamored of each other's society, had resolved to stay, overcrowded though they might be, and make an indefinite sitting of it. In a modest niche, set apart like a vestibule from the apartments of the medical gentlemen, lay a shallow case, which disclosed, on the lifting of a cover, the neatly ordered rank of tweezers, probe, and lancet, which constituted my friend's claim to the confidence of the plethoric community; for, although unblessed with metropolitan fame, he was still no "Cromwell guiltless of his country's blood."

Here many an hour have I sat buried in the statistics of human life or the history of the make-shifts for its preservation. Here the details of surgical or medical experiment have held me in as complete engrossment as the positions and crises of romance; and here especially, with a disregard to my own safety which would have done credit to Quintus Curtius have I made upon myself the trial of the effects of every strange drug and chemical which the laboratory could produce. Now with the chloroform bottle beneath my nose have I set myself careering upon the wings of a thrilling and accelerating life, until I had just enough power remaining to restore the liquid to its place upon the shelf, and sink back into the enjoyment of the delicious apathy which lasted through the few succeeding moments. Now ether was substituted for chloroform, and the difference of their phenomena noted, and now some other exhilarant, in the form of an opiate or stimulant, was the instrument of my experiments, until I had run through the whole gamut of queer agents within my reach.

In all these experiences research and not indulgence was my object, so that I never became the victim of any habit in the prosecution of my headlong investigations. When the circuit of all the accessible tests was completed, I ceased experimenting, and sat down like a pharmaceutical Alexander, with no more drug-worlds to conquer.

One morning, in the spring of 185–, I dropped in upon the doctor for my accustomed lounge.

"Have you seen," said he, "my new acquisitions?"

I looked toward the shelves in the direction of which he pointed, and saw, added since my last visit, a row of comely pasteboard cylinders inclosing vials of the various extracts prepared by Tilden & Co. Arranged in order according to their size, they confronted me, as pretty a little rank of medicinal sharpshooters as could gratify the eye of an amateur. I approached the shelves, that I might take them in review.

A rapid glance showed most of them to be old acquaintances. "Conium, taraxacum, rhubarb—ha! what is this? Cannabis indica?" "That," answered the doctor, looking with a parental fondness upon his new treasure, "is a preparation of the East Indian hemp, a powerful agent in case of lock-jaw." On the strength of this introduction, I took down the little archer, and, removing his outer verdant coat, began the further prosecution of his acquaintance. To pull out a broad and shallow cork was the work of an instant, and it revealed to me an olive-brown extract, of the consistency of pitch, and a decided aromatic odor. . . .

. . . I waited till my friend was out of sight, that I might not terrify him by that which he considered a suicidal venture, and then quietly uncapping my little archer a second time, removed from his store of offensive armor a pill sufficient to balance the ten grain weight of the sanctorial scales. This, upon the authority of Pereira and the Dispensatory, I swallowed without a tremor as to the danger of the result.

Making all due allowance for the fact that I had not taken my hasheesh bolus fasting, I ought to experience its effects within the next four hours. That time elapsed without bringing the shadow of a phenomenon. It was plain that my dose had been insufficient.

For the sake of observing the most conservative prudence, I suffered several days to go by without a repetition of the experiment, and then, keeping the matter equally secret, I administered to myself a pill of fifteen grains. This second was equally ineffectual with the first.

Gradually, by five grains at a time, I increased the dose to thirty grains, which I took one evening half an hour after tea. I had now almost come to the conclusion that I was absolutely unsusceptible of the hasheesh influence. Without any expectation that this last experiment would be more successful than the former ones, and indeed with no realization of the manner in which the drug affected those who did make the experiment successfully, I went to pass the evening at the house of an intimate friend. In music and conversation the time passed pleasantly. The clock struck ten, reminding me that three hours had elapsed since the dose was taken, and as yet not an unusual symptom had appeared. I was provoked to think that this trial was as fruitless as its predecessors.

Ha! what means this sudden thrill? A shock, as of some unimagined vital force, shoots without warning through my entire frame, leaping to my fingers' ends, piercing my brain, startling me till I almost spring from my chair.

I could not doubt it. I was in the power of the hasheesh influence. My first emotion was one of uncontrollable terror —a sense of getting something which I had not bargained for. That moment I would have given all I had or hoped to have to be as I was three hours before.

No pain anywhere—not a twinge in any fibre—yet a cloud of unutterable strangeness was settling upon me, and wrapping me impenetrably in from all that was natural or familiar. Endeared faces, well known to me of old, surrounded me, yet they were not with me in my loneliness. I had entered upon a tremendous life which they could not share. If the disembodied ever return to hover over the hearth-stone which once had a seat for them, they look upon their friends as I then looked upon mine. A nearness of place, with an infinite distance of state, a connection which had no possible sympathies for the wants of that hour of revelation, an isolation none the less perfect for seeming companionship.

Still I spoke; a question was put to me, and I answered it; I even laughed at a bon mot. Yet it was not my voice which spoke; perhaps one which I once had far away in another time and another place. For a while I knew nothing that was going on externally, and then the remembrance of the last remark which had been made returned slowly and indistinctly, as some trait of a dream will return after many days, puzzling as to say where we have been conscious of it before.

A fitful wind all the evening had been sighing down the chimney; it now grew into the steady hum of a vast wheel in accelerating motion. For a while this hum seemed to resound through all space. I was stunned by it—I was absorbed in it. Slowly the revolution of the wheel came to a stop, and its monotonous din was changed for the reverberating peal of a grand cathedral organ. The ebb and flow of its inconceivably solemn tone filled me with a grief that was more than human. I sympathized with the dirge-like cadence as spirit sympathizes with spirit. And then, in the full conviction that all I heard and felt was real, I looked out of my isolation to see the effect of the music on my friends. Ah! we were in separate worlds indeed. Not a trace of appreciation on any face.

Perhaps I was acting strangely. Suddenly a pair of busy hands, which had been running neck and neck all the evening with a nimble little crochet-needle over a race-ground of pink and blue silk, stopped at their goal, and their owner looked at me steadfastly. Ah! I was found out—I had betrayed myself. In terror I waited, expecting every instant to hear the word "hasheesh." No, the lady only asked me some questions connected with the previous conversation. As mechanically as an automaton I began to reply. As I heard once more the alien and unreal tones of my own voice, I became convinced that it was someone else who spoke, and in another world. I sat and listened; still the voice kept speaking. Now for the first time I experienced that vast change which hasheesh makes in all measurements of time. The first word of the reply occupied a period sufficient for the action of a drama; the last left me in complete ignorance for any point far enough back in the past to date the commencement of the sentence. Its enunciation might have occupied years. I was not in the same life which had held me when I heard it begun.

And now, with time, space expanded also. At my friend's house one particular arm-chair was always reserved for me. I was sitting in it at a distance of hardly three feet from the centre-table around which the members of the family were grouped. Rapidly that distance widened. The whole atmosphere seemed ductile, and spun endlessly out into great spaces surrounding me on every side. We were in a vast hall, of which my friends and I occupied opposite extremities. The ceiling and the walls ran upward with a gliding motion, as if vivified by a sudden force of resistless growth.

Oh! I could not bear it. I should soon be left alone in the midst of an infinity of space. And now more and more every moment increased the conviction that I was watched. I did not know then, as I learned afterward, that suspicion of all earthly things and persons was the characteristic of the hasheesh delirium.

In the midst of my complicated hallucination, I could perceive that I had a dual existence. One portion of me was whirled unresistingly along the track of this tremendous experience, the other sat looking down from a height upon its double, observing, reasoning, and serenely weighing all the phenomena. This calmer being suffered with the other by sympathy, but did not lose its self-possession. Presently it warned me that I must go home, lest the growing effect of the hasheesh should incite me to some act which might frighten my friends. I acknowledged the force of this remark very much as if it had been made by another person, and rose to take my leave. I advanced toward the centre-table. With every step its distance increased. I nerved myself as for a long pedestrian journey. Still the lights, the faces, the furniture receded. At last, almost unconsciously, I reached them. It would be tedious to attempt to convey the idea of the time which my leave-taking consumed, and the attempt, at least with all minds that have not passed through the same experience, would be as impossible as tedious. At last I was in the street.

Beyond me the view stretched endlessly away. It was an unconverging vista, whose nearest lamps seemed separated from me by leagues. I was doomed to pass through a merciless stretch of space. A soul just disenthralled, setting out for his flight beyond the farthest visible star, could not be more overwhelmed with his new-acquired conception of the sublimity of distance than I was at that moment. Solemnly I began my infinite journey.

Before long I walked in entire unconsciousness of all around me. I dwelt in a marvelous inner world. I existed by turns in different places and various states of being. Now I swept my gondola through the moonlit lagoons of Venice. Now Alp on Alp towered above my view, and the glory of the coming sun flashed purple light upon the topmost pinnacle. Now in the primeval silence of some unexplored tropical forest I spread my feathery leaves, a giant fern, and swayed and nodded in the spice-gales over a river whose waves at once sent up clouds of music and perfume. My soul changed to a vegetable essence,

thrilled with a strange and unimagined ecstasy. The palace of
Al Haroun could not have brought me back to humanity.

I will not detail all the transmutations of that walk. Ever
and anon I returned from my dreams into consciousness, as
some well-known house seemed to leap out into my path,
awaking me with a shock. The whole way homeward was a
series of such awakings and relapses into abstraction and
delirium until I reached the corner of the street in which I
lived.

Here a new phenomenon manifested itself. I had just awaked
for perhaps the twentieth time, and my eyes were wide open.
I recognized all surrounding objects, and began calculating the
distance home. Suddenly, out of a blank wall at my side a
muffled figure stepped into the path before me. His hair, white
as snow, hung in tangled elf-locks on his shoulders, where he
carried also a heavy burden, like unto the well-filled sack of
sins which Bunyan places on the back of his pilgrim. Not liking
his manner, I stepped aside, intending to pass around him and
go on my way. This change of our relative position allowed the
blaze of a neighboring street-lamp to fall full on his face, which
had hitherto been totally obscured. Horror unspeakable! I shall
never, till the day I die, forget that face. Every lineament was
stamped with the records of a life black with damning crime; it
glared upon me with a ferocious wickedness and a stony despair
which only he may feel who is entering on the retribution of
the unpardonable sin. He might have sat to a demon painter as
the ideal of Shelley's Cenci. I seemed to grow blasphemous in
looking at him, and, in an agony of fear, began to run away.
He detained me with a bony hand, which pierced my wrist
like talons, and, slowly taking down the burden from his own
shoulders, laid it upon mine. I threw it off and pushed him
away. Silently he returned and restored the weight. Again I
repulsed him, this time crying out, "Man, what do you mean?"
In a voice which impressed me with the sense of wickedness
as his face had done, he replied, "You *shall* bear my burden
with me," and a third time laid it on my shoulders. For the last
time I hurled it aside, and, with all my force, dashed him from
me. He reeled backward and fell, and before he could recover
his disadvantage I had put a long distance between us.

Through the excitement of my struggle with this phantasm
the effects of the hasheesh had increased mightily. I was burst-
ing with an uncontrollable life; I strode with the thews of a
giant. Hotter and faster came my breath; I seemed to pant like
some tremendous engine. An electric energy whirled me resist-
lessly onward; I feared for myself lest it should burst its fleshly
walls, and glance on, leaving a wrecked frame-work behind it.

At last I entered my own house. During my absence a family connection had arrived from abroad, and stood ready to receive my greeting. Partly restored to consciousness by the naturalness of home-faces and the powerful light of a chandelier which shed its blaze through the room, I saw the necessity of vigilance against betraying my condition, and with an intense effort suppressing all I felt, I approached my friend, and said all that is usual on such occasions. Yet recent as I was from my conflict with the supernatural, I cast a stealthy look about me, that I might learn from the faces of the others, if, after all, I was shaking hands with a phantom, and making inquiries about the health of a family of hallucinations. Growing assured as I perceived no symptoms of astonishment, I finished the salutation and sat down.

It soon required all my resolution to keep the secret which I had determined to hold inviolable. My sensations began to be terrific—not from any pain that I felt, but from the tremendous mystery of all around me and within me. By an appalling introversion, all the operations of vitality which, in our ordinary state, go on unconsciously, came vividly into my experience. Through every thinnest corporeal tissue and minutest vein I could trace the circulation of the blood along each inch of its progress. I knew when every valve opened and when it shut; every sense was preternaturally awakened; the room was full of a great glory. The beating of my heart was so clearly audible that I wondered to find it unnoticed by those who were sitting by my side. Lo, now, that heart became a great fountain, whose jet played upward with loud vibrations, and, striking upon the roof of my skull as on a gigantic dome, fell back with a splash and echo into its reservoir. Faster and faster came the pulsations, until at last I heard them no more, and the stream became one continuously pouring flood, whose roar resounded through all my frame. I gave myself up for lost, since judgment, which still sat unimpaired above my perverted senses, argued that congestion must take place in a few moments, and close the drama with my death. But my clutch would not yet relax from hope.The thought struck me, Might not this rapidity of circulation be, after all, imaginary? I determined to find out.

Going to my own room, I took out my watch, and placed my hand upon my heart. The very effort which I made to ascertain the reality gradually brought perception back to its natural state. In the intensity of my observations, I began to perceive that the circulation was not as rapid as I had thought. From a pulseless flow it gradually came to be apprehended as a hurrying succession of intense throbs, then less swift and less intense, till finally, on comparing it with the second hand, I found that about 90 a minute was its average rapidity. Greatly comforted, I desisted from the experiment. Almost instantly the hallucination returned. Again I dreaded apoplexy, congestion, hemorrhage, a multiplicity of nameless deaths, and drew my picture as I might be found on the morrow, stark and cold, by those whose agony would be redoubled by the mystery of my end. I reasoned with myself; I bathed my forehead—it did no good. There was one resource left: I would go to a physician.

With this resolve, I left my room and went to the head of the staircase. The family had all retired for the night, and the gas was turned off from the burner in the hall below. I looked down the stairs: the depth was fathomless; it was a journey of years to reach the bottom! The dim light of the sky shone through the narrow panes at the sides of the front door, and seemed a demon-lamp in the middle darkness of the abyss. I never could get down! I sat me down despairingly upon the topmost step.

Suddenly a sublime thought possessed me. If the distance be infinite, I am immortal. It shall be tried. I commenced the descent, wearily, wearily down through my league-long, year-long journey. To record my impressions in that journey would be to repeat what I have said of the time of hasheesh. Now stopping to rest as a traveler would turn aside at a wayside inn, now toiling down through the lonely darkness, I came by-and-by to the end, and passed out into the street.

THE KINGDOM OF THE DREAM

The moment that I closed my eyes a vision of celestial glory burst upon me. I stood on the silver strand of a translucent, boundless lake, across whose bosom I seemed to have been just transported. A short way up the beach, a temple, modeled like the Parthenon, lifted its spotless and gleaming columns of alabaster sublimely into a rosy air—like the Parthenon, yet as much excelling it as the godlike ideal of architecture must transcend that ideal realized by man. Unblemished in its purity of whiteness, faultless in the unbroken symmetry of every line and angle, its pediment was draped in odorous clouds, whose tints outshone the rainbow. It was the work of an unearthly builder, and my soul stood before it in a trance of ecstasy. Its folded doors were resplendent with the glory of a multitude of eyes of glass, which were inlaid throughout the marble surfaces at the corners of diamond figures from the floor of the porch to the topmost moulding. One of these eyes was golden, like the midday sun, another emerald, another sapphire, and thus onward through the whole gamut of hues, all of them set in such collocations as to form most exquisite harmonies, and whirling upon their axes with the rapidity of thought. At the mere vestibule of the temple I could have sat and drunk in ecstasy forever; but lo! I am yet more blessed. On silent hinges the doors swing open, and I pass in.

I did not seem to be in the interior of a temple. I beheld myself as truly in the open air as if I had never passed the portals, for whichever way I looked there were no walls, no roof, no pavement. An atmosphere of fathomless and soul-satisfying serenity surrounded and transfused me. I stood upon the bank of a crystal stream, whose waters, as they slid on, discoursed notes of music which tinkled on the ear like the tones of some exquisite bell-glass. The same impression which such tones produce, of music refined to its ultimate ethereal spirit and borne from a far distance, characterized every ripple of those translucent waves. The gently sloping banks of the stream were luxuriant with a velvety cushioning of grass and moss, so living green that the eye and the soul reposed on them at the same time and drank in peace. Through this amaranthine herbage strayed the gnarled, fantastic roots of giant cedars of Lebanon, from whose primeval trunks great branches spread above me, and interlocking, wove a roof of impenetrable shadow; and wandering down the still avenues below those grand arboreal arches went glorious bards, whose snowy beards fell on their breasts beneath countenances of ineffable benignity and nobleness.

They were all clad in flowing robes, like God's high priests, and each one held in his hand a lyre of unearthly workmanship. Presently one stops midway down a shady walk, and, baring his right arm, begins a prelude. While his celestial chords were trembling up into their sublime fullness, another strikes his strings, and now they blend upon my ravished ear in such a symphony as was never heard elsewhere, and I shall never hear again out of the Great Presence. A moment more, and three are playing in harmony; now the fourth joins the glorious rapture of his music to their own, and in the completeness of the chord my soul is swallowed up. I can bear no more. But yes, I am sustained, for suddenly the whole throng break forth in a chorus, upon whose wings I am lifted out of the riven walls of sense, and music and spirit thrill in immediate communion. Forever rid of the intervention of pulsing air and vibrating nerve, my soul dilates with the swell of that transcendent harmony, and interprets from it arcana of a meaning which words can never tell. I am borne aloft upon the glory of sound. I float in a trance among the burning choir of the seraphim. But, as I am melting through the purification of that sublime ecstasy into oneness with the Deity himself, one by one those pealing lyres faint away, and as the last throb dies down along the measureless ether, visionless arms swiftly as lightning carry me far into the profound, and set me down before another portal. Its leaves, like the first, are of spotless marble, but ungemmed with wheeling eyes of burning color.

Before entering on the record of this new vision I will make a digression, for the purpose of introducing two laws of the hasheesh operation, which, as explicatory, deserve a place here. First, after the completion of any one fantasia has arrived, there almost invariably succeeds a shifting of the action to some other stage entirely different in its surroundings. In this transition the general character of the emotion may remain unchanged. I may be happy in Paradise and happy at the sources of the Nile, but seldom, either in Paradise or on the Nile, twice in succession. I may writhe in Etna and burn unquenchably in Gehenna, but almost never, in the course of the same delirium, shall Etna or Gehenna witness my torture a second time.

Second, after the full storm of a vision of intense sublimity has blown past the hasheesh-eater, his next vision is generally of a quiet, relaxing, and recreating nature. He comes down from his clouds or up from his abyss into a middle ground of gentle shadows, where he may rest his eyes from the splendor of the seraphim or the flames of fiends. There is a wise philosophy in this arrangement, for otherwise the soul would soon burn out in the excess of its own oxygen. Many a time, it seems to me, has my own thus been saved from extinction.

This next vision illustrated both, but especially the latter of these laws. The temple-doors opened noiselessly before me, but it was no scene of sublimity which thus broke in upon my eyes. I stood in a large apartment, which resembled the Senate-chamber at Washington more than anything else to which I can compare it. Its roof was vaulted, and at the side opposite the entrance the floor rose into a dais surmounted by a large arm-chair. The body of the house was occupied by similar chairs disposed in arcs; the heavy paneling of the walls was adorned with grotesque frescoes of every imaginable bird, beast, and monster, which, by some hidden law of life and motion, were forever changing, like the figures of the kaleidoscope. Now the walls bristled with hippogriffs; now, from wainscot to ceiling, toucans and maccataws swung and nodded from their perches amid emerald palms; now Centaurs and

Lapithæ clashed in ferocious tumult, while crater and cyathus were crushed beneath ringing hoof and heel. But my attention was quickly distracted from the frescoes by the sight of a most witchly congress, which filled all the chairs of that broad chamber. On the dais sat an old crone, whose commanding position first engaged my attention to her personal appearance, and, upon rather impolite scrutiny, I beheld that she was the product of an art held in preeminent favor among persons of her age and sex. She was *knit* of purple yarn! In faultless order the stitches ran along her face; in every pucker of her re-entrant mouth, in every wrinkle of her brow, she was a yarny counterfeit of the grandam of actual life, and by some skillful process of stuffing her nose had received its due peak and her chin its projection. The occupants of the seats below were all but reproductions of their president, and both she and they were constantly swaying from side to side, forward and back, to the music of some invisible instruments, whose tone and style were most intensely and ludicrously Ethiopian. Not a word was spoken by any of the woolly conclave, but with untiring industry they were all knitting, knitting, knitting ceaselessly, as if their lives depended on it. I looked to see the objects of their manufacture. They were knitting old women like themselves! One of the sisterhood had nearly brought her double to completion; earnestly another was engaged in rounding out an eyeball; another was fastening the gathers at the corners of a mouth; another was setting up stitches for an old woman in petto.

With marvelous rapidity this work went on; ever and anon some completed crone sprang from the needles which had just achieved her, and, instantly vivified, took up the instruments of reproduction, and fell to work as assiduously as if she had been a member of the congress since the world began. "Here," I cried, "here, at last, do I realize the meaning of endless progression!" and, though the dome echoed with my peals of laughter, I saw no motion of astonishment in the stitches of a single face, but, as for dear life, the manufacture of old women went on unobstructed by the involuntary rudeness of the stranger.

An irresistible desire to aid in the work possessed me; I was half determined to snatch up a quartette of needles and join the sisterhood. My nose began to be ruffled with stitches, and the next moment I had been a partner in their yarny destinies but for a hand which pulled me backward through the door, and shut the congress forever from my view.

For a season I abode in an utter void of sight and sound, but I waited patiently in the assurance that some new changes of magnificence were preparing for me. I was not disappointed. Suddenly, at a far distance, three intense luminous points stood on the triple wall of darkness, and through each of them shot twin attenuated rays of magic light and music. Without being able to perceive anything of my immediate surroundings, I still felt that I was noiselessly drifting toward those radiant and vocal points. With every moment they grew larger, the light and the harmony came clearer, and before long I could distinguish plainly three colossal arches rising from the bosom of a waveless water. The mid arch towered highest; the two on either side were equal to each other. Presently I beheld that they formed the portals of an enormous cavern, whose dome rose above me into such sublimity that its cope was hidden from my eyes in wreaths of cloud. On each side of me ran a wall of gnarled and rugged rock, from whose jutting points, as high as the eye could reach, depended stalactites of every imagined form and tinge of beauty, while below me, in the semblance of an ebon pavement, from the reflection of its overshadowing crags, lay a level lake whose exquisite transparency wanted but the smile of the sun to make it glow like a floor of adamant. On this lake I lay in a little boat divinely carved from pearl after the similitude of Triton's shelly shallop; its rudder and its oarage were my own unconscious will, and, without the labors of especial volition, I floated as I list with a furrowless keel swiftly toward the central giant arch. With every moment that brought me nearer to my exit, the harmony that poured through it developed into a grander volume and an intenser beauty.

And now I passed out.

Claude Lorraine, freed from the limitations of sense, and gifted with an infinite canvas, may, for aught I know, be upon some halcyon island of the universe painting such a view as now sailed into my vision. Fitting employment would it be for his immortality were his pencil dipped into the very fountains of the light. Many a time in the course of my life I yearned for the possession of some grand old master's soul and culture in the presence of revelations of Nature's loveliness which I dared not trust to memory; before this vision, as now in the remembrance of it, that longing became a heartfelt pain. Yet, after all, it was well; the mortal limner would have fainted in his task. Alas! how does the material in which we must embody the spiritual cramp and resist its execution! Standing before windows where the invisible spirit of the frost had traced his exquisite algæ, his palms and his ferns, have I said to myself, with a sigh, Ah! Nature alone, of all artists, is gifted to work out her ideals!

Shall I be so presumptuous as to attempt in words that which would beggar the palette and the pencil of old-time disciples of the beautiful? I will, if it be only to satisfy a deep longing.

From the arches of my cavern I had emerged upon a horizonless sea. Through all the infinitudes around me I looked out, and met no boundaries of space. Often in after times have I beheld the heavens and the earth stretching out in parallel lines forever, but this was the first time I had ever stood un-"ringed by the azure world," and I exulted in all the sublimity of the new conception. The whole atmosphere was one measureless suffusion of golden notes, which throbbed continually in cadence and showered radiance and harmony at the same time. With ecstasy vision spread her wings for a flight against which material laws locked no barrier, and every moment grew more and more entranced at further and fuller glimpses of a beauty which floated like incense from the pavement of that eternal sea. With ecstasy the spiritual ear gathered in continually some more distant and unimaginable tone, and grouped the growing harmonies into one sublime chant of benediction. With ecstasy the whole soul drank in revelations from every province, and cried out, "Oh, awful loveliness!" And now out of my shallop I was borne away into the full light of the mid firmament; now seated on some toppling peak of a cloud-mountain, whose yawning rifts disclosed far down the mines of reserved lightning; now bathed in my ethereal travel by the rivers of the rainbow, which, side by side, coursed through the valleys of heaven; now dwelling for a season in the environment of unbroken sunlight, yet bearing it like the eagle with undazzled eye, now crowned with a coronal of prismatic beads of dew. Through whatever region or circumstances I passed, one characteristic of the vision remained unchanged: peace—everywhere godlike peace, the sum of all conceivable desires satisfied.

Slowly I floated down to earth again. There Oriental gardens waited to receive me. From fountain to fountain I danced in graceful mazes with inimitable houris, whose foreheads were bound with fillets of jasmine. I pelted with figs the rare exotic birds, whose gold and crimson wings went flashing from branch to branch, or wheedled them to me with Arabic phrases of endearment. Through avenues of palm I walked arm-in-arm with Halfiz, and heard the hours flow singing through the channels of his matchless poetry. In gay kiosques I quaffed my sherbet, and in the luxury of lawlessness kissed away by drops that other juice which is contraband unto the faithful. And now beneath citron shadows I laid me down to sleep.

When I awoke it was morning—actually morning, and not a hasheesh hallucination. The first emotion that I felt upon opening my eyes was happiness to find things again wearing a natural air. Yes; although the last experience of which I had been conscious had seemed to satisfy every human want, physical or spiritual, I smiled on the four plain white walls of my bedchamber, and hailed their familiar unostentatiousness with a pleasure which had no wish to transfer itself to arabesque or rainbows. It was like returning home from an eternity spent in loneliness among the palaces of strangers. Well may I say an eternity, for during the whole day I could not rid myself of the feeling that I was separated from the preceding one by an immeasurable lapse of time. In fact, I never got wholly rid of it.

I rose that I might test my reinstated powers, and see if the restoration was complete. Yes, I felt not one trace of bodily weariness nor mental depression. Every function had returned to its normal state, with the one exception mentioned; memory could not efface the traces of my having passed through a great mystery. I recalled the events of the past night, and was pleased to think that I had betrayed myself to no one but Dr. H. I was satisfied with my experiment. . . .

THE BOOK OF SYMBOLS

Of all experiences in the hasheesh state, my indoctrination into spiritual facts through means of symbols was the most wonderful to myself. In other visions I have reveled in more delicious beauty, and suffered horrors even more terrible; but in this I was lifted entirely out of the world of hitherto conceivable being, and invested with the power of beholding forms and modes of existence which, on earth, are impossible to be expressed, for the reason that no material emblems exist which even faintly foreshadow them.

Among men we communicate entirely by symbols. Upon any thought which has not its symbol in the Outer, "untransferable" is stamped indelibly. A certain relation between two thoughts is beheld by one human mind. How shall the man inform his neighbor of this relation? There is no means for it through any of the labyrinths of material sense; it can not be seen, heard, felt, smelt, or tasted. What is to be done?

A flock of cranes are assembling from the four quarters of heaven to hold their aerial council on some tall crag above him. Into our thinker's mind flashes a bright idea. Those birds shall mediate for his relation a passage into his brother's understanding. The cranes (grues) are coming together (con), and in this visible symbol he embodies his invisible relation, and the name henceforth that passes for it among men is "congruous."

Yet there is one condition beyond the mere discovery of an apt symbol which is necessary before that symbol can be circulated as the bank-note which bases its security on the intangible coin within the spiritual treasury. That coin must be universally felt to exist, or the bill will be good for nothing. In the present instance, the idea of the relation expressed by "congruous" must already have been perceived by the communicatee, or the communicator will be unable to express himself intelligibly. Rather should we say, the idea of the possiblity of this relation must exist before the former can perceive it; for, if he recognizes such a possibility, then, by virtue of this very capacity, he will immediately actualize the possible, and on the communication of the symbol perceive the idea of "congruity," though it be for the first time.

The question now arises, What state of mind lies back of, and conditions the capacity to recognize, through symbols, the mental phenomena of another? Plainly this: the two who are in communication must be situated so nearly upon the same plane of thought that they behold the same truths and are affected by the same emotions. In proportion as this condition is violated will two men be unappreciating of each other's inner states.

Now in hasheesh it is utterly violated. In the hasheesh-eater a virtual change of worlds has taken place, through the preternatural scope and activity of all his faculties. Truth has not become expanded, but his vision has grown telescopic; that which others see only as the dim nebula, or do not see at all, he looks into with a penetrating scrutiny which distance, to a great extent, can not evade. Where the luminous mist or the perfect void had been, he finds wondrous constellations of spiritual being, determines their bearings, and reads the law of their sublime harmony. To his neighbor in the natural state he turns to give expression to his visions, but finds that to him the symbols which convey the apocalypse to his own mind are meaningless, because, in our ordinary life, the thoughts which they convey have no existence; their two planes are utterly different.

This has not only occurred in my own case, but in several others—in persons upon whom I have experimented with hasheesh. At their highest exaltation, so earnest has been the desire to communicate the burden which overpowered them, that they have spoken forth the symbols presented to their minds; yet from these symbols men around them, in the unexalted state, drew an entirely different significance from the true one, or, perceiving none at all, laughed at what was said as an absurdity, seeing nothing in the name of some ordinary thing or mode of being to excite such emotions of terror or of ecstasy as were produced in the hasheesh-eater. Yet many a time, as I stood near, by these symbols thus expressed, have I been able to follow the ecstatic wanderer, and recognize the exact place in his journey at which he had arrived as something which I had once seen myself.

It is this process of symbolization which, in certain hasheesh states, gives every tree and house, every pebble and leaf, every footprint, feature, and gesture, a significance beyond mere matter or form, which possesses an inconceivable force of tortures or of happiness.

Perhaps one of the most difficult things to convey to a mind not in the hasheesh delirium, by the symbols which there teach the manner of its process, or by any others, is the interchange of senses. The soul is sometimes plainly perceived to be but one in its own sensorium, while the body is understood to be all that so variously modifies impressions as to make them in the one instance smell, in another taste, another sight, and thus on, ad finem. Thus the hasheesh-eater knows what it is to be burned by *salt* fire, to *smell* colors, to *see* sounds, and, much more frequently, to *see* feelings. How often do I remember vibrating in the air over a floor bristling with red-hot needles, and, although I never supposed I came in contact with them, *feeling* the sensation of their frightful pungency through *sight* as distinctly as if they were entering my heart.

In the midst of sufferings unfathomable or raptures measureless, I often thought of St. Paul's God-given trance, and the "ἄρρητα ῥήματα ἃ δὺκ ἐξὸν ἀνθρώπῳ λαλῆσαι." Never was I more convinced of anything in my life than that our translation, "which it is not lawful for a man to utter," is wholly inadequate. It should be, "which it is impossible to utter to man"; for this alone harmonizes with that state of intuition in which words are "speechless words," and the truths beheld have no symbols on earth which will embody them. Though far from believing that my own ecstasy, or that of any hasheesh-eater, has claim to such inspiration as an apostle's, the states are still analogous in this respect, that they both share the nature of disembodiment, and the soul, in both, beholds realities of greater or less significance, such as may never be apprehended again out of the light of eternity.

There is one thought suggested by the symbolization of hasheesh which I can not refrain from introducing here. In

some apocalyptic states of delirium like that which I have
mentioned, and others succeeding it, there were symbols of
an earthly nature used, which not only had never before con-
veyed to me such truth as I then saw, but never had expressed
any truth at all. Things the least suspected of having any
significance beyond their material agency were perceived to
be the most startling illustrations and incarnations of spiritual
facts.

Now where, among created things, shall we set the boundaries to this capacity for symbolizing? In view of that which
I saw, especially upon the last detailed memorable night, I
felt, and still feel, forced to the conclusion that there is no
boundary. If, as the true philosopher must believe, the material was created for the spiritual, as the lower for the higher,
the means for the end, it is impossible that any minutest lichen
should exist as mere inert matter, lessonless to the soul of all
creation's viceroy—man.

CHAPTER FIVE

THE STORY OF LAHCEN AND IDIR

Paul Bowles

Paul Bowles, who studied music with Aaron Copland and Virgil Thomson, has achieved fame both as a composer and as a writer. His brilliant scores have embellished literally dozens of films, opera, and ballets, from Watch on the Rhine *and* The Glass Menagerie *to* Twelfth Night *and* Cyrano de Bergerac. *Bowles' rich talents won him a Guggenheim Fellowship in 1941, and in 1959 he was the recipient of a Rockefeller Grant.*

As a writer, he is known especially for his fiction: The Sheltering Sky, Let It Come Down, *and* The Delicate Prey. *The following short story originally appeared in a small collection entitled* 100 Camels in the Courtyard. *The derivation of that title is of particular interest here, for it stems from an ancient Arabic proverb which assures us that "a pipeful of kif (marihuana) before breakfast gives a man the strength of a hundred camels in the courtyard."*

In "The Story of Lahcen and Idir," "Lahcen liked to drink and Idir smoked kif." The implications and outcome of the relative merits of alcohol and hemp constitute the substance of this marihuana morality tale.

Two friends, Lahcen and Idir, were walking on the beach at Merkala. By the rocks stood a girl, and her djellaba blew in the wind. Lahcen and Idir stopped walking when they saw her.

They stood still, looking at her. Lahcen said: "Do you know that one?"

"No. I never saw her."

"Let's go over," said Lahcen. They looked up and down the beach for a man who might be with the girl, but there was no one. "A whore," said Lahcen. When they got closer to the girl, they saw that she was very young. Lahcen laughed. "This is easy."

"How much have you got?" Idir asked him.

"You think I'm going to pay her?" cried Lahcen.

Idir understood that Lahcen meant to beat her. ("If you don't pay a whore you have to beat her.") And he did not like the idea, because they had done it before together, and it nearly always meant trouble later. Her sister or someone in her family went to the police and complained, and in the end everybody was in jail. Being shut into prison made Idir nervous. He tried to keep out of it, and he was usually able to. The difference between Lahcen and Idir was that Lahcen liked to drink and Idir smoked kif. Kif smokers want to stay quiet in their heads, and drinkers are not like that. They want to break things.

Lahcen rubbed his groin and spat onto the sand. Idir knew he was going over the moves in the game he was going to play with the girl, planning when and where he would knock her down. He was worried. The girl looked the other way. She held down the skirt of her djellaba so the wind would not blow it. Lahcen said: "Wait here." He went on to her and Idir saw her lips moving as she spoke to him, for she wore no veil. All her teeth were gold. Idir hated women with gold teeth because at fourteen he had been in love with a gold-toothed whore named Zohra, who never had paid him any attention. He said to himself: "He can have her." Besides, he did not want to be with them when the trouble began. He stood still until Lahcen whistled to him. Then he went over to where they stood.

"Ready?" Lahcen asked. He took the girl's arm and started to walk along beside the rocks.

"It's late. I've got to go," Idir told him. Lahcen looked surprised, but he said nothing. "Some other day," Idir told Lahcen, looking at him and trying to warn him. The girl laughed spitefully, as if she thought that might shame him into coming along.

He was glad he had decided to go home. When he went by the Mendoub's fig orchard a dog barked at him. He threw a rock at it and hit it.

The next morning Lahcen came to Idir's room. His eyes were red from the wine he had been drinking. He sat down on the floor and pulled out a handkerchief that had a knot tied in one corner. He untied the knot and let a gold ring fall out into his lap. Picking up the ring, he handed it to Idir. "For you, I got it cheap." Idir saw that Lahcen wanted him to take the ring, and he put it on his finger, saying: "May Allah give you health."

Lahcen rubbed his hand across his chin and yawned. Then he said: "I saw you look at me, and afterward when we got to the quarry I thought that would be the best place. And then I remembered the night the police took us at Bou Khach Khach, and I remembered you looking at me. I turned around and left her there. Garbage!"

"So you're not in jail and you're drunk," said Idir, and he laughed.

"That's true," said Lahcen. "And that's why I give you the ring."

Idir knew the ring was worth at least fifty dirhams, and he could sell it if he needed money badly. That would end his friendship with Lahcen, but there would be no help for it.

Sometimes Lahcen came by in the evening with a bottle of wine. He would drink the whole bottle while Idir smoked his kif pipe, and they would listen to the radio until the end of the program at twelve o'clock. Afterward, very late, they would walk through the streets of Dradeb to a garage where a friend of Lahcen's was night watchman. When the moon was full, it was brighter than the street lights. With no moon, there was nobody in the streets, and in the few late cafés the men told one another about what thieves had done, and how there were more of them than ever before. This was because there was almost no work to be had anywhere, and the country people were selling their cows and sheep to be able to pay their taxes, and then coming to the city. Lahcen and Idir worked now and then, whenever they found something to do. They had a little money, they always ate, and Lahcen sometimes was able to afford his bottle of Spanish wine. Idir's kif was more of a problem, because each time the police decided to enforce the law they had made against it, it grew very scarce and the price went up. Then when there was plenty to be had, because the police were busy looking for guns and rebels instead, the price stayed high. He did not smoke any less, but he smoked by himself in his room. If you smoke in a café, there is always someone who has left his kif at home and wants to use yours. He told his friends at the Café Nadjah that he had given up kif, and he never accepted a pipe when it was offered to him.

Back in his room in the early evening, with the window open and the sleepy sounds of the town coming up, for it was summer and the voices of people filled the streets, Idir sat in the chair he had bought and put his feet on the windowsill. That way he could see the sky as he smoked. Lahcen would come in and talk. Now and then they went together to Emsallah to a barraca there near the slaughterhouse where two sisters lived with their feeble-minded mother. They would get the mother drunk and put her to bed in the inner room. Then they would get the girls drunk and spend the night with them, without paying. The cognac was expensive, but it did not cost as much as whores would have.

In midsummer, at the time of Sidi Kacem, it suddenly grew very hot. People set up tents made of sheets on the roofs of their houses and cooked and slept there. At night in the moonlight Idir could see all the roofs, each one with its box of sheets flapping in the wind, and inside the sheets the red light made by the fire in the pot. Daytimes, the sun shining on the sea of white sheets hurt his eyes, and he remembered not to look out when he passed the window as he moved about his room. He would have liked to live in a more expensive room, one with a blind to keep out the light. There was no way of being protected from the bright summer day that filled the sky outside, and he waited with longing for dusk. His custom was not to smoke kif before the sun went down. He did not like it in the daytime, above all in summer when the air is hot and the light is powerful. When each day came up hotter than the one before it, he decided to buy enough food and kif to last several days, and to shut himself into his room until it got cooler. He had worked two days at the port that week and had some money. He put the food on the table and locked the door. Then he took the key out of the lock and threw it into the drawer of the table. Lying with the packages and cans in his market basket was a large bundle of kif wrapped in a newspaper. He unfolded it, took out a sheaf and sniffed of it. For the next two hours he sat on the floor picking off the leaves and cutting them on a breadboard, sifting, and cutting, again and again. Once, as the sun reached him, he had to move to get out of its heat. By the time the sun went down he had enough ready for three or four days. He got up off the floor and sat in his chair with his pouch and his pipe in his lap, and smoked, while the radio played the Chleuh music that was always broadcast at this hour for the Soussi shopkeepers. In cafés men often got up and turned it off. Idir enjoyed it. Kif smokers usually like it, because of the *naqous* that always pounds the same design.

The music played a long time, and Idir thought of the market at Tiznit and the mosque with the tree trunks sticking out of its mud walls. He looked down at the floor. The room still had daylight in it. He opened his eyes wide. A small bird was walking slowly along the floor. He jumped up. The kif pipe fell, but its bowl did not break. Before the bird had time to move, he had put his hand over it. Even when he held it between his two hands it did not struggle. He looked at it, and thought it was the smallest bird he had ever seen. Its head was grey and its wings were black and white. It looked at him, and it did not seem afraid. He sat down in the chair with the bird in his lap. When he lifted his hand it stayed still. "It's a young bird and can't fly," he thought. He smoked several pipes of kif. The bird did not move. The sun had gone down and the houses were growing blue in the evening light. He stroked the bird's head with his thumb. Then he took the ring from his little finger and slipped it over the smooth feathers of its head. The bird paid no attention. "A gold collar for the sultan of birds," he said. He smoked some more kif and looked at the sky. Then he began to be hungry, and he thought the bird might like some bread crumbs. He put his pipe down on the table and tried to take the ring from the bird's head. It would not come off over the feathers. He pulled at it, and the bird fluttered its wings and struggled. For a second he let go of it, and in that instant it flew straight from his lap into the sky. Idir jumped up and stood watching it. When it was gone, he began to smile. "The son of a whore!" he whispered.

He prepared his food and ate it. After that he sat in the chair smoking and thinking about the bird. When Lahcen came he told him the story. "He was waiting all the time for a chance to steal something," he said.

Lahcen was a little drunk, and he was angry. "So he stole my ring!" he cried.

"Ah," said Idir. "Yours? I thought you gave it to me."

"I'm not crazy yet," Lahcen told him. He went away still angry, and did not return for more than a week.

The morning he came into the room Idir was certain that he was going to begin to talk again about the ring, and he quickly handed him a pair of shoes he had bought from a friend the day before. "Do these fit you?" he asked him. Lahcen sat down in the chair, put them on, and found they did fit. "They need new bottoms, but the tops are like new," Idir told him.

"The tops are good," said Lahcen. He felt of the leather and squeezed it between his thumb and fingers.

"Take them," said Idir.

Lahcen was pleased, and he said nothing about the ring that day. When he got the shoes to his room he looked carefully at them and decided to spend the money that it would cost to have new soles made.

The next day he went to a Spanish cobbler, who agreed to

repair the shoes for fifteen dirhams. "Ten," said Lahcen. After a long discussion the cobbler lowered his price to thirteen, and he left the shoes there, saying that he would call for them in a week. The same afternoon he was walking through Sidi Bouknadel, and he saw a girl. They talked together for two hours or more, standing not very near to each other beside the wall, and looking down at the ground so that no one could see they were talking. The girl was from Meknes, and that was why he had never seen her before. She was visiting her aunt, who lived there in the quarter, and soon her sister was coming from Meknes. She looked to him the best thing he had seen that year, but of course he could not be sure of her nose and mouth because her veil hid them. He got her to agree to meet him at the same place the next day. This time they took a walk along the Hafa, and he could see that she would be willing. But she would not tell him where her aunt's house was.

Only two days later he got her to his room. As he had expected, she was beautiful. That night he was very happy, but in the morning when she had gone, he understood that he wanted to be with her all the time. He wanted to know what her aunt's house was like and how she was going to pass her day. In this way a bad time began for Lahcen. He was happy only when she was with him and he could get into bed and see her lying on one side of him and a bottle of cognac on the other, upright on the floor beside his pillow, where he could reach it easily. Each day when she had gone he lay thinking about all the men she might be going to see before she came back to him. When he talked about it to her she laughed and said she spent all her time with her aunt and sister, who now had arrived from Meknes. But he could not stop worrying about it.

Two weeks went by before he remembered to go and get his shoes. On his way to the cobbler's he thought about how he would solve his problem. He had an idea that Idir could help him. If he brought Idir and the girl together and left them alone, Idir would tell him afterward everything that had happened. If she let Idir take her to bed, then she was a whore and could be treated like a whore. He would give her a good beating and then make it up with her, because she was too good to throw away. But he had to know whether she was really his, or whether she would go with others.

When the cobbler handed him his shoes, he saw that they looked almost like new, and he was pleased. He paid the thirteen dirhams and took the shoes home. That night when he was going to put them on to wear to the café, he found that his feet would not go into them. They were much too small. The cobbler had cut down the last in order to stitch on the new soles. He put his old shoes back on, went out, and slammed the door. That night he had a quarrel with the girl. It took him until almost dawn to stop her crying. When the sun came up and she was asleep, he lay with his arms folded behind his head looking at the ceiling, thinking that the shoes had cost him thirteen dirhams and now he was going to have to spend the day trying to sell them. He got rid of the girl early and went in to Bou Aragia with the shoes. No one would give him more than eight dirhams for them. In the afternoon he went to the Joteya and sat in the shade of a grapevine, waiting for the buyers and sellers to arrive. A man from the mountains finally offered him ten dirhams, and he sold the shoes. "Three dirhams gone for nothing," he thought when he put the money into his pocket. He was angry, but instead of blaming the cobbler, he felt that the fault was Idir's.

That afternoon he saw Idir, and he told him he would bring a friend with him to Idir's room after the evening meal. Then he went home and drank cognac. When the girl arrived he had finished the bottle, and he was drunk and more unhappy than ever. "Don't take it off," he told her when she began to unfasten her veil. "We're going out." She said nothing. They took the back streets to Idir's room.

Idir sat in his chair listening to the radio. He had not expected a girl, and when he saw her take off her veil the beating of his heart made his head ache. He told her to sit in the chair, and then he paid no more attention to her and sat on the bed talking only with Lahcen, who did not look at her either. Soon Lahcen got up. "I'm going out to get some cigarettes," he said. "I'll be right back." He shut the door after him, and Idir quickly went and locked it. He smiled at the girl and sat on the table beside her, looking down at her. Now and then he smoked a pipe of kif. He wondered why Lahcen was taking so long.

Finally he said: "He's not coming back, you know." The girl laughed and shrugged. He jumped up, took her hand, and led her to the bed.

In the morning when they were getting dressed, she told him she lived at the Hotel Sevilla. It was a small Moslem hotel in the center of the Medina. He took her there and left her. "Will you come tonight?" she asked him.

Idir frowned. He was thinking of Lahcen. "Don't wait for me after midnight," he said.

On his way home he stopped at the Café Nadjah. Lahcen was there. His eyes were red and he looked as though he had not slept at all. Idir had the feeling that he had been waiting for him to appear, for when he came into the café Lahcen quickly got up and paid the *qahouaji*. They walked down the main street of Dradeb without saying anything, and when they got to the road that leads to the Merkala beach, they turned down it, still without speaking.

It was low tide. They walked on the wet sand while the small waves broke at their feet. Lahcen smoked a cigarette and threw stones into the water. Finally he spoke. "How was it?"

Idir shrugged, tried to keep his voice flat. "All right for one night," he said.

Lahcen was ready to say carelessly: "Or even two." But then he realized that Idir did not want to talk about the night, which meant that it had been a great event for him. And when he looked at his face he was certain that Idir wanted the girl for himself. He was sure he had already lost her to him, but he did not know why he had not thought of that in the beginning. Now he forgot the true reason why he had wanted to take her to Idir.

"You thought I brought her just to be good to you!" he cried. "No, sidi! I left her there to see if you were a friend. And I see what kind of friend you are! A scorpion!" He seized the front of Idir's garments and struck him in the face. Idir moved backward a few steps, and got ready to fight. He understood that Lahcen had seen the truth, and that now there was nothing at all to say, and nothing to do but fight. When they were both bloody and panting, he looked for a flash at Lahcen's face, and saw that he was dizzy and could not see very well. He drew back, put his head down, and with all his force ran into Lahcen, who lost his balance and fell onto the sand. Then quickly he kicked him in the head with the heel of his shoe. He left him lying there and went home.

In a little while Lahcen began to hear the waves breaking on the sand near him. "I must kill him," he thought. "He sold my ring. Now I must go and kill him." Instead, he took off his clothes and bathed in the sea, and when he had finished, he lay in the sun on the sand all day and slept. In the evening he went and got very drunk.

At eleven o'clock Idir went to the Hotel Sevilla. The girl was sitting in a wicker chair by the front door, waiting for him. She looked carefully at the cuts on his face. Under her veil he saw her smile.

"You fought?" Idir nodded his head. "How is he?" He shrugged. This made her laugh. "He was always drunk, anyway," she said. Idir took her arm, and they went out into the street.

CHAPTER SIX

RED-DIRT MARIHUANA

Terry Southern

Terry Southern is a social satirist whose closest American literary antecedent is Nathaniel West. His novels, The Magic Christian, Flash and Filagree, *and* Candy *(written in collaboration with Mason Hoffenberg), are wildly destructive, wildly comic attacks on outmoded sexual and moral conventions. Southern believes that the roots of contemporary American existentialism spring from the more realistic, organically oriented values encountered in Negro culture. The following short story illustrates that belief: it is the poor and uneducated (but intelligent, knowledgeable and resourceful) hired Negro ranch hand who first introduces his employer's twelve-year-old son to the pleasures of homegrown "red-dirt marihuana"; it is the Negro, rather than the educated white middle-class father, who "turns on" the boy, who takes on the responsibility of giving him his first instruction in that age-old art of transcendence known today as consciousness expansion.*

The white boy came into the open-end, dirt-floor shed where the Negro was siting on the ground against the wall reading a *Western Story* magazine.

In one hand the boy was carrying a pillowcase that was bunched out at the bottom, about a third filled with something, and when the Negro looked up it appeared from his smile that he knew well enough what it was.

"What you doin', Hal', bringin' in the *crop?*"

The white boy's name was Harold; the Negro pronounced it *Hal'*.

The boy walked on over to one side of the shed where the kindling was stacked and pulled down an old sheet of newspaper which he shook out to full size and spread in front of the Negro. He dumped the gray-grass contents of the pillow-case onto the paper and then straightened up to stand with his hands on his hips, frowning down at it. He was twelve years old.

The Negro was looking at it, too; but he was laughing. He was about thirty-five, and he laughed sometimes in a soft, almost soundless way, shaking his head as though this surely were the final irony, while his face, against very white teeth, gleamed with the darks of richest pipebriar. His name was C.K.

"*Sho'* is a lotta gage," he said.

He reached out a hand and rolled a dry pinch of it between his thumb and forefinger.

"You reckon it's dried out enough?" the boy asked, nasal, sounding almost querulous, as he squatted down opposite. "Shoot, I don't wanta leave it *out* there no more—not hangin' on that dang sycamore anyway—it's beginnin' to *look* too funny." He glanced out the end of the shed toward the big white farmhouse that was about thirty yards away. "Heck, Dad's been shootin' *dove* down in there all week—I was down there this mornin' and that damned old dog of Les Newgate's was runnin' around with a piece of it in his *mouth!* I had to git it away from 'im 'fore they seen it."

The Negro took another pinch of it and briskly crushed it between his flat palms, then held them up, cupped, smelling it.

"They wouldn't of knowed what it was noway," he said.

"You crazy?" said Harold, frowning. "You think my dad don't know *Mex'can loco-weed* when he sees it?"

"Don't look much *like* no loco-weed now though, do it?" said the Negro flatly, raising expressionless eyes to the boy.

"*He's* seen it dried out, too, I bet," said the boy, loyally, but looking away.

"*Sho'* he is," said C.K., weary and acid. "*Sho'*, I bet he done *blow* a lot of it too, ain't he? Sho', you daddy pro'bly one of the biggest ole hop-heads in Texas—why I bet he *smoke* it an' *eat* it an' jest anyway he can git it into his old haid! Hee-hee!" He laughed at the mischievous image. "Ain't *that* right, Hal'?"

"You *crazy?*" demanded Harold, frowning terribly; he took the Negro's wrist. "Lemme smell it," he said.

He drew back after a second.

"I can't smell nothin' but your dang sweat," he said.

" 'Course not," said C.K., frowning in his turn, and brushing his hands, "you got to git it jest when the *flower* break—that's the *boo*-kay of the plant, you see; that's what we call that."

"Do it again," said Harold.

"I ain't goin' *do* it again," said C.K., peevish, closing his eyes for a moment; ". . . it's jest a waste on you—I do it again, you jest say you smell my *sweat*. You ain't got the nose for it noway—you got to know you business 'fore you start foolin' round with *this* plant."

"I can do it, C.K.," said the boy earnestly; ". . . *come* on, dang it!"

The Negro sighed, elaborately, and selected another small bud from the pile.

"Awright now when I rub it in my *hand*," he said sternly, "you let out you breath—then I *cup* my hand, you put your nose in an' smell strong . . . you got to suck in *strong* thru you nose!"

They did this.

"You smell it?" asked C.K.

"Yeah, sort of," said Harold, leaning back again.

"That's the *boo*-kay of the plant—they ain't no smell like it."

"It smells like tea," said the boy.

"Well, now that's why they calls it that, you see—but it smell like somethin' *else* too."

"What?"

"Like mighty fine gage, that's what."

"Well, whatta you keep on callin' it *that* for?" asked the boy crossly. ". . . That ain't what that Mex'can called it neither —he called it *'pot.'* "

"That ole *Mex*," said C.K., brushing his hands and laughing, "he sho' were funny, weren't he? . . . thought he could pick *cotton* . . . told *me* he use to *pick-a-bale-a-day!* I had to laugh when he say that . . . oh, sho', you didn't talk to that Mex'can like I did—he call it *lotta* things. He call it *'baby,'* too! Hee-hee. Yeah, he say: 'Man, don't forget the *baby* now!' He mean bring a few *sticks* of it out to the field, you see, that's what he mean by that. He call it *'charge,'* too. Sho'. Them's *slang* names. Them names git started people don't want the *po*-lice nobody like that to know they business, you see. Sho' they make *up* them names, go on an' talk about they business nobody know what they *sayin',* you see what I mean."

He stretched his legs out comfortably and crossed his hands over the magazine that was still in his lap.

"Yes indeed," he said after a minute, staring at the pile

on the newspaper, and shaking his head, "I tell you right now, boy—that sho' is a lotta gage."

About two weeks earlier, on a day when C.K. wasn't helping Harold's father, they had gone fishing together, Harold and C.K., and on the way back to the house that afternoon, Harold had stopped and stood looking into an adjacent field, a section of barren pasture-land where the cows almost never went, but where there was a cow at that moment, alone, lying on its stomach, with its head stretched out on the ground in front of it.

"What's wrong with that dang *cow?*" he demanded, not so much of C.K. as of himself, or perhaps of God—though in a sense C.K. *was* responsible for the stock, it being his job at least to take them out to pasture and back each day.

"Do look like she takin' it *easy,* don't it?" said C.K., and they went through the fence and started toward her. *"Look* like ole Maybelle," he said, squinting his eyes at the distance.

"I ain't never seen a cow act like *that* before," said Harold crossly, ". . . layin' there with her head on the ground like a damned old hound-dog."

The cow didn't move when they reached it, just stared up at them; she was chewing her cud, in a rhythmic and contented manner.

"Look at that dang cow," Harold muttered, ever impatient with enigma; ". . . it is old Maybelle, ain't it?" He felt of her nose and then began kicking her gently on the flank. "Git up, dang it."

"Sho' that's old Maybelle," said C.K., patting her neck. "What's the matter with you, Maybelle?"

Then C.K. found it, a bush of it, about twenty feet away, growing in the midst of a patch of dwarf-cactus, and he was bent over it, examining it with great care.

"This here is a *full-grown* plant," he said, touching it in several places, gently bending it back, almost caressingly. Finally he stood up again, hands on his hips, looking back at the prostrate cow.

"Must be mighty fine gage," he said.

"Well, I ain't never seen loco-weed make a cow act like *that,"* said Harold, as if that were the important aspect of the whole incident, and he began absently kicking at the plant.

"That ain't no ordinary loco-weed," said C.K.; ". . . that there is *red-dirt marihuana,* that's what *that* is."

Harold spat, frowning.

"Shoot," he said then, "I reckon we oughta pull it up and burn it."

"I reckon we oughtta," said C.K.

They pulled it up.

"Don't gen'lly take to *red-dirt*," C.K. remarked, casually, brushing his hands; ". . . they say if it *do*, then it's mighty fine indeed—they reckon it's got to be *strong* to do it, you see."

"Must be pretty dang *strong* awright," Harold dryly agreed, looking back at the disabled cow. "You think we oughtta git Doc Parks?"

They walked over to the cow.

"Shoot," said C.K., "they ain't nothin' wrong with *this* cow."

The cow had raised her head, and her eyes followed them when they were near. They stared down at her for a minute or two, and she looked at them, interestedly, still chewing.

"Ole Maybelle havin' a *fine* time," said C.K., leaning over to stroke her muzzle. "Hee-hee. She *high*, that's what she is!" He straightened up again. "I tell you right now, boy," he said to Harold, "you lookin' at a *ver'* contented cow there!"

"You reckon it'll ruin her milk?"

"Shoot, that make her milk all the more *rich*! Yeah, she goin' give some Grade-A milk indeed after *that* kinda re-laxation. Ain't that right, Maybelle?"

They started back to the fence, Harold dragging the bush along and swinging it back and forth.

"Look at the ole *root* on that plant," said C.K., laughing, ". . . big ole juicy root—sho' would make a fine soup-bone I bet!"

He had twisted off a branch of the plant and plucked a little bunch of leaves from it, which he was chewing now, like mint.

"What's it taste like?" asked Harold.

C.K. plucked another small bunch and proffered it to the boy.

"Here you is, my man," he said.

"Naw, it jest makes me sick," said Harold, thrusting his free hand in his pocket and making a face; so, after a minute, C.K. put that piece in his mouth too.

"We could dry it out and smoke it," said Harold.

C.K. laughed, a short derisive snort.

"Yes, I reckon we could."

"Let's dry it out and sell it," said the boy.

C.K. looked at him, plaintive exasperation dark in his face.

"Now, Hal', don't go talkin' without you knows what you talkin' *about*."

"We could sell it to them Mex'can sharecroppers over at Farney," said Harold.

"Hal', what is you *talkin'* about—them people ain't got no money."

They went through the fence again, silent for a while.

"Well, don't *you* wanta dry it out?" Harold asked, bewildered, boy of twelve, aching for action and projects—*any* project that would bring them together.

C.K. shook his head.

"Boy, you don't catch me givin' no advice on that kinda business—you daddy run me right off this place somethin' like that ever happen."

Harold was breaking it up.

"We'd have to put it some place where the dang stock wouldn't git at it," he said.

So they spread the pieces of it up in the outside branches of a great sycamore, where the Texas sun would blaze against them, and then they started back on up to the house.

"Listen, Hal'," said C.K. about halfway on. "I tell you right now you don't wanta say nothin' 'bout this to nobody up at the house."

"You crazy?" said the boy. "You don't reckon I *would* do you?"

They walked on.

"What'll we do with it when it's dried *out,* C.K.?"

C.K. shrugged, kicked at a rock.

"Shoot, we find *some* use for it I reckon," he said, with a little laugh.

"You think it's dried *out* enough?" Harold was asking, as they sat with the pile of it between them, he crumbling some of it now in his fingers, scowling at it.

C.K. took out his sack of *Bull-Durham.*

"Well, I tell you what we goin' have to do," he said with genial authority, " . . . we goin' have to *test* it."

He slipped two cigarette-papers from the attached packet, one of which he licked and placed alongside the other, slightly overlapping it.

"I use *two* of these papers," he explained, concentrating on the work, "that give us a nice *slow*-burnin' stick, you see."

He selected a small segment from the pile and crumpled it, letting it sift down from his fingers into the cupped cigarette-paper; and then he carefully rolled it, licking his pink-white tongue slowly over the whole length of it after it was done. "I do that," he said, "that seal it in good, you see." And he held it up then for them both to see; it was much thinner than an ordinary cigarette, and still glittering with the wet of his mouth.

"That cost you half-a-*dollah* in *Dallas*," he said.

"Shoot," said the boy, uncertain.

"Sho' would," said C.K.; ". . . oh you git you three for a dollah, you *know* the man—'course that's mighty good gage I'm talkin' 'bout you pay half-a-dollah . . . that's you *quality* gage. I don't know how good quality this here is yet, you see."

He lit it.

"Sho' *smell* good though, don't it?"

Harold watched him narrowly as he wafted the smoking stick back and forth beneath his nose.

"*Taste* mighty good too! Shoot, I jest bet this is *ver'* good quality gage. You wanta taste of it?" He held it out.

"Naw, I don't want none of it right now," said Harold. He got up and walked over to the kindling-stack, and drew out from a stash there a package of Camels; he lit one, returned the pack to its place, and came back to sit opposite C.K. again.

"*Yeah*," said C.K. softly, gazing at the thin cigarette in his hand, "I feel this gage aweady . . . this is *fine.*"

"What does it feel like?" asked Harold.

C.K. had inhaled again, very deeply, and was holding his breath, severely, chest expanded like a person who is learning to float, his dark brow slightly knit in the awareness of actually *working* at it physically.

"It feel *fine,*" he said at last, smiling.

"How come it jest made me *sick?*" asked the boy.

"Why *I* tole you, Hal'," said C.K. impatiently, " 'cause you tried to fight *against* it, that's why . . . you tried to *fight* that gage, so it jest make you *sick!* Sho', that was *good* gage that ole Mex had."

"Shoot, all I felt besides gettin' sick at my stomach was jest right *dizzy.*"

C.K. had taken another deep drag and was still holding it, so that now when he spoke, casually but without exhaling, it was from the top of his throat, and his voice sounded odd and strained:

"Well, that's 'cause you *mind* is young an un*formed* . . . that gage jest come into you mind an' *cloud* it over!"

"My *mind?*" said Harold.

"Sho', you *brain!*" said C.K. in a whispery rush of voice as he let out the smoke. "*You* brain is young an' un*formed,* you see . . . that smoke come in, it got no where to go, it jest *cloud* you young brain over!"

Harold flicked his cigarette a couple of times.

"It's as good as any dang nigger-brain I guess," he said after a minute.

"Now boy, don't *mess* with me," said C.K., frowning;

". . . you ast me somethin' an' I tellin' you! *You* brain is young an' un*formed* . . . it's all *smooth,* you brain, smooth as that piece of shoe-leather. That smoke jest come in an' cloud it over!" He took another drag. "Now you take a full-*growed* brain," he said in his breath-holding voice, "it *ain't* smooth—it's got all *ridges* in it, all over, go this way an' that. Shoot, a man know what he doin' he have that smoke runnin' *up* one ridge an' *down* the other! He *con*trol his high, you see what I mean, he don't fight against it. . . ." His voice died away in the effort of holding breath and speaking at the same time—and, after exhaling again, he finished off the cigarette in several quick little drags, then broke open the butt with lazy care and emptied the few remaining bits from it back onto the pile. "*Yeah* . . ." he said, almost inaudibly, an absent smile on his lips.

Harold sat or half reclined, though somewhat stiffly, supporting himself with one arm, just staring at C.K. for a moment before he shifted about a little, flicking his cigarette. "Shoot," he said, "I jest wish you'd tell me what it *feels* like, that's all."

C.K., though he was sitting closs-legged now with his back fairly straight against the side of the shed, gave the appearance of substance wholly without bone, like a softly filled sack that has slowly, imperceptibly sprawled and found its final perfect contour, while his head lay back against the shed, watching the boy out of half-closed eyes. He laughed.

"Boy, I done *tole* you," he said quietly, "it feels *good*."

"Well, that *ain't* nothin', dang it," said Harold, almost angrily, "*I* aw*ready* feel good!"

"Uh-huh," said C.K. with dreamy finality.

"Well, I *do,* god-dang it," said Harold, glaring at him hatefully.

"That's right," said C.K., nodding, closing his eyes, and they were both silent for a few minutes, until C.K. looked at the boy again and spoke, as though there had been no pause at all: "But you don't feel as good now as you do at *Christmas*-time though, do you? Like when right after you daddy give you that new *Win*chester? An' then you don't feel as *bad* as that time he was whippin' you for shootin' that doe with it neither, do you? Yeah. Well now that's how much difference they *is,* you see, between that cigarette you got in you hand an' the one I jest put out! Now that's what I tellin' *you*."

"Shoot," said Harold, flicking his half-smoked Camel and then mashing it out on the ground, "you're crazy."

C.K. laughed. "Sho' I is," he said.

They fell silent again, C.K. appearing almost asleep, humming to himself, and Harold sitting opposite, frowning down to where his own finger traced lines without pattern in the dirt-floor of the shed.

"Where we gonna keep this stuff at, C.K.?" he demanded finally, his words harsh and reasonable. "We can't jest leave it sittin' out like this."

C.K. seemed not to have heard, or perhaps simply to consider it without opening his eyes; then he did open them, and when he leaned forward and spoke, it was with a fresh and remarkable cheerfulness and clarity:

"Well, now the first thing we got to do is to *clean* this gage. We got to git them *seeds* outta there an' all them little sticks. But the *ver'* first thing we do . . ." and he reached into the pile, "is to take some of this here *flower,* these here *ver'* small leaves, an' put them off to the side. That way you got you *two* kinds of gage, you see—you got you a *light* gage an' a *heavy* gage."

C.K. started breaking off the stems and taking them out, Harold joining in after a while; and then they began crushing the dry leaves with their hands.

"How we ever gonna git all them dang seeds outta there?" asked Harold.

"Now I show you a *trick* about that," said C.K., smiling and leisurely getting to his feet. "Where's that pilly-cover at?"

He spread the pillowcase flat on the ground and, lifting the newspaper, dumped the crushed leaves on top of it. Then he folded the cloth over them and kneaded the bundle with his fingers, pulverizing it. After a minute of this, he opened it up again, flat, so that the pile was sitting on the pillowcase now as it had been on the newspaper.

"You hold on hard to that end," he told Harold, and he took the other himself and slowly raised it, tilting it, and agitating it. The round seeds started rolling out of the pile, down the taut cloth and onto the ground. C.K. put a corner of the pillowcase between his teeth and held the other corner out with one hand; then, with his other hand, he tapped gently on the bottom of the pile, and the seeds poured out by the hundreds, without disturbing the rest.

"Where'd you learn all that at, C.K.?" asked Harold.

"Shoot, you got to know you business you workin' with *this* plant," said C.K.; ". . . waste our time pickin' out them ole seeds." He stood for a moment looking around the shed. "Now we got to have us somethin' to *keep* this gage in—we got to have us a *box,* somethin' like that, you see."

"Why can't we jest keep it in that?" asked Harold, referring to the pillowcase.

C.K. frowned. "Naw we can't *keep* it in that," he said, ". . . keep it in that like ole sacka turnip . . . we got to git us somethin'—a nice little *box*, somethin' like that, you see. How 'bout one of you empty shell-boxes? You got any?"

"They ain't big enough," said Harold.

C.K. resumed his place, sitting and slowly leaning back against the wall, looking at the pile again.

"They sho' ain't, is they," he said, happy with that fact.

"We could use two or three of 'em," Harold said.

"Wait a minute now," said C.K., "we talkin' here, we done forgit about this *heavy* gage." He laid his hand on the smaller pile, as though to reassure it. "One of them shell-boxes do fine for that—an' I *tell* you what we need for this *light* gage now I think of it . . . is one of you momma's quart *fruit*-jars!"

"Shoot, I can't fool around with them dang jars, C.K.," said the boy.

C.K. made a little grimace of impatience.

"*You* momma ain't begrudge you one of them fruit-jars, Hal'—she *ast* you 'bout it, you jest say it got *broke*! You say you done *use* that jar put you fishin' minners in it! *Hee-hee* . . . she won't even wanta *see* that jar no more, you tell her *that*."

"I ain't gonna fool around with them jars, C.K."

C.K. sighed and started rolling another cigarette.

"I jest goin' twist up a few of these sticks now," he explained, "an' put them off to the side."

"When're you gonna smoke some of the other?" asked Harold.

"What, that *heavy* gage?" said C.K., raising his eyebrows in surprise at the suggestion. "Shoot, *that* ain't no workin'-hour gage there, that's you *Sunday* gage . . . oh you mix a little bit of that *into* you light gage now and then you *feel* like it—but you got to be sure ain't nobody goin' to mess with you 'fore you turn *that* gage full on. 'Cause you jest wanta lay back then an' take it *easy*." He nodded to himself in agreement with this, his eyes intently watching his fingers work the paper. "You see . . . you don't *swing* with you heavy gage, you jest *goof* . . . that's what you call that. Now you light gage, you *swing* with you light gage . . . you *control* that gage, you see. Say a man have to go out an' *work*, why he able to *enjoy* that work! Like now you seen me turn on some of this light gage, didn't you? Well, I may have to go out with you *daddy* a little later an' lay on that fence-wire, or work with my post-hole digger. Why I able to *swing* with my post-hole digger with my light gage on. Sho', that's you *sociable* gage, you light gage is—this here other, well, that's what you call you *thinkin'* gage. . . . Hee-hee! Shoot, I wouldn't even wanta *see* no post-hole digger I turn *that* gage full on!"

He rolled the cigarette up, slowly, licking it with great care.

"Yeah," he said half-aloud, ". . . ole fruit-jar be *fine* for this light gage." He chuckled. "That way we jest look right in there, know how much we got on hand at all time."

"We got *enough* I reckon," said Harold, a little sullenly it seemed.

"Sho' is," said C.K., "more'n the law allows at that."

"Is it against the law then sure enough, C.K.?" asked Harold in eager interest, ". . . like that Mex'can kept sayin' it was?"

C.K. gave a soft laugh.

"I jest reckon it *is*," he said, ". . . it's against all kinda law—what we got here is. Sho', they's one law say you can't have *none* of it, they put you in the jailhouse you do . . . then they's another law say they catch you with more than *this* much . . ." he reached down and picked up a handful to show, "well, then you in *real* trouble! Sho', you got more than *that* why they say: 'Now that man got more of that gage than he *need* for his personal use, he must be *sellin'* it!' Then they say you a *pusher*. That's what they call that, an' boy I mean they put you *way* back in the jailhouse then!" He gave Harold a severe look. "I don't wanta tell you you business, nothin' like that, Hal', but if I was you I wouldn't let on 'bout this to nobody—not to you frien' Big Law'ence or *any* of them people."

"Heck, don't you think I know better than to do that?"

"You ain't scared though, is you Hal'?"

Harold spat.

"Shoot," he said, looking away, as though in exasperation and disgust that the thought could have occurred to anyone.

C.K. resumed his work, rolling the cigarettes, and Harold watched him for a few minutes and then stood up, very straight.

"I reckon I could git a fruit-jar outta the cellar," he said, "if she ain't awready brought 'em up for her cannin'."

"That sho' would be fine, Hal'," said C.K., without raising his head, licking the length of another thin stick of it.

When Harold came back with the fruit-jar and the empty shell-box, they transferred the two piles into those things.

"How come it's against the *law* if it's so all-fired good?" asked Harold.

"Well, now I use to study 'bout that myself," said C.K., tightening the lid of the fruit-jar and giving it a pat. He laughed.

"It ain't because it make young boys like you sick, I tell you *that* much!"

"Well, what the heck is it then?"

C.K. put the fruit-jar beside the shell-box, placing it neatly, carefully centering the two just in front of him, and seeming to consider the question while he was doing it.

"I *tell* you what it is," he said then, "it's cause a man *see* too much when he git high, that's what. He see right *through* ever'thing . . . you understan' what I say?"

"What the heck are you talkin' about, C.K.?"

"Well, maybe you too young to know what I talkin' 'bout— but I tell you they's a lotta trickin' an' lyin' go on in the world . . . they's a lotta ole *bull-crap* go on in the world . . . well, a man git high, he see right through all them tricks an' lies, an' all that ole bull-crap. He see right through there into the *truth* of it!"

"Truth of *what?*"

"*Ever*'thing."

"Dang you sure talk crazy, C.K."

"Sho', they *got* to have it against the law. Shoot, ever'body git high, wouldn't be nobody git up an' feed the chickens! Hee-hee . . . ever'body jest *lay in bed!* Jest lay in bed till they *ready* to git up? Sho', you take a man high on good gage, he got no use for they old bull-crap, 'cause he done see right through there. Shoot, he lookin' right down into his ver' *soul!*"

"I ain't never heard nobody talk so dang crazy, C.K."

"Well, you young, boy—you goin' hear plenty crazy talk 'fore you is a grown man."

"Shoot."

"Now we got to think of us a good place to *put* this gage," he said, "a *secret* place. Where you think, Hal'?"

"How 'bout that old smoke-house out back—ain't nobody goes in there."

"Shoot, that's a *good* place for it, Hal'—you sure they ain't goin' tear it down no time soon?"

"Heck no, what would they tear it down for?"

C.K. laughed.

"Yeah, that's right," he said. "Well, we take it out there after it gits dark."

They fell silent, sitting there together in the early afternoon. Through the open end of the shed the bright light had inched across the dirt floor till now they were both sitting half in the full sunlight.

"*I* jest wish I knowed or not you daddy goin' to work on that south-quarter *fence* today," said C.K. after a bit.

"Aw him and Les Newgate went to *Dalton,*" said Harold;

". . . heck, I bet they ain't back 'fore dark. You wanta go fishin'?"

"Shoot, that sound like a *good* idea," said C.K.

"I seen that dang drum-head jumpin' on the west side of the pond again this mornin'," said Harold; ". . . shoot, I bet he weighs seven or eight pounds."

"*I* think we do awright today," C.K. agreed, glancing out at the blue sky and sniffing a little. ". . . Shoot, we try some calf-liver over at the second *log*—that's jest where that ole drum-head is 'bout now."

"I reckon we oughtta git started," said Harold. "I guess we can jest leave that dang stuff here till dark . . . we can stick it back behind that fire-wood."

"Sho'," said C.K., "we stick it back in there for the time bein'—I think I jest twist up one or two more 'fore we set out though . . . put a taste of this heavy in 'em." He laughed as he unscrewed the lid of the fruit-jar. "Shoot, this sho' be fine for fishin'," he said; ". . . ain't nothin' like good gage give a man the strength of patience—you want me to twist up a couple for you, Hal'?"

Harold spat.

"Aw I guess so," he said; ". . . you let *me* lick 'em though, dang it, C.K."

CHAPTER SEVEN

FIRST MANIFESTO TO END THE BRINGDOWN

Allen Ginsberg

Millions of Americans first read about Allen Ginsberg's poetry long before they had a chance to read a line of it. From the writer's point of view, it might even be argued that it has proved ironically fortuitous that such a huge potential audience was created practically overnight by that handful of self-righteously vocal, self-appointed literary critics who raised such a nationally publicized furor when, in 1957, Howl *quickened the literary atmosphere—violating, they claimed, the pornographic speed limit.*

The battle was soon joined: the San Francisco Customs and Post Office, forced to release foreign-printed copies of Howl *because the United States District Attorney refused to institute condemnation proceedings, passed the buck to the local police. They promptly arrested, not Ginsberg, but his poet-publisher friend Lawrence Ferlinghetti, of City Lights Books, and his assistant, Shigeyoshi Murao, charging that* Howl *was obscene and not fit for children to read.*

The trial, which went on for months, was attended by enormous press coverage, largely because the long list of defense witnesses included many of America's leading writers and critics. The bench, in its historic decision acquitting the defendants, stated that Howl *was a poetic work of social criticism that rather than purveying obscene ideas, entered "a plea for holy living."*

Further admonishing the prosecution, the presiding magistrate suggested that "in considering material claimed to be obscene, it is well to remember the motto: Honi soit qui mal y pense *(Evil to him who thinks evil.)"*

In the subsequent decade, Allen Ginsberg has, on the basis of his poetic achievement alone, been accorded international acclaim as a major American poet. He has both traveled and lived for several years in North Africa and India and has visited the eastern European socialist countries. His works have been anthologized and translated into dozens of languages, and he recently received a Guggenheim fellowship.

In addition to Ginsberg's commitment to poetry, he has been publicly active in both the peace and the civil rights movements. He feels that the campaign to legalize marihuana, now being actively organized and waged, is an important aspect of this decade's vital social movements. In the following essay, written especially for this volume, Ginsberg presents an impassioned defense of marihuana based on the evidence that supports the fact that the consciousness-expanding effects of the herb constitute "a reality kick."

I The first half of the essay was written while the author was smoking marihuana.

7:38 P.M. Nov. 13, 1965
San Francisco, California, USA, Kosmos

How much to be revealed about marijuana especially in this time and nation for the *general* public! for the actual experience of the smoked herb has been completely clouded by a fog of dirty language by the diminishing crowd of fakers who have not had the experience and yet insist on being centers of propaganda about the experience. And the key, the paradoxical key to this bizarre impasse of awareness is precisely that the marijuana consciousness is one that, ever so gently, shifts the center of attention *from* habitual shallow purely verbal guidelines and repetitive secondhand ideological interpretations of experience to *more direct, slower, absorbing, occasionally microscopically minute, engagement with sensing phenomena during the high* moments or hours after one has smoked.

One who has the experience needs no explanations in the world of explanatory language, which is, after all, a limited charming part of the whole phenomenal show of life. A few people don't *like* the experience and report back to the language world that it's a drag and make propaganda against this particular area of nonverbal awareness. But the vast majority all over the world, who have smoked the several breaths necessary to feel the effect, adjust to the strangely familiar sensation of Time slow-down, and explore this new space thru natural curiosity, report that it's a useful area of mind-consciousness to be familiar with, a creative show of the silly side of an awful big army of senseless but habitual thought-formations risen out of the elements of a language world. a metaphysical herb less habituating than tobacco, whose smoke is no more disruptive than Insight—in short, for those who have made the only objective test, a vast majority of satisfied smokers.

This essay in explanation, conceived by a mature middle-aged gentleman, the holder at present of a Guggenheim Fellowship for creative writing, a traveler on many continents with experience of customs and modes of different cultures, is dedicated in the author's right mind (i.e., not high) to those who have *not* smoked marijuana, as an attempt to bridge the conceptual gap, or cultural gap as may be, to explain the misunderstanding that has too long existed between those who know what pot is by experience and those who don't know exactly what it is but have been influenced by sloppy, or secondhand, or unscientific, or (as in the case of drug-control bureaucracies) definitely self-interested language used to describe the marijuana high pejoratively. I offer the pleasant suggestion that a negative approach to the whole issue (as presently obtains in what are aptly called square circles in the USA) is not necessarily the best, and that it is time to shift to a more positive attitude toward this specific experience.[1] If one is not inclined

---

1   Editorial in The English Journal of Medicine *The Lancet*, November 9, 1963.

> . . . At most of the recent references the question was raised whether the marijuana problem might be abolished by removing the substance from the list of dangerous drugs, where it was placed in 1951, and giving it the same social status as alcohol by legalising its import and consumption.
>
> This suggestion is worth considering. Besides the undoubted attraction of reducing, for once, the number of crimes that a member of our society can commit, and of allowing the wider spread of something that can give pleasure, a greater revenue would certainly come to the State from taxation than from fines. Additional gains might be the reduction of interracial tension, as well as that between generations; for "pot" spread from South America to Britain via the United States and the West Indies. Here it has been taken up by the younger members of a society in which alcohol is the inheritance of the more elderly.

to have the experience oneself, this is a free country and no one is obliged to have an experience merely because a great number of one's friends, family, or business acquaintances have had it and report themselves pleased. On the other hand, an equal respect and courtesy is required for the sensibilities of one's familiars for whom the experience has not been closed off by the door of Choice.

The main negative mythic images of the marijuana state that the general public is familiar with emanate from one particular source: the U.S. Treas. Dept. Narcotics Bureau.[2] If the tendency (a return to common sense) to leave the opiate problem with qualified M.D.'s prevails, the main function of this large Bureau will shift to the persecution of marijuana. Otherwise the Bureau will have no function except as a minor tax office for which it was originally purposed, under the aegis of Secty. of Treasury. Following Parkinson's Law that a bureaucracy will attempt to find work for itself, or following a simpler line of thought, that the agents of this Bureau have a business interest in perpetuating the idea of a marijuana "menace" lest they lose their employment, it is not unreasonable to suppose that a great deal of the violence, hysteria & energy of the antimarijuana language propaganda emanating from this source has as its motive a rather obnoxious self-interest, all the

2   Anslinger, Harry J. and Fulton Oursler: *The Murderers,* Farrar, Strauss & Cudahy, N. Y., 1961 (p. 38).

Much of the irrational juvenile violence and killing that has written a new chapter of shame and tragedy is traceable directly to this hemp intoxication . . .

As the Marijuana situation grew worse, I knew action had to be taken to get proper control legislation passed. By 1937, under my direction, the Bureau launched two important steps: First, a legislative plan to seek from Congress a new law that would place Marijuana and its distribution directly under federal control. Second, on radio and at major forums, such as that presented annually by the New York *Herald Tribune,* I told the story of this evil weed of the fields and river beds and roadsides. I wrote articles for magazines; our agents gave hundreds of lectures to parents, educators, social and civic leaders. In network broadcasts I reported on the growing list of crimes, including murder and rape. I described the nature of Marijuana and its close kinship to hashish. I continued to hammer at the facts.

I believe we did a thorough job, for the public was alerted, and the laws to protect them were passed, both nationally and at the state level.

more objectionable for its tone of moralist evangelism.[3] This hypocrisy is recognizable to anybody who has firsthand experience of the so-called narcotic; which, as the reader may have noticed, I have termed an herb, which it is—a leaf or blossom —in order to switch away from negative terminology and inaccurate language.

A marvelous project for a sociologist, and one which I am sure will be in preparation before my generation grows old, will be a close examination of the actual history and tactics of the Narcotics Bureau and its former chief Power, Harry J. Anslinger, in planting the seed of the marihuana "menace" in the public mind and carefully nurturing its growth in the course of a few decades until the unsuspecting public was forced to accept an outright lie.[4] I am not a thorough patient sociologist and this is not my task here, so I will limit myself to telling a few stories from personal experience, or relating stories that have been told me.

I must begin by explaining something that I have already said in public for many years: that I occasionally use marijuana in preference to alcohol, and have for several decades. I say occasionally and mean it quite literally; I have spent about as many hours high as I have spent in movie theaters—sometimes 3 hours a week, sometimes 12 or 20 or more, as at a film festival—with about the same degree of alteration of my normal awareness.

To continue, I therefore do know the subjective possibilities of marijuana and herein take evidence of my own senses between my own awareness of the mysterious ghastly universe of

3 H. J. Anslinger, Commissioner of Narcotics, Correspondence, *Jour. A.M.A.*, Jan. 16, 1943 (p. 212).

> . . . information in our possession . . . that marihuana precipitates in certain persons psychoses and unstable and disorganized personality . . . may be an important contributory cause to crime . . . by relaxing inhibitions may permit antisocial tendencies . . .
> Of course, the primary interest of the Bureau of Narcotics is in the enforcement aspect. From that point of view it is very unfortunate that Drs. Allentuck and Bowman should have stated so unqualifiedly that use of marihuana does not lead to physical, mental, or moral degeneration and that no permanent deleterious effects from its continued use were observed.

4 "Traffic in Opium and Other Dangerous Drugs." Report by the Government of the United States of America for the Year Ended December 31st, 1938, by Hon. H. J. Anslinger, Commissioner of Narcotics (p. 7). "The Narcotics Section recognizes the great danger of marihuana due to its definite impairment of the mentality and the fact that its continuous use leads direct to the insane asylum."

joy, pain, discovery, birth and death, the emptiness and awesomeness of its forms and consciousness described in the Prajna Paramita Sutra central to a Buddhist or even Christian or Hindu view of Kosmos which I sometimes experience while high, as for the last two paragraphs, and the cheap abstract inexperienced version of exactly the same thing one may have read in the newspapers, written by reporters (who smoke pot themselves occasionally nowadays) taking the main part of their poorly written squibs of misinformation from the texts and mouths of Chiefs of Narcotics Bureaus, Municipal or Federal—or an occasional doctor notorious for his ungracious stupidity and insulting manners.

One doctor, facing me across a microphone in a radio broadcasting booth on a six o'clock chat show, pre-recorded, opened our conversation reading aloud a paragraph of *Kaddish* (a poem I had written in memory of my mother, and a tribute to her which made my own father weep; a text widely read, set to music or anthologized in portions, translations of which had met with some critical approval in various languages—Spanish, French, Italian and German, by now some Bengali or Hebrew; a text which I submitted as among my major "Poems" in applying for monies from great foundations; a text applauded in recitation before academies; a text recorded for a large commercial business establishment's circulation; a text which I'd spent months daily transcribing as a movie scenario—in short a straightforward piece of communication integrating the subjective and objective, private and public, and what is common between them)—disapproving and confused—declared firmly that the dashes used as this—indicated that the broken measures of phrase—moment-to-moment consciousness during which syntax and meaning and direction of the—pauses for thought—were a sign of marijuana intoxication and were incomprehensible. He could not follow the thought. He said, as I remember—marijuana retains association and goes from one thought to another if verbalized—that I was, in fact, quite mad.

Such a notion I thought quite mad on his part; my mother had been that. They were both quite insistent in their obsessions, or opinions, and sometimes harsh and premature in their judgments. This doctor and my mother did not differ so much from myself; the announcer was sympathetic to both of us. After the show I got quite angry with the doctor—it seemed quite a self-righteous remark; but I suppose I could not match his Power by any other means at the moment and felt that Frankness and a show of emotion might shake his composure —alas, I yelled Fascist in his face, and had to be reprimanded by my companion Mr. Orlovsky for losing my temper with Dr. Baird. I have a most excellent reason in such cases and so calmed myself, but I did believe that he was a quack-mind of sorts and a sort of negative Judger with professional credentials. I had as friends many psychiatrists who treated me as interesting and no madder than themselves; and had in fact graduated from 8 months in a psychiatric institute to be told smilingly by a doctor that I was not schizophrenic but in fact a bearable neurotic, like many other people—but this was years earlier when I was a poet with a tie and an obsession with eternity. True, I had changed much in the intervening 13 years. I had pursued my thoughts to India and was now satisfied with my self and bodily existence, and a little more in harmony with desire for Life, I had begun singing mantras daily—Hindu practice of Japa and Kirtan—and I had smoked a lot of marijuana in those years; but I had not, despite my odd little biography in *Who's Who* maintained so much confusion over my identity as to forget to end a sentence, if I wished to, tying together simultaneously association and language and memory with correct punctuation and obvious thought for the reader (to make it obvious, I am doing it now): I had not so much changed and broken away from communication from my fellow selves on earth that anyone should judge me mad. His remark (on the radio) only made me feel slightly paranoid; and I suppose it is no cure to try to make the other fellow feel paranoid, so perhaps I misunderstood the doctor and must take a charitable position and assume that I am Mad (or Not-Mad) but that the doctors also misunderstood my syntax; and judged too abruptly before the Revelations possible thru pot had been deciphered. . . . In any case I had *not* been high on marijuana when *Kaddish* was composed. The original mms. were bought by NYU library and are clearly labeled as written primarily under the influence of amphetamines, more popularly known as Benzedrine or Dexadrine, familiar to many a truck driver, doctor student, housewife, and harried business executive and soldier in battle—a common experience not generally termed mad.

The mind does wander and that's another way around; to give by example a manifestation of the precise record of the effects of marijuana during composition on the subject itself, showing the area of reality traversed, so that the reader may see that it is a harmless gentle shift to a "more direct, slower, absorbing, occasionally microscopic minute, engagement with sensing phenomena"—in *this* case the phenomenon of transmuting to written language a model of the marijuana experi-

ence, which can be understood and related to in some mode by
those who have not yet met the experience but who are willing
to slow their thought and judgment and decipher the syntax
clause by clause not necessarily as slowly as composed, so the
affect will differ; and of course two bodies cannot, they say,
occupy the same place in space. Yet in another light, they say
we are one being of thought and to that common being—perceived in whatever mode one perceives—I address this syntax.[5]

Returning to the mundane world of order,[6] may I compare
the mental phenomena of the preceding anecdote with the
criminal view of it as presented by the Narcotics Dept. for
years in cheap sex magazines and government reports—reports
uninfluenced by the Narco Dept. take a contrasting view[7]—
base paranoia close to murder; frothing at the mouth of
Egyptian dogs, sex orgies in cheap dives, debilitation and terror
and physiological or mysterious psychic addiction. An essentially grotesque Image, a thought-hallucination magnified myri-
ad thru massmedia, a byproduct of Fear—something quite
fiendish—"Dope Fiend" the old language, a language abandoned in the early sixties where enough of the general public
had sufficient personal experience to reject such palpable pop-
pycock and the bureaucratic line shifted to defense of its own
existence with the following reason:[8] necessary to control

---

5   As stated in the text, which stands almost completely unrevised from
first composition, the author smoked one marijuana cigarette at the beginning of the fourth paragraph.

6   The author is still high to the end of Section I.

7   The Pharmacological Basis of Therapeutics, Goodman and Gillman,
1956 ed. (p. 20). "The federal narcotic regulations and a number of
supplementary laws include drugs such as papaverine and marihuana
which do not produce narcosis."
    (pp. 170–177). "There are no lasting ill effects from the acute use of
marihuana, and fatalities have not been known to occur.
    "Careful and complete medical and neuropsychiatric examinations of
habitués reveal no pathological conditions or disorders of cerebral functions attributable to the drug.
    "Although habituation occurs, psychic dependence is not as promi-
nent or compelling as in the case of morphine, alcohol, or perhaps even
tobacco habituation."

8   Hearings before the Committee on Ways and Means, U.S. House of
Representatives, 75th Congress, 1st session April and May 1937: House
Marijuana Hearings (p. 24).
    Rep. John Dingall: "I am just wondering whether the marijuana ad-
dict graduates into a heroin, an opium, or a cocaine user?"
    Anslinger: "No, sir. I have not heard of a case of that kind. I think
it is an entirely different class. The marijuana addict does not go in
that direction."

marijuana because smoking leads to search for thrills, kicks; this leads to next step the monster Heroin. And a terrible Fate.[9]

In sound good health I smoked legal ganja (as marihuana is termed in India where it is traditionally used in preference to alcohol) bought from government tax shops in Calcutta, in a circle of devotees, yogis, and hymn-singing pious Shaivite worshippers in the burning ground at Nimtallah Ghat in Calcutta, where it was the custom of these respected gentlemen to meet on Tues. and Saturday nights, smoke before an improvised altar of blossoms, sacramental milk-candy and perhaps a fire taken from the burning wooden bed on which lay a newly dead body, of some friend perhaps, likely a stranger if a corpse is a stranger, pass out the candy as God's gift to friend and stranger, and sing holy songs all night, with great strength and emotion, addressed to different images of the Divine Spirit. Ganja was there considered a beginning of saddhana[10] by some; others consider the Ascetic Yogi Shiva Himself to have smoked marijuana; on His birthday marijuana is mixed as a paste with almond milk by the grandmothers of pious families and imbibed as sacrament by this polytheistic nation, considered by some a holy society. The professors of English at Benares University brought me a bottle for the traditional night of Shivaratri, birthday of the Creator and Destroyer who is the patron god of this oldest continuously inhabited city on Earth. "Bom Bom Mahadev!" (Boom Boom Great God!) is the Mantra Yogis' cry as they raise the ganja pipe to their brows before inhaling.

All India is familiar with ganja, and so is all Africa, and so is all the Arab world; and so were Paris and London in smaller

9   In historical context this excuse for repression of marijuana seemed to the author so irrational that it was unnecessary to analyze. Yet public confusion may warrant some precise analysis. A) There are no legitimate sociological/medical study documents warranting the Narcotics Department's assertion of causal relation between use of marijuana and graduation to opiates. B) There never had been any hint of such association before the two classes of drugs were forcibly juxtaposed in black market by said department; Anslinger testified to that in 1937 (see footnote #8). C) A greater number of opiate users started with bananas, cigarettes and alcohol than started with marijuana—no causal relationship is indicated in any case. D) The number of millions of respectable Americans who smoke marijuana have obviously not proceeded to opiates. E) In test sociological cases, i.e. societies such as Morocco and India where marijuana use is universal, there is very small use of opiates and no social association or juxtaposition between the two classes of drugs. What juxtaposition there is in America has been created and encouraged by the propaganda and repression tactics of the Narcotics Bureau.

10   Saddhana: Yogic Path or Discipline.

measure in high-minded but respectable 19th-century circles; and so on a larger scale is America even now. Young and old millions perhaps smoke marijuana and see no harm. And we have not measured the Latin-American world, Mexico particularly who gave the local herb its familiar name. In some respects we may then see its prohibition as an arbitrary cultural taboo.

There has been a tendency toward its supression in the Arab world with the too hasty adoption of Western rationality and the enlarged activity of the American fanatic Mr. Anslinger as US representative to the UN World Health Organization Single Narcotics Commission—a position from which he circulates hysterical notices and warnings, manufactured in Washington's Treas. Dept., to the police forces of the cities of the world—so I was told by a police official in Tel Aviv, an old school chum who laughed about the latest release, a grim warning against the dangers of Khat, a traditional energizing leaf chewed by Bedouins of Arabia and businessmen and princes in Ethiopia, as well as a few traditional Yemenite Jews.

There seems to be a liaison between Anslinger and some policemen in Egypt, which has now formally outlawed its hashish or kif form of marijuana (even though masses of non-drinking faithful Muslims prefer a contemplative pipe of kif to the dangers of violent alcohol forbidden by the Koran). We find government bureaucrats and the well-to-do (as in India) taking knowing delight in alcohol as a more sophisticated and *daring* preference; and stories of mad dogs frothing at the mouth and asylums full of people driven mad by some unheard-of brand of hashish (would god it were imported to America like some fine brand of Scotch or pernod) circulated from the police information bureaus of Egypt—or perhaps some single cranky Egyptian Dr. Baird—thru the Treas. Dept. Narcotics Bureau and thence by interview and press release to the mass media of America and an inexperienced public (encouraged to drink intoxicating beer by millions of dollars' worth of advertisement). The Egyptian evidence has been quoted for years, most recently by the present head of the Narcotics Bureau, a Mr. Giordano, one of Mr. Anslinger's former intimates in the department.

Professor Lindesmith has already objected in public print to the Department's manipulation and attempted quashing of various medical-juridic reports; a Canadian documentary film on the drug subject has been blocked from being shown in this country thru activity of the Treas. Dept.—perhaps an import license was refused; the impartial LaGuardia Report was rudely attacked by Anslinger; a President's Judicial Advisory Council Policy Statement (1964) has characterized the activities of the Bureau as exceeding legal rightfulness in "criminalizing" by executive fiat and administrative dictum those addicted to addicting drugs who for decades have been prevented from going to a doctor for treatment unless it was under the aegis of Lexington jail and thru police channels. Memory of the British East India Hemp Commission report, the largest in history, done in the 1880s, which concluded that marijuana was *not* a problem, has been ignored,[11] memories of our own Panama Canal Military reports giving marijuana a clean bill of health have been unavailing in consideration of the Bureau,[12] doctors have complained of being harassed and framed by one

11 Report of the Indian Hemp Drugs Commission, 1893–4, Ch. XIII (263–4, par. 552).

Summary of conclusions regarding effects. The Commission have now examined all the evidence before them regarding the effects attributed to hemp drugs. It will be well to summarize briefly the conclusions to which they come. It has been clearly established that the occasional use of hemp in moderate doses may be beneficial; but this use may be regarded as medicinal in character. It is rather to the popular and common use of the drugs that the Commission will now confine their attention. It is convenient to consider the effects separately as affecting the physical, mental or moral nature. In regard to the physical effects, the Commission have come to the conclusion that the moderate use of hemp drugs is practically attended by no evil results at all. There may be exceptional cases in which, owing to idiosyncracies of constitution, the drugs in even moderate use may be injurious. There is probably nothing the use of which may not possibly be injurious in cases of exceptional intolerance . . .

In respect to the alleged mental effects of the drugs, the Commission have come to the conclusion that the moderate use of hemp drugs produces no injurious effects on the mind . . .

In regard to the moral effects of the drugs, the Commission are of opinion that their moderate use produces no moral injury whatever. There is no adequate ground for believing that it injuriously affects the character of the consumer . . . for all practical purposes it may be laid down that there is little or no connection between the use of hemp drugs and crime.

Viewing the subject generally, it may be added that the moderate use of these drugs is the rule, and that the excessive use is comparatively exceptional.

12 Panama Canal Zone Governor's Committee, Apr.-Dec. 1925: (*The Military Surgeon,* Journal of the Association of Military Surgeons of the United States, November 1933, p. 274).

After an investigation extending from April 1 to December 1925, the Committee reached the following conclusions:

There is no evidence that marihuana as grown here is a "habit-forming" drug in the sense in which the term is applied to alcohol,

or another police agency; sick junkies have died in jail; thousands of intelligent citizens have been put in jail for uncounted years for possession or sale of marijuana,[13] even if they grew it themselves and only smoked in private; youths have been entrapped into selling small or large quantities of the grass to police agents and consequently found themselves faced with all the venomous bullshit that an arbitrary law can create from the terror of arrest to the horror of years in jail; the author receives letters of complaint and appeals for help from many US cities, from acquaintances, fellow litterateurs, even scholarly investigators of the subject writing books about it, as well as from one energetic poet founding a fine project for an Artist's workshop (John Sinclair in Detroit, presently sentenced to 6 months for letting an agent buy marijuana for the second time) — one becomes awed by the enormity of the imposition.[14]

It is not a healthy activity for the State to be annoying so many of its citizens thusly; it creates a climate of topsy-turvy law and begets disrespect for the law and the society that tolerates execution of such barbarous law,[15] and a climate of fear and hatred for the administrators of the law. Such a law

opium, cocaine, etc., or that it has any appreciably deleterious influence on the individual using it.

Panama Canal Zone Governor's Committee, June 1931 (vide supra, p. 278):

Delinquencies due to marijuana smoking which results in trial by military court are negligible in number when compared with delinquencies resulting from the use of alcoholic drinks which also may be classed as stimulants and intoxicants.

13   12,229 convictions for marijuana in 1963 and 1964 reported from California alone, according to Prof. Lindesmith. The whole scene is so shrouded in bureaucratic mystery that there are no national figures available *anywhere*.

14   By March 1966 Dr. Timothy Leary faced a minimum of 5 years in jail and A.P. reported that the celebrated novelist Ken Kesey was a refugee in Mexico threatened with extradition by the FBI to face marijuana charges in California.

15   Proceedings White House Conference on Narcotic and Drug Abuse, September 27–28, 1962, State Department Auditorium, Washington, D.C. (p. 286).

It is the opinion of the Panel that the hazards of Marijuana per se have been exaggerated and that long criminal sentences imposed on an occasional user or possessor of the drug are in poor social perspective. Although Marijuana has long held the reputation of inciting individuals to commit sexual offenses and other antisocial acts, the evidence is inadequate to substantiate this. Tolerance and physical dependence do not develop and withdrawal does not produce an abstinence syndrome.

is a threat to the existence of the State itself, for it sickens and debilitates its most adventurous and sensitive citizens. Such a law, in fact, can drive people mad.

It is no wonder then that most people who have smoked marijuana in America often experience a state of anxiety, of threat, of paranoia in fact, which may lead to trembling or hysteria, at the microscopic awareness that they are breaking a Law, that thousands of Investigators all over the country are trained and paid to smoke them out and jail them, that thousands of their community are in jail, that inevitably a few friends are "busted" with all the hypocrisy and expense and anxiety of that trial and perhaps punishment—jail and victimage by the bureaucracy that made, propagandized, administers, and profits from such a monstrous law.

From my own experience and the experience of others I have concluded that most of the horrific affects and disorders described as characteristic of marijuana "intoxication" by the US Federal Treasury Department's Bureau of Narcotics are, quite the reverse, precisely traceable back to the effects on consciousness not of the narcotic but of the law and the threatening activities of the US Bureau of Narcotics itself. Thus, as the Buddha said to a lady who offered him a curse, the gift is returned to the giver when it is not accepted.

I myself experience this form of paranoia when I smoke marijuana, and for that reason smoke it in America more rarely than I did in countries where it is legal. I noticed a pronounced difference of affect in my case. The anxiety was directly traceable to fear of being apprehended and treated as a deviant criminal and put thru the hassle of social disapproval, ignominious Kafkian tremblings in vast court buildings coming to be Judged, the helplessness of being overwhelmed by force or threat of deadly force and put in brick and iron cell.

This apprehension deepened when on returning this year from Europe I was stopped, stripped, and searched at Customs. The dust of my pockets was examined with magnifying glass for traces of weed. I had publicly spoken in defense of marijuana and attacked the conduct of the Bureau, and now my name was down on a letter dossier at which I secretly peeked, on the Customs search-room desk. I quote the first sentence, referring to myself and Orlovsky: "These persons are reported to be smuggling (or importing) narcotics. . . ."

On a later occasion, when I was advised by several friends and near-acquaintances that Federal Narcotics personnel in NYC had asked them to "set me up" for an arrest, I became incensed enough to write a letter of complaint to my Congressman. He replied that he thought I was being humorless about the reason for my being on a list for Customs investigation, since it was natural (I had talked about the dread subject so much in public); anyway, not Kafkian as I characterized it. As for my complaint about being set up—that, with my letter, was forwarded to the Treasury Dept. in Washington for consideration and reply.[16] I had schemed writing some essay, such as this in addition to a letter of reminder to my Representative, for it would be to my safety to publish.

I had had the earlier experience after a nationwide TV discussion show, during which the moderator, John Crosby, the anthropologist Ashley Montagu, and celebrated fellow-writer Norman Mailer all concluded—perhaps for the first time over a nationally publicized medium of communication in the last three decades—that as far as we knew there was nothing wrong with marijuana—of learning that the Treasury Department, true to its obsession, had forced its opinion back on the medium thru a 7-minute video-taped Refutation (including an incredible rehash of the Egyptian mad dogs), and placed it on the air against the wishes of Mr. Crosby on the insistence of his network, which had received a communication from the Narco. Bureau, possibly thru intervention of FCC. Years later I read an account of the incident by Mr. Crosby in his syndicated column, formally complaining about the affair.[17]

At that time, looking forward to the occasion of this essay, a difficult one, I made a preliminary epistle on the subject to Anslinger himself, a ten-page composition saying I thought he was a dangerous fraud, responsible for untold death and suffering, and that some day soon, those who had experience of the matter would band together with reasoning and documentation—such as one may find in this book—to come out in the open to explain the actual horror of the US Treas. Dept. Fed. Narcotic Bureau to an already suspecting public.

Allen Ginsberg   2 A.M. Nov. 14, 1965

II

Rather than alter the preceding composition—let it remain, for the reader who has not smoked marihuana, a manifestation

16 Reply received December 22, 1965:

"I would advise you that I have been in touch with the Bureau of Narcotics and am of the opinion that nothing has been done in your case that is illegal or inconsistent with law enforcement practices designed to enforce the narcotics laws." In this case it was police request to arrested friends that they carry marijuana to *my* apartment and to that of the novelist William S. Burroughs.

17 New York *Herald Tribune*, November 22, 1963.

of marijuana-high thought structure in a mode which intersects our mutual consciousness, namely language—the author wishes to add here a few thoughts.

The author has spent half a year in Morocco, smoking kif often: old gentlemen and peaceable youths sit amiably, in cafes or under shade trees in outdoor gardens drinking mint tea, passing the tiny kif pipe, and looking quietly at the sea. This is the true picture of the use of kif in North Africa, exactly the opposite of the lurid stereotype of mad-dog human beings deliberately spread by our Treasury Department police branch. And I set this model of tranquil sensibility beside the tableau of aggravated New York executives sipping whiskey before a 1966 TV set's imagery of drunken American violence covering the world from the highways to Berkeley all the way to the dirt roads of Vietnam.

No one has yet remarked that the suppression of Negro rights, culture, and sensibility in America has been complicated by the marijuana laws. African sects have used pot for divine worship (much as I have described its sacred use in India). And to the extent that jazz has been an adaption of an African religious form to American context (and will have been in no small measure the salvation of America, if America survives the decades of coming change), marijuana has been closely associated with the development of this indigenous American form of chant and prayer. Use of marijuana has always been widespread among the Negro population in this country, and suppression of its use, with constant friction and bludgeoning of the Law, has been one of the major unconscious, or unmentionable, methods of suppression of Negro rights. The mortal sufferings of our most celebrated heroic Negro musicians, from Billie Holiday thru Thelonious Monk, at the hands of police over the drug issue are well known. Such sadistic persecutions have outraged the heart of America for decades. I mean the cultural and spiritual Heart—US Music.

Although most scientific authors who present their reputable evidence for the harmlessness of marijuana make no claim for its surprising *usefulness,* I do make that claim:

Marijuana is a useful catalyst for specific optical and aural aesthetic perceptions. I apprehended the structure of certain pieces of jazz and classical music in a new manner under the influence of marijuana, and these apprehensions have remained valid in years of normal consciousness. I first discovered how to see Klee's *Magic Squares* as the painter intended them (as optically 3-dimensional space structures) while high on marijuana. I perceived ("dug") for the first time Cezanne's "petit sensation" of space achieved on a 2-dimensional canvas (by means of advancing and receding colors, organization of triangles, cubes, etc., as the painter describes in his letters) while looking at *The Bathers* high on marijuana. And I saw anew many of nature's panoramas and landscapes that I'd stared at blindly without even noticing before; thru the use of marijuana, awe and detail were made conscious. These perceptions are permanent—any deep aesthetic experience leaves a trace, and an idea of what to look for that can be checked back later. I developed a taste for Crivelli's symmetry; and saw Rembrandt's *Polish Rider* as a sublime Youth on a Deathly horse for the first time—saw myself in the rider's face, one might say—while walking around the Frick Museum high on pot. These are not "hallucinations"; these are deepened perceptions that one might have catalyzed not by pot but by some *other* natural event (as natural as pot) that changes the mind, such as an intense love, a death in the family, a sudden clear dusk after rain, or the sight of the neon spectral reality of Times Square one sometimes has after leaving a strange movie. So it's all *natural*.

At this point it should be announced that most of the major (best and most famous too) poets, painters, musicians, cinéasts, sculptors, actors, singers and publishers in America and England have been smoking marihuana for years and years. I have gotten high with the majority of the dozens of contributors to the Don Allen *Anthology of New American Poetry 1945–1960;* and in years subsequent to its publication have sat down to coffee and a marijuana cigarette with not a few of the more academic poets of the rival Hall-Pack-Simpson anthology. No art opening in Paris, London, New York, or Wichita at which one may not sniff the incense-fumes of marijuana issuing from the ladies' room. Up and down Madison Avenue it is charming old inside knowledge; in the clacketing vast city rooms of newspapers on both coasts, copyboys and reporters smoke somewhat less marijuana than they take tranquillizers or benzedrine, but pot begins to rival liquor as a non-medical delight in conversation. Already 8 years ago I smoked marijuana with a couple of narcotic department plainclothesmen who were trustworthy enough to invite to a literary reception. A full-page paid advertisement in *The New York Times,* quoting authoritative medical evidence of the harmlessness of marijuana, and signed by a thousand of its most famous smokers, would once and for all break the cultural ice and end once and for all the tyranny of the Treasury Department Narcotics Bureau. For it would only manifest in public what everybody sane in the centers of communication in America knows anyway, an enormous open secret—that it is time to end Prohibition again. And with it put an end to the gangsterism, police mania, hypocrisy, anxiety, and national stupidity generated by administrative abuse of the Marijuana Tax Act of 1937.

It should be understood once and for all that in this area we have been undergoing police-state conditions in America, with characteristic mass brainwashing of the public, persecutions and deaths in jails, elaborate systems of plainclothes police and police spies and stool-pigeons, abuse of constitutional guarantees of privacy of home and person (even *mode of consciousness*) from improper search and seizure. The police prohibition of marijuana (accompanied with the even more obnoxious persecution of sick heroin addicts who all along should have been seeing the doctor) has directly created vast black markets, crime syndicates, crime waves in the cities, and a breakdown of law and order in the State itself. For the courts of large cities are clogged with so-called narcotic crimes and behind schedule, and new laws (such as the recent NY Rockefeller Stop and Frisk and No-Knock) spring up against the citizen to cope with the massive unpopularity of prohibition.

Not only do I propose end of prohibition of marijuana, and total shift of treatment of actually addictive drugs to the hands of the medical profession, but I propose a total dismantling of the whole cancerous bureaucracy that has perpetrated this historic fuck-up on the United States. And not only is it necessary that the Bureau of Narcotics be dismantled and consigned to the wax-museum of history, where it belongs, but it is also about time that a full-scale Congressional Investigation, utilizing all the resources of the embattled medical, legal and sociological authorities, who for years have been complaining in vain, should be undertaken to fix the precise responsibility for this vast swindle on the administrative, business and mass-media shoulders where it belongs. What were the motive and method in perpetrating this insane hoax on public consciousness? Have any laws of malfeasance in public office been violated?

Not only an investigation of how it all happened, but some positive remuneration is required for those poor citizens, many of them defenseless against beatings, sickness, and anxiety for years—a minority directly and physically persecuted by the police of every city and state and by agents of the nation; a minority often railroaded to jail by uncomprehending judges for months, for years, for decades; a minority battling idiotic laws, and even then without adequate legal representation for the slim trickery available to the rich to evade such laws. Pension must be made obviously for the cornered junkies. But for the inoffensive charming smokers of marihuana who have undergone disgraceful jailings, money is due as compensation. This goes back decades for thousands and thousands of people who, I would guess, are among the most sensitive citizens of the nation; and their social place and special honor of character should be rewarded by a society which urgently needs this kind of sensibility where it can be seen in public.

I have long left that there were certain political implications to the suppression of marijuana, beyond the obvious revelation (which Burroughs points out in *Naked Lunch*) of the cancerous nature of the marihuana-suppression bureaucracy. When the citizens of this country see that such an old-time, taken-for-granted, flagwaving, reactionary truism of police, press, and law as the "reefer menace" is in fact a creepy hoax, a scarecrow, a national hallucination emanating from the perverted brain of one single man (perhaps) such as Anslinger, what will they begin to think of the whole of taken-for-granted public REALITY?

What of other issues filled with the same threatening hysteria? The spectre of Communism? Respect for the police and courts? Respect for the Treasury Department? If marihuana is a hoax, what is Money? What is the War in Vietnam? What are the Mass Media?

As I declared at the beginning of this essay, marijuana consciousness shifts attention from stereotyped verbal symbols to "more direct, slower, absorbing, occasionally microscopically minute, engagement with sensing phenomena during the high . . ." Already millions of people have got high and looked at the images of their Presidents and governors and Representatives on television and seen that all were betraying signs of false character. Or heard the impersonal robot tones of radio newscasters announcing mass deaths in Asia.

It is no wonder that for years the great centers of puritanism of consciousness, blackout and persecution of the subtle vibrations of personal consciousness catalyzed by marijuana have been precisely Moscow and Washington, the centers of the human power war. Fanatical rigid mentality pursuing abstract ideological obsessions make decisions in the right-wing mind of America, pursuing a hateful war against a mirror-image of the same "sectarian, dogmatic" ideological mentality in the Communist camp. It is part of the same pattern that both centers of power have the most rigid laws against marijuana. And that marijuana and versions of African ritual music (rock and roll) are slowly catalyzing anti-ideological consciousness of the new generations on both sides of the Iron-Time curtain.

I believe that future generations will have to rely on new faculties of awareness, rather than new versions of old idea-systems, to cope with the increasing godlike complexity of our planetary civilization, with its overpopulation, its threat of atomic annihilation, its centralized network of abstract word-image communications, its power to leave the earth. A new consciousness, or new awareness, will evolve to meet a changed ecological environment. It has already begun evolving in younger generations from Prague to Calcutta; part of the process of re-examination of certain heretofore discarded "primitive" devices of communication with Self and Selves. Negro worship rituals have invaded the West via New Orleans and Liverpool, in altered but still recognizably functional form. The consciousness-expanding drugs (psychedelics) occupy attention in the highest intellectual circles of the West, as well as among a great mass of youth. The odd perceptions of Zen, Tibetan Yoga, Mantra Yoga, and indigenous American shamanism affect the consciousness of a universal generation, children who can recognize each other by hairstyle, tone of voice, attitude to nature and attitude to Civilization. The airwaves are filled with songs of hitherto unheard-of frankness and beauty.

These then are some of the political or social implications of the legalization of marijuana as a catalyst to self-awareness. The generalizations I have made may also apply to the deeper affects and deeper social changes that may be catalyzed thru the already massive use of psychedelic drugs.

And it is significant that, as Marijuana was once monopolized by a small rabid bureaucracy in the Treasury Department, the psychedelic drugs have this year in America been officially monopolized by the Pure Food and Drug Administration—within months a large amateur police force has mushroomed. I've heard it rumored that the precise group of citizens *least* equipped for "responsibility" in this area—the *least* "mature" pressure-group in the States—already acts in an advisory capacity on licensing. This group is the Chemical Warfare Division of the Pentagon.

CHAPTER EIGHT

EXPERIMENTS WITH HASHISH

Victor Robinson, MD

Dr. Robinson's experiments with hashish were performed on his friends under informal circumstances, usually at home. Though they are humorous and anecdotal, they nevertheless contain vivid descriptions of the psychological reactions of relatively normal people who were taking hashish for the first time.

Idiosyncrasy may not be the star performer, but it certainly plays an important role in the therapeutic drama. No drug in the entire materia medica is capable of producing such a diversity of effects as *Cannabis indica*. "Of the actions of hashish," writes Alfred Stillé, "many and various descriptions have been given which differ so widely among themselves that they would scarcely be supposed to apply to the same agent, had we not every day a no less remarkable instance of the same kind before us in the case of alcohol. As the latter enlivens or saddens, excites or depresses, fills with tenderness, or urges to brutality, imparts vigor and activity, or nauseates and weakens, so does the former give rise to even a still greater variety of phenomena, according to the natural disposition of the person, his existing state of mind, the quantity of the drug and the combinations in which it is taken."

Cannabis is certainly the coquette of drugdom. It is because of the unending variety of its action that the writer experimented with hashish and a few of the cases are here reported:

Experiment with Mr. A.

Mr. A. took 25 minims of the fluid extract of *Cannabis indica* (U.S.P.) in the presence of some ladies. An hour passed without results. A second hour followed without any noticeable result. The third hour promised to be equally fruitless, and as it was already late in the evening, the ladies said good-by. No sooner did they leave the room than the characteristic hashish-laugh rang out. The hemp was doing its work. In a shrill voice Mr. A. was exclaiming: "What foo-oolish people, what foo-oo-ool-ish people to leave just when the show is beginning." The ladies came back. And it was a show. Mr. A. made socialistic speeches, and argued warmly for the cause of Woman Suffrage. He grew most affectionate and insisted on holding a lady's hand. His face was flushed, his eyes were half closed, his abdomen seemed uneasy, but his spirit was happy. He sang, he rhymed, he declaimed, he whistled, he mimicked, he acted. He pleaded so passionately for the rights of Humanity that it seemed he was using up the resources of his system. But he was tireless. With both hands he gesticulated, and would brook no interruption.

Peculiar ideas suggested themselves. For instance, he said something was "sheer nonsense," and then reasoned as follows: "Since shears are the same as scissors, instead of sheer nonsense I can say scissors nonsense." He also said, "I will give you a kick in the tickle"—and was much amused by the expression.

At all times he recognized those about him, and remained conscious of his surroundings. When the approach of dawn forced the ladies to depart, Mr. A. uttered a Rabelaisian jest, and immediately exclaimed triumphantly, "I wouldn't have said that if the ladies were here for a million dollars." Someone yawned deeply, and being displeased by the unexpected appearance of a gaping orifice, Mr. A. melodramatically gave utterance to this Gorky-like phrase: "From the depths of dirtiness and despair there rose a sickly odorous yawn"—and instantly he remarked that the first portion of this sentence was alliterative! Note that consciousness and intoxication can exist in the same brain simultaneously. The next day he remembered all that occurred, was in excellent spirits, laughed much and easily, and felt himself above the petty things of this world.

Experiment with Mr. B.

On May 19, 1910, this world was excited over the visit of Halley's comet. It is pleasant to remember that the celestial guest attracted considerable newspaper attention. On the evening of this day, at 10 o'clock, Mr. B., a court stenographer, took 45 minims. At 11:30 the effects of the drug became apparent, and Mr. B. lost consciousness of his surroundings to such an extent that he imagined himself an inhabitant of Sir Edmund Halley's nebulous planet. He despised the earth and the dwellers thereon; he called it a miserable little flea-bite, and claimed its place in the cosmos was no more important than a flea-jump. With a scornful finger he pointed downward, and said in a voice full of contempt. "That little joke down there, called the earth."

Pointing to an onlooker he said, "You're a fine fellow, you're the smartest man in the city, you've got the god in you, but the best thoughts you write are low compared to the things we think up here." A little later he condescended to take this individual up with him, and said, "We're up in the realm now, and we'll make money when we get down on that measly earth again; they respect Mr. B. on earth."

He imitated how Magistrate Butts calls a prisoner to the bar. "Butts," he explained, "is the best of them. Butts—Butts —cigarette-butts." If this irreverent line fell beneath the dignified eyes of His Honor, instead of rebuking his devoted stenographer for contempt of court, it is hoped he recalled that under the influence of narcotics men are mentally irresponsible.

By this time Mr. B.'s vanity was enormous. "God, Mark Twain and I are chums," he remarked casually. "God is wise, and I am wise. And to think that people *dictate* to me!"

He imagined he had material for a great book. "I'm giving you the thoughts; slap them down, we'll make a fortune and go whacks. We'll make a million. I'll get half and you'll get half. With half a million we'll take it easy for a while on this measly earth. We'll live till a hundred and two, and then we'll skedaddle didoo. At one hundred and two it will be said of Mr. B. that he shuffled off this mortal coil. We'll skip into the great idea—hooray! hooray! Take down everything that is signifi*cant*—with an accent on the *cant*—Immanuel Kant was a wise man, and I'm a wise man; I am wise, because I'm wise." In spite of all the gabble concerning the volume that was to bring fame and fortune, not even one line was dictated by the inspired author. In fact he never got beyond the title: "Wise is God; God is Wise."

Later came a variation in the form of a hissing sound which was meant to be an imitation of the whizzing of Halley's comet; there was a wild swinging of the sheets as a welcome to the President; some hashish-laughter, and the utterance of this original epigram: Shakespeare, seltzerbeer, be cheerful.

A little later all variations ceased, for the subject became the victim of a fixed idea. He became thoroughly imbued with the great idea that the right attitude to preserve toward life is to take all things on earth as a joke. Hundreds and hundreds and hundreds of times he repeated: "The idea of the great idea, the idea of the great idea, the idea of the great idea." No question could steer him out of this track. "Who's up on this comet? Any pretty girls there?" he was asked. "The great idea is up there," was the answer.

"Where would you fall if you fell off the comet?"

"I'd fall into the great idea."

"What do you do when you want to eat and have no money?"

"You have to get the idea."

"When will you get married?"

"When I get the idea."

Midnight came, and he was still talking about his great idea. At one o'clock everyone was bored. "If you don't talk about anything else except the idea, we'll have to quit," he was warned.

"Yes," he replied, "we'll all quit, we'll all be wrapped up in the great idea." He took out his handkerchief to blow his nose, remarking, "The idea of my nose." A spectator approached him. "Don't interfere," he cried, "I'm off with the great idea." The spectators began to descend the stairs. When halfway down they stopped to listen. Mr. B. was still a monomaniac. As he was still harping on the idea of the great idea, it was time to go to bed.

In the morning his countenance was ashen, which formed a marked contrast to its extreme flushed appearance the evening before. He should have slept longer, but the thought of the duties to be performed for Judge Butts made it necessary to arouse him. The human touch may have cast him down from the glorious Halley's comet to the little flea-bite of an earth, besides jarring the idea of the great idea, but instead of manifesting anger, he smiled and extended his hand cordially, as if he had been absent for a long time. The effects of the drug had not entirely disappeared, and his friends at work thought him drunk, and asked with whom he had been out all night. Mr. B. was in first-class spirits, he bubbled over with idealism, and felt a contempt for all commercial transactions. He claimed he was the American Bernard Shaw, and looked upon the universe as a joke of the gods. While adding some figures of considerable importance—as salaries depended upon the results—a superintendent passed. Mr. B. pointed to the column that needed balancing, and asked, "This is all a joke, isn't it?" Not appreciating the etiology of the query, the superintendent nodded and passed on.

Experiment with Mr. C.

One midnight, while preparing to retire, it occurred to Mr. C. that this was a good time for him to try hashish. As he received no discouragement, 30 minims were forthwith swallowed, with the result that he had an unusual night. It must be remarked that over the bed on which he lay hangs a portrait of Ralph Waldo Emerson. For an hour and a quarter he discussed decadent poetry, and Marx's influence on the revolutionary youth of Russia. The conversation was interrupted by the hashish-laugh.

It had begun: the flood of laughter was loose, the deluge of mirth poured forth, the cascade of cachinnation rushed on till it swelled into a torrent of humor while the waves of snickering and tittering mingled with the freshets of hilarity and jollity till the whole flowed into a marvelous Niagara of merriment. What a pity the audience was so small! What a shame the old humorists could not be present! How the belly of Aristophanes would have thundered a loud *papa-pappax,* how Scarron would have grinned, how Sydney Smith would have enjoyed, how Tom Moore would have held his aching sides, how Rabelais would have raised the rafters with his loud ho-ho-hos! Mr. C. was a Leyden-jar of laughter, charged to the limit.

"I feel a satisfaction," he says, "in seeing Emerson's picture, as I always felt like laughing at him." Rolls on the bed and laughs uncontrollably. "It makes my face tired," he explains. In reply to a question, he answers that he enjoys laughing. Begins to expound something, but is stopped by a laughing fit. Says he would like to have his photo taken now, and then laughs immoderately. Remarks that it doesn't seem so much like laughing as like letting wind out of a bag. Says it is worthwhile staying up to see such a show. Giggles terrifically. "Open the window, as I am using up all the air." Laughs loud and long. Strangely enough his laughter begins to sound exactly like that of a stage Negro. He recognizes this and says: "I'se laughin' now jes' like a colored man." He is extraordinarily comical. From top to bottom his body is shaking with laughter. He twirls his arms, kicks his feet, and exemplifies Milton's "light, fantastic toe."

"I feel as if any way I put my leg I have to keep it. If I stuck it in the air and kept it there—wouldn't that be funny?" Loud laughter. Imitates the music of a military band. His eyes glisten with pleasure, his whole countenance is beaming, and he seems infinitely delighted with himself. "Forward march!" he exclaims. He plays a fife and beats a drum: Boom! Boom! Boom! Says sternly: "I don't want this band to play a patriotic air, not even in my sleep.

"Ladies and gentlemen, I tell you a story. You think I'm a fool, don't you?" Laughter. "This reminds me of a story." Laughter. "O what a fool am I!" Laughter. "I'm going to tell that story," he says determinedly. Makes several attempts, but it is a difficult feat, on account of the frequent outbursts of laughter, and because it is next to impossible for him to concentrate his thoughts. At last he gets this out: "A man said he hadn't laughed so much since his mother-in-law died. Oh, how funny!

"Mr. C.: Imitation of laughter. Pretty good, eh?" Makes a speech, imitates the gestures, and bows as politely as it is possible for one who is stretched out in bed.

"This would be a good dope to try on a fellow who is accused of having no sense of humor. Oh, I'm getting funnier every minute.

"Emerson, O you, you were a kid once, too, weren't you? I don't believe you ever were. If I had a rotten egg I'd throw it at you.

"There's a blue phosphorescent light in your face . . .

"I'd rather laugh than vomit any day." Strikes the bowl which was placed near him in case the cannabis produced emesis. "But I'm not a dog and I'll not return to my vomit. That Biblical dog was a fool.

"I've been doing all sorts of laughter. Couldn't you have a system of prosody, and divide it off into feet like poetry, and have a Laughing Poet whose contributions would be accepted by the comic papers?" Whistles and sings and drums rhythmically with fingertips on the bowl.

When one of his statements is confirmed, he says, "Don't be butting in, this is my show." Points his finger and laughs. Sensations must be very acute, for while hearing someone clear his throat to say something, but before uttering anything, he exclaims: "There you go, butting in again. But don't be afraid, I'm not getting pugnacious; it all ends in laughter." But for a moment he does become quarrelsome.

"I had a good thought, but I don't know what's best: to stick to the thought, or stick to the laughter?

"If Chauncey Depew would be wrecked in the New York Central, wouldn't that be funny? Would it be poetic justice? No, it would be the justice of laughter. Oh, it would be the laughter of the gods!" He raises himself and swings his arm dramatically. Laughter leaps from his insides as if it were a geyser spouting up, and rushes from his lips as if it were a cataract bounding down a boulder.

He theorizes about egoism and Max Stirner, but it is difficult to jot down the reflection in its entirety. He says his auditor has no sense of humor to sit there taking notes, instead of joining him in laughing.

"Of course you understand why I am laughing. But your old cook—if she hears me, she'll send for the police.

"It's too bad that when I'm having such a good time, I should be troubled by a dry taste in the mouth. It's another evidence that the world was created by a lunatic. There is always some little thing that interferes."

Talks sensibly awhile, and then says impatiently: "I want to stop all this talking, and get to laughing again. I'm not complaining about the effects from hashish, because I consider it worth everything.

"Oh, tell me, pretty maiden, why can't a little canary bird whistle a symphony, for instance, Tschaikowsky's *Le Pathétique?*" Whistles, waves his hand fantastically. "As little as I know about music, not having been gifted by Nature in that direction"—twists his arms in a grotesque manner—"I'm able to get a bunch out of Tschaikowsky. I don't mean Comrade Tschaikowsky, the revolutionist in Russia, I mean Peter Ilich Tschaikowsky. The itch of that Ilich—it seems like a personal ailment, it sounds insulting."

Throws a piece of paper, but says, "Don't be afraid, I'll break no bones."

He is asked to tell the time. He gazes intently at the clock, and says, "I want to get it exactly on the fraction of a second. But it changes so quickly, I can't." Gives it up in disgust.

Claims a heavy feeling is creeping over him, and wonders if it is due to increased blood-pressure. "But what am I beginning to talk serious for? I could keep on laughing for a couple of weeks, except that I don't want to keep you up.

"If Spencer had been more of a sport and had taken some of the stuff, he would have had material for his essay 'The Physiology of Laughter.'" To see a man drugged with hashish quoting the profoundest of synthetic philosophers is too much for the gravity of his auditor, and for a moment he screams with laughter.

"Ah, I'm beginning to get light again. It's much nicer to be light and delicate. To be a filmy butterfly, and float in fancy"—his face assumes an expression of poetic beauty, and he speculates whether man should like a life of beauty or of duty.

"Oh, I'm willing to laugh. . . ." Throws off the blankets and cries, "Throw off the bonds of all existence!"

He is asked what day it is. "I hope," says he, with a melodramatic wave of the hand. "I will express the modest hope, that in accordance to my wishes, and in conformity to my desires, it is Sunday night! Sunday night! Sunday night!" Sits up, looks roguish, and laughs. "I feel a metalliferous touch within me. I'd rather have a cramp in my leg than in my brain. Some people would call this a brain-cramp, wouldn't they?" Laughs and kicks up his legs.

"If you got erotic while laughing, wouldn't it be blasphemy? Worse than laughing in church.

"Have no illusions of death yet. I am still in a position to laugh death in the face, to laugh death in the face, to laugh . . ." —and he proves it. He claps his hands together merrily.

Has a lucid moment, looks at the clock, and says simply and correctly, "10 to 3."

Imitates a Frenchman most admirably, accent, gestures, and so forth.

The door opens, and an inmate—who has found it impossible to sleep with a roaring volcano in the house—enters. Mr. C. is requested to repeat his reflections about Chauncey Depew and the New York Central. Mr. C. is highly pleased, and gazes over the story with intense zest. He enlarges it, and claims Depew has got Elbert Hubbard beat as a hypocrite. He says all who believe Depew deserves to be killed should signify it by saying Aye, and then he himself, as if he were a whole assembly, shouts out, Aye! Aye! Aye! "The Ayes have it," he announces with the air of a man who has just won an important victory. His visitors laugh heartily. There is no limit to Mr. C.'s happiness. "That's right," he says, "it's good, take it down, old man."

He cannot bear a moment's abstinence from laughter. "Cast aside all irrelevant hypotheses, and get to the laughing. I proclaim the supremacy of the laugh, laughter inextinguishable, laughter eternal, the divine laughter of the gods."

His second visitor leaves the room. "Everything has a comic element if you look at it right. It seemed to me that he went down into the cellar because he couldn't sleep on account of all my foolishness." He wallows in amusement, but at the same time expresses regret that he is preventing us from sleeping, and says next time he will take hashish in the daytime.

The second visitor re-enters, and desires to feel his pulse. At first Mr. C. objects vehemently to being touched, but then smiles the sweetness of smiles, and with the demeanor of a martyred Bruno marching to the stake, stretches forth his hand, saying, "In the interests of science I am willing," but after a few seconds Mr. C. pulls his hand impatiently away, and exclaims angrily, "You've been holding it half an hour.

"Come on in, the hashish is fine! You laugh and laugh and laugh and laugh like an imbecile. Who can laugh in more ways than me? Not any fellow that I can see."

Begins to philosophize about savages, but loses the thread of his thoughts. He is reminded what he was talking about; he thinks a moment; taps his forehead significantly, and says, "There was a laugh there before, and now I've lost it."

"Every tick of the clock is another instant that you're wasting time over all this foolishness.

"Laughter is indisputable and for its own sake. I proclaim the laugh for the laugh's sake." The English tongue is insufficient for him; he coins words of his own: "Laughfinity!" he shouts. "Laughinosity!" he screams. "The whole world is a blooming joke."

"Which is best," he says innocently, "the Laughing Goddess, or the Goddess of Laughter?" "The Laughing Goddess," is the answer. Exultation shines through the dilated pupils of the questioner, as he responds, "I knew I would catch you. The Laughing Goddess reminds you by the association of ideas of the laughing hyena, and then instead of being the goddess presiding over the divine function of laughter, she becomes a laughing stock."

He is asked something about figures. "Figures," he answers, "are intellectually beneath me. In short, I would never be a great mathematician. Yet I appreciate the metaphysics of mathematics. I adore, I prostrate myself before mathematics as long as there are no figures in it." Hearing laughter, he explains, "Yet this isn't so foolish as it seems. Up to a certain point in geometry there are no figures.

"I would have talked more sensibly if Emerson had not been there." Bangs his legs against the edge of the bed; he is asked if he hurt himself. "Not on a material plane; it was a psychic jar of which you cannot conceive."

Speaks in a declamatory tone: "I am all the time on the border-line between Science and Folly. Which god shall ye follow, young man?"

He is told he can stop laughing if he wishes. "No, sir," comes the emphatic response, "not if you lived in my world. It is a categorical imperative in the world of hashish: Thou shalt laugh."

It is already four o'clock in the morning. The spectator is loath to leave this frolicsome dynamo of blithesomeness, this continuous current of good cheer, this generator of joyousness, but there is work to be done in the world, for which sleep is necessary, so with a last look at his Mirthful Majesty, he is left alone in his glory and his giggles.

Four hours later, the intellectual merry-andrew who criticizes the Concord Transcendentalist and juggles philosophic conceptions even under the effects of dope is motionless. Lassitude has usurped the throne of laughter.

Experiment with Mr. C. (Subject's Report)

Mr. C. has written the following memorandum of the subjective features of his experience:

The first symptom which told me that the drug was beginning to take effect was a feeling of extreme lightness. I seemed to be hollowing out inside, in some magical manner, until I became a mere shell, ready to float away into space. This was soon succeeded, in one of the breathless intervals of my prodigious laughter, by a diametrically opposite sensation of extreme solidity and leaden weight. It seemed to me that I had changed into metal of some sort. There was a metallic taste in my mouth; in some inexplicable way the surfaces of my body seemed to communicate to my consciousness a metalliferous feeling; and I imagined that if struck I would give forth a metallic ring. This heavy and metallic feeling traveled rapidly upwards from the feet to the chest, where it stopped, leaving my head free for the issuance of the storms of laughter. Most of the time my arms and legs seemed to be so leaden that it required Herculean effort to move them, but under any special stimulus, such as the entrance of a third person, the vagrant conception of a new idea, or an unusually hearty fit of laughing, this feeling of unliftable heaviness in the limbs and torso would be forgotten and I would move freely, waving my arms with great vigor and enthusiasm.

Throughout the experiment I experienced a peculiar double consciousness. I was perfectly aware that my laughter, etc., was the result of having taken the drug, yet I was powerless to stop it, nor did I care to do so, for I enjoyed it as thoroughly as if it had arisen from natural causes. In the same way the extension of the sense of time induced by the drug was in itself indubitable and as cogent as any normal evidence of the senses, yet I remained able to convince myself at any moment by reflection that my sense of time was fallacious. I divided these impressions into hashish-time and real time. But in their alterations, so rapid as to seem simultaneous, both these standards of time seemed equally valid. For instance, once or twice when my friend spoke of something I had said a second before, I was impatient and replied: "What do you want to go back to that for? That was a long time ago. What's the use of going back into the past?" At the next moment, however, I would recognize, purely as a matter of logic, that he was replying to the sentence before the last that I had uttered, and would thus realize that the remark to which he referred was separated from the present only by a moment's interval. I did not, however, at any time on this occasion, attain the state sometimes reached in the second stage of hashish intoxication in which mere time disappears in an eternity wherein ages rush by like ephemera; nor did I experience any magnification of the sense of space, my experiences in regard to such extensions being confined to an intermittent multiplication of the sense of time.

When my laughter began it seemed for an instant to be mechanical, as if produced by some external power which forced air in and out of my lungs; it seemed for an instant to proceed from the body rather than from the mind; to be, in its inception, merely physical laughter without a corresponding psychic state of amusement. But this was only momentary. After the first few moments I enjoyed laughing immensely. I felt an inclination to joke as well as to laugh, and I remember saying: "I am going to have some reason for this laughing, so I will tell a story; if I have to laugh anyway, I'm going to supply good reasons for doing so, as it would be idiotic to laugh about nothing." I thereupon proceeded to relate an anecdote. Although I knew that my condition was the result of the drug, I was nevertheless filled with a genuine sense of profound hilarity, an eager desire to impart similar merriment to others, and a feeling of immense geniality and mirth, accompanied by sentiments of the most expansive good-will.

Against the effects of the drug, much as I enjoyed and yielded to it, there was opposed a preconceived intention. I had determined to tell my friend Victor Robinson, who was taking notes of my condition, just how I felt; had determined to supply as much data as possible in regard to my sensations. The result was that I repeatedly summoned all the rational energy that remained to me, and fought desperately to express the thoughts that came to me, whether ridiculous or analytical. Sometimes when I felt myself slipping away again into laughter or dreaminess I summoned all my strength to say what I had in mind, and would lose the thread of my thought and could not remember what I wanted to say, but would return to it again and again with the utmost determination and tenacity until I succeeded in saying what I wished to—sometimes an observation about my sensations, often only a jest about my condition. I believe that this acted as a great resistant to the effect of the drug. The energy of the drug was dissipated, I think, in overcoming my will to observe and analyze my sensations, and it was probably for this reason that I did not pass very far on this occasion into the second stage in which laughter gives place to grandiose visions and charming hallucinations.

After my friend turned out the light and left the room, my laughter gradually subsided into a few gurgles of ineffable mirth and benevolence, and after a period of the amorous visions sometimes induced by this philtre from the land of harems, I fell into a sound sleep after my three hours of continuous and exhausting laughter.

I awoke next morning after seven hours' sleep, with a ravenous appetite, which I think was probably as much due to the great expenditure of energy in laughing as to any direct effect of the drug itself. I was also very thirsty and my skin was parched and burning. Although I immediately dressed and went down to breakfast, I felt very drowsy and disinclined to physical exertion or mental concentration. And while no longer given to causeless laughter, I felt a lingering merriment and was easily moved to chuckling. I slept several hours in the afternoon and after dinner I slept all evening, awaking at 11 P.M., when I arose feeling very much refreshed and entirely normal, and went out to get another meal, being still hungry. I should say that the immediate after-effect, the reaction from the stimulation of hashish, is not much greater, except for the drowsiness, than that following the common or beer garden variety of intoxication. My memory of what I said and did while under the hashish was complete and accurate.

Experiment of Dr. X. (Subject's Report)

On March 4, 1910, I came home, feeling very tired. I found that some *Cannabis indica* which I had expected had arrived. After supper, while finishing up an article, I began to debate with myself whether I should join the hashish-eaters that night. The argument ended in my taking 20 minims at 9 o'clock. I was alone in the room, and no one was aware that I had yielded to temptation. An hour later I wrote in my memoranda book: Absolutely no effect. At 10:30, I completed my article, and entered this note: No effect at all from the hemp. By this time I was exhausted, and being convinced that the hashish would not act, I went to bed in disappointment. I fell asleep immediately.

I hear music. There is something strange about this music. I have not heard such music before. The anthem is far away, but in its very faintness there is a lure. In the soft surge and swell of the minor notes there breathes a harmony that ravishes the sense of sound. A resonant organ, with a stop of sapphire and a diapason of opal, diffuses endless octaves from star to star. All the moonbeams form strings to vibrate the perfect pitch, and this entrancing unison is poured into my enchanted ears. Under such a spell, who can remain in a bed? The magic of that melody bewitches my soul. I begin to rise horizontally from my couch. No walls impede by progress, and I float into the outside air. Sweeter and sweeter grows the music; it bears me higher and higher, and I float in tune with the infinite— under the turquoise heavens where globules of mercury are glittering.

I become an unhindered wanderer through unending space. No airship can go here, I say. I am astonished at the vastness of Infinity. I always knew it was large, I argue, but I never dreamed it was as huge as this. I desire to know how fast I am floating through the air, and I calculate that it must be about a billion miles a second.

I am transported to wonderland. I walk in streets where gold is dirt, and I have no desire to gather it. I wonder whether it is worthwhile to explore the canals of Mars, or rock myself on the rings of Saturn, but before I can decide, a thousand other fancies enter my excited brain.

I wish to see if I can concentrate my mind sufficiently to recite something, and I succeed in correctly quoting this stanza from a favorite poem which I am perpetually re-reading:

> Come into the garden, Maud,
> For the black bat, night, has flown,
> Come into the garden, Maud,
> I am here at the gate alone;
> And the woodbine spices are wafted abroad,
> And the musk of the rose is blown.

It occurs to me that it is high honor for Tennyson to have his poetry quoted in Heaven.

I turn, I twist, I twirl. I melt, I fade, I dissolve. No diaphanous cloud is so light and airy as I. I admire the ease with which I float. My gracefulness fills me with delight. My body is not subject to the law of gravitation. I sail dreamily along, lost in exquisite intoxication.

New scenes of wonder continually unravel themselves before my astonished eyes. I say to myself that if I could only record one-thousandth of the ideas which come to me every second, I would be considered a greater poet than Milton.

I am on the top of a high mountain-peak. I am alone—only the romantic night envelops me. From a distant valley I hear the gentle tinkling of cowbells. I float downwards, and find immense fields in which peacocks' tails are growing. They wave slowly, to better exhibit their dazzling ocelli, and I revel in the gorgeous colors. I pass over mountains and I sail over seas. I am the monarch of the air.

I hear the songs of women. Thousands of maidens pass near me; they bend their bodies in the most charming curves, and scatter beautiful flowers in my fragrant path. Some faces are strange, some I knew on earth, but all are lovely. They smile, and sing and dance. Their bare feet glorify the firmament. It is more than flesh can stand. I grow sensual unto satyriasis. The aphrodisiac effect is astonishing in its intensity. I enjoy all the women of the world. I pursue countless maidens through the confines of Heaven. A delicious warmth suffuses my whole body. Hot and blissful I float through the universe, consumed with a resistless passion. And in the midst of this unexampled and unexpected orgy, I think of the case reported by the German Dr. Reidel, about a drug-clerk who took a huge dose of hashish to enjoy voluptuous visions, but who heard not even the rustle of Aphrodite's garment, and I laugh at him in scorn and derision.

I sigh deeply, open my eyes, and find myself sitting with one foot in bed, and the other on my desk. I am bathed in warm sweat, which is pleasant. But my head aches, and there is a feeling in my stomach which I recognize and detest. It is nausea. I pull the basket near me, and await the inevitable result. At the same time I feel like begging for mercy, for I have traveled so far and so long, and I am tired beyond limit and I need a rest. The fatal moment approaches, and I lower my head for the easier deposition of the rising burden. And my head seems monstrously huge, and weighted with lead. At last the deed is done, and I lean back on the pillow.

I hear my sister come home from the opera. I wish to call her. My sister's name is Margaret; I try to say it, but I cannot. The effort is too much. I sigh in despair. It occurs to me that I may achieve better results if I compromise on Marge, as this contains one syllable instead of three. Again I am defeated. I am too weary to exert myself to any extent, but I am determined. I make up my mind to collect all my strength, and call out: Marge. The result is a fizzle. No sound issues from my lips.

My lips do not move. I give it up. My head falls on my breast, utterly exhausted and devoid of all energy.

Again my brain teems. Again I hear that high and heavenly harmony, again I float to the outposts of the universe and beyond, again I see the dancing maidens with their soft yielding bodies, white and warm. I am excited unto ecstasy. I feel myself a brother to the Oriental, for the same drug which gives him joy is now acting on me. I am conscious all the time, and I say to myself in a knowing way with a suspicion of a smile: All these visions because of 20 minims of *Cannabis indica*. My only regret is that the trances are ceaseless. I wish respite, but for answer I find myself floating over an immense ocean. Then the vision grows so wond'rous that body and soul I give myself up to it, and I taste the fabled joys of Paradise. Ah, what this night is worth!

The music fades, the beauteous girls are gone, and I float no more. But the black rubber covering of my typewriter glows like a chunk of yellow phosphorus. By one door stands a skeleton with a luminous abdomen who brandishes a wooden sword. By the other door a little red devil keeps guard. I open my eyes wide, I close them tight, but these spectres will not vanish. I know they are not real, I know I see them because I took hashish, but they annoy me nevertheless. I become uncomfortable, even frightened. I make a superhuman effort, and succeed in getting up and lighting the gas. It is two o'clock. Everything is the way it should be, except that in the basket I notice the remains of an orange—somewhat the worse for wear.

I feel relieved, and fall asleep. Something is handling me, and I start in fright. I open my eyes and see my father. He has returned from a meeting at the Academy of Medicine, and, surprised at seeing a light in my room at such a time, has entered. He surmises what I have done, and is anxious to know what quantity I have taken. I should have answered, with a wink, *quantum sufficit;* but I have no inclination for conversation; on hearing the question repeated, I answer, "Twenty minims." He tells me I look as pale as a ghost, and brings me a glass of water. I drink it, become quite normal, and thus ends the most wonderful night of my entire existence.

In the morning my capacity for happiness is considerably increased. I have an excellent appetite, the coffee I sip is nectar, and the white bread, ambrosia. I take my camera, and walk to Central Park. It is a glorious day. Everyone I meet is idealized. The lake never looked so placid before. I enter the hothouses, and a gaudy-colored insect buzzing among the lovely flowers fills me with joy. I am too languid to take any pictures; to set the focus, to use the proper stop, to locate the image, to press the bulb—all these seem Herculean feats which I dare not even attempt. But I walk and walk, without apparent effort, and my mind eagerly dwells on the brilliant pageantry of the night before. I do not wish to forget my frenzied nocturnal revelry upon the vast dome of the broad blue heavens. I wish to remember forever the floating, the mercury-globules, the peacock-feathers, the colors, the music, the women. In memory I enjoy the carnival again.

"For the brave Meiamoun," writes Théophile Gautier, "Cleopatra danced; she was apparelled in a robe of green, open at either side; castanets were attached to her alabaster hands. . . . Poised on the pink tips of her little feet, she approached swiftly to graze his forehead with a kiss; then she recommenced her wond'rous art, and flitted around him, now backward-leaning, with head reversed, eyes half-closed, arms lifelessly relaxed, locks uncurled and loose-hanging like a bacchante of Mount Menelaus; now again active, animated, laughing, fluttering, more tireless and capricious in her movements than the pilfering bee. Heart-consuming love, sensual pleasure, burning passion, youth inexhaustible and ever-fresh, the promise of bliss to come—she expressed all. . . . The modest stars had ceased to contemplate the scene; their golden eyes could not endure such a spectacle; the heaven itself was blotted out, and a dome of flaming vapor covered the hall."

But for me a thousand Cleopatras caroused—and did not present me a vase of poison to drain at a draught. Again I repeated to myself: "And all these charming miracles because of 20 minims of *Fluidextractum Cannabis Indicae*, U.S.P."

By the afternoon I had so far recovered as to be able to concentrate my mind on technical studies. I will not attempt to interpret my visions psychologically, but I wish to refer to one aspect. Spencer, in *Principle of Psychology*, mentions hashish as possessing the power of reviving ideas. I found this to be the case. I spoke about airships because there had been a discussion about them at supper; I quoted from Tennyson's "Maud" because I had been rereading it; I saw mercury-globules in the heavens because that same day I had worked with mercury in preparing mercurial plaster; and I saw the peacock tails because a couple of days previous I had been at the Museum of Natural History and had closely observed a magnificent specimen. I cannot account for the women in my visions.

All poets—with the possible exception of Margaret Sangster—have celebrated Alcohol, while Rudyard Kipling has gone so far as to solemnize delirium tremens; B. V. has glorified Nicotine; De Quincey has immortalized Opium; Murger is full of praise for Caffeine; Dumas in *Monte Cristo* has apotheosized Hasheesh, Gautier has vivified it in *Club des Hachichins,* Baudelaire has panegyrized it in *Paradis artificiels,* but as few American pens have done so, I have taken it upon myself to write a sonnet to the most interesting plant that blooms:

> Near Punjab and Pab, in Sutlej and Sind,
> Where the cobras-di-capello abound,
> Where the poppy, palm and the tamarind,
> Where cummin and ginger festoon the ground—
> And the capsicum fields are all abloom
> From the hills above to the vales below,
> Entrancing the air with a rich perfume,
> There, too, does the greenish Cannabis grow:
> Inflaming the blood with the living fire,
> Till the burning joys like the eagles rise,
> And the pulses throb with a strange desire,
> While passion awakes with a wild surprise:
> O to eat that drug, and to dream all day,
> Of the maids that live by the Bengal Bay!

CHAPTER NINE

NOTES ON THE USE
OF HASHISH

Sheldon Cholst, MD

*Sheldon Cholst received his BA from New York University,
where he studied medieval literature and folklore. Upon becoming interested in the Freudian interpretation of literature,
he decided to study psychoanalysis. He was awarded his MD
from the Long Island College of Medicine and was a research
associate in the Department of Neurophysiology at the Yale
University School of Medicine, where he engaged in studies of
animal hypnosis. From 1953 to 1955, Dr. Cholst served in the
U.S. Air Force, becoming chief psychiatric officer at the Elmen-
dorf Air Force Base in Alaska. He was the Director of the
Child Guidance Clinic of University Settlement House as well
as an Instructor in the Department of Psychiatry of the N.Y.U.
Medical School. At present, Dr. Cholst resides in Europe,
where he devotes his full attention to scientific and literary
writing.*
*No effort has been made to alter or edit the following essay,
since much of its interest and value derive from the fact that it
was written by a trained psychiatrist while under the influence
of hashish.*

19 Jan. 1965

I am writing now of the effect of hashish. I smoked it in a cigarette. Had some childish thoughts or memories—of me as a

child knocking over a refrigerator and then hitting my mother for being mad at me and jumping into the fireplace and emerging unscathed and saying look what a delusion of grandeur I am. Unscathed—I can now do anything. I stopped doing hypnosis when I age-regressed a patient who got all shook up at the experience—apparently he remembered it and also saw a drawing he did at 5 in kindergarten. He remembered the President was Hoover Coolidge which he didn't remember when he awoke. Hashish I think does something similar and makes you

> Younger by far
> Than ever you are.

So it makes you a child again—in mind or emotions or soul or unboring restless behavior. You move easily in thoughts and fantasies—one to another like a child. More honest (like seeing paintings without the brainwashing of prestige or learning) but you are still a grown-up. Both child and grown-up at the same time. Lothar Gidro-Frank, a psychiatrist and friend of mine, did an experiment years ago in which he age-regressed someone and found the person had electronic muscular changes similar to what is obtained by a Babinski reflex. (The big toe goes up when the sole of the foot is scratched or indented with a pin or key from the heel around the outer aspect to the big toe, describing an elliptic semicircle.) Now with hashish there was a tendency for my big toe to move upward. My muscles were very relaxed and the general reflexes accentuated (knee and elbow). Now after the wearing off of the effect, I have the distinct impression of no Babinski and my reflexes at knee and ulnar are what they usually are for me. Tentatively then, the hashish affects the pyramidal tract in some way producing the minor changes listed before and is similar to hypnotic age regression. Thus I was adult and child at the same moment. The fountain of youth has been found. The child lives in a world of wonders, he searches, finds, turns away and is afraid sometimes of being hurt or "put down" by adults. But now he is both—so he feels "high," tall like an adult and yet still a child. O wonder of wonders! What more can this "child at heart" want—for that is what a "head" or hashish taker who really "turns on" is. He has turned off adult reality—"what to do, where to go, what am I allowed to do" and has returned to the life of the free, primitive child who wanders in his happiness. It is the ultimate cure for boredom. For the highest types of humans are very restless. "Man is a restless animal"—and the highest types are the most restless—looking for challenges—

traveling lands afar—creating new things—for what has been done is already done and thus would be a bore to do—but the limitations of the adult life—money, commitments (emotional and otherwise), time, place, the presence or not of a lover, fate's very prancing self—all these are overcome in one fell swoop—for with a few puffs of a cigarette one gets a new childhood approach. One's mind is free to wander, think, and all the restlessness is taken care of in the mind. No longer to go out and kill a tiger or hunt the wooly bear or see what lies over the mountains—that can be done too—but here he has instant joy. The limitations of motility of the adult world (reality, laws, etc.) are gotten rid of, and so his motor nerves are no longer charged with the job but return to a primitive early state. Children have Babinskis until about 6 months of age—before they can walk, certainly, for the nerve sheaths are not fully myelinated except during this first year of life. One returns in a sense to a very youthful state and doesn't need the motor nerves to escape, wander, search, find, experiment, think, fight, run away, run towards. One is already there and so the hashish is like removing the motor cortex which occurs in real life in a man who has a "stroke" or in tumors interrupting this pyramidal, area 4, part of the cortex and brain. Thus a man who is "stoned" is in a sense desirably paralyzed (partially or wholly) without the need for that motor activity which is indicative of the adult world. When a child reaches the age of 18 months (average) he is then able to walk or run away from danger and to go to pleasure; before that he is at the mercy of his parents and the particular environment he's in. Now he, under hashish, need no longer be concerned about the environmental dangers which he previously concerned himself with and compromised with, for in the real world the concern with danger, insecurity, fear of evil, have made him dress a certain way, listen to rules, frustrate himself, keep himself from being free—"able to do what he wants when he wants to do it." Were he able to be so as an adult at will (and only the good and decent truly want this freedom) he would continuously feel "high" and would know of no difference in states. That society causes pressures against absolute freedom goes without saying, and so the artist—that individual most desirous of freedom— no matter what field he is in—longs the most for the hashish release so that he can pursue and feel his joy in self as a child— for the child is the most free—not having yet been brainwashed into conformity—and the artist (and also the great artists, geniuses) retains always part of himself as this curious, naive, child-like self, the self that probes, that does not take rules easily, that does not believe unless he has checked it out himself. Scientific discoveries are by and large done by non-conformists who do not allow the written word or the prestigious person to influence them from studying the material themselves and reaching their own opinions—they are not afraid—like the child who fears nothing, but walks on a line, tries this and that and looks wondrously and newly at the butterflies, trees, and says why are the stars in the sky and where are we going and why—interminable questions of honesty which the many adults have gotten pat answers for from their parents or books or famous people—or fear to ask for fear they'll look and sound ridiculous and thus will not be accepted by the milieu and thus not receive some of the gains—food, money, prestige, too.

So hashish obviates the motor cortex, inhibits it, renders it unnecessary and sends it to the path of the old paralyzed man or the unfully formed nerve heads of the child. "What need to run to and fro which is inhibited anyway and also here in my mind I explore, find, lose my boredom, find an outlet for my restlessness and become truly a man, a human being who finds truths in this state, sees pictures for what they really are and is still an adult with all the years of memory and experience to probe. How joyous is this state—like love—for in love with another one is completely free to be oneself in its noblest meanings and

> My love is like hemp
> That brings me to faery lands afar.

This hashish, this drug, this chemical, this resin from female *Cannabis sativa* flowers, these leaves of marihuana, this poisoner of frustrating reality, this antidote for restlessness that is frustrated, this instant joy and relaxation, this chemical age-regression that allows us to be young and old at the same moment of time. Like being in two places at the same time when one crosses the international date line in the Pacific on the same day and experiences the unreal "way out" sensation of being in two places at the same time—it is just such an unreal feeling that comes up in the hashish smoker. This smoke like from Aladdin's lamp that contains the genie that brings all things to the wisher, this smoke when inhaled does the same as Aladdin's lamp and brings out the genius in the inhaler for he becomes fresh and comes fresh to thoughts and ideas and he joys with laughter at his childhood pleasure. And if he is with congenial friends he finds himself happy with them too. The drug hashish, the "fountain of youth," causes no harm—for what harm is there in being a child in the heart and in the mind—and those who do not have this capacity—those who are too square, too limited, too conformist, too brainwashed, not too bright, these people want the closed in adult life—closed in because of overpopulation and the consequent limitations on freedom. These people who either constitutionally or environmentally cannot or do not want this release into childhood life—they will not "turn on," they will not feel "high."

By and large, in general, those who wish to smoke already do, but there are some on the borderline who are too afraid they will like it too much and be drawn into the artistic or free life thus losing out on their Faustian bargain. They have sold their souls (their honesty, their desire for freedom, their insistence on truth, honor, dignity for all mankind) for the mess of pottage called financial success, prestige, and acceptance by society.

The legislation against homosexuality and other sexual acts between consenting adults is similar to the legislation against hashish. There is no earthly reason for it. You cannot legislate homosexuality for sexual urges cannot be repressed except by causing the most grievous harm to the repressing individual (virtually all is not repressed) but these people become paranoid, insecure, and even go to jail. So too with the need and desire for hashish among those who know and have experienced it. Legislation in an overpopulated society should be against those who commit heinous crimes of violence or deception but not for thinking or feeling a certain way or acting a certain way with friends that causes no harm to others and certainly not to society. Society fears letting down the gates, but the gates are already down, it is just a question of recognizing that in a world of difficulties, limitations, fate's harrowing movements, at least society ought to allow people to enjoy their mind's play, to laugh without harboring a fear of prison or other similar dangers. They will do it anyway, for what would their lives be but a prison—for those who have found their freedom limited in society and so they really have nothing to lose. But they have and do gain tremendous freedom and joy while they partake and they wish all who could also share and enjoy could come over and do so. They want to "turn on" the world and they want men free to be free if they wish in the real world if possible thru proper and decent legislation of economy and politics and at least in the meantime a freedom of the mind purchased at very little cost in the form of smoke from this remarkable Aladdin's lamp.

There are many who fear man would become poverty stricken, indolent and succumb to the ways of the East, but the ways of the East were good prior to the advent of the young West who went out to conquer and plunder and despoiled the East and leaves it where we now find it, suffering in body as much as Western man suffers in soul. They, faced with their older culture and population, formed a culture which allowed for these private escapes into freedom in the mind. In the West until the past 100 years there was a great deal of physical environmental freedom but this has almost gone, and until we find a way to live comfortably and freely with each other and the East the least we can do is not imprison those artistic searchers for truth who use hashish as escape into freedom. Happiness should be the key goal of life—human happiness— and hashish is able to help us in this.

7 Feb. 1965

As a corollary, I should like to state that there is a fear on the part of the general public that this drug or others will cause violence or crime. The evil will commit evil, come what may. Whether they use drugs as the excuse or money, power, job in the military or police or even in love. He who is evil is evil and will do so no matter what job or drug he takes. There are those who overindulge in alcohol and get into car accidents causing harm. They might also do this with hashish or even with nothing at all but psychological problems. The man who is arrested for selling hashish has usually been bothersome to others and comes to their attention and they put him away —if he is cool he is not bothered. So given the circumstances some violate public policy to such an extent they get put away. Others remain cool, but it puts a pressure on them that shouldn't be there. Even in love some will hound and badger another or nag them or treat them like a dog. There are evil people and whatever they come in touch with takes on their odor. But they will do it and some will murder in the name of love, some will murder in the name of money or governments or power or institutions or religions. But the good will never murder altho it is conceivable that in some extremity unbe- knownst to themselves, their actions predispose to murder or they are placed in such extremity that they might protect themselves and thereby cause an accident. So rare is this that I have not yet seen a clear case but its possibility remains.

So if the laws are consistent then love, autos, money, alcohol, should be banned along with hashish. If only we could ban evil or the evil ones we'd have no evil problems. But if, at least, the good are not attacked, they can get strong enough to handle and control the evil which is the best way.

> Since evil contained is not evil
> And good sustained, brings on good.

2 hours later

The laws should be against evil acts not the drug or chemical or means that is used prior to or with it or is used in the name of. Many evils were done in the name of God but this does not make God evil. Nor should hashish or hashish-takers be branded evil, but only the evil should be branded evil.

2 hours later

Those who take drugs such as hashish or even heroin or LSD have a remarkable knowledge and awareness of the drugs they take, far outdistancing those who prescribe the drug rarely or even frequently. They are users themselves. They know needles, gauges, antidotes, techniques, organ function, that far surpass the knowledge of the average physician—for they have made it an important study—their lives depend on it—their lives are on the line at each moment they live. I have seen physicians overdose patients with consequent danger and even death on more occasions than I have seen non-physicians give themselves medicines that proved harmful. I have seen mothers overdosed with demerol give birth to somnolent, dying children. I have seen physicians err with dosages to the extent of their own care and interest whether it be with insulin, tranquilizers, or even antibiotics and heart drugs.

I have seen them operate without the proper preparation out of a greed and a hunger for prestige and recognition. I have seen them operate on nonexistent conditions unnecessarily. I have seen them make mistakes. They are no different from other groups of people. Some are excellent, some mediocre, and some bad. Like art, there are some great artists, many mediocre, and some bad—or any field. For someone to have a license to dispense drugs is like having a license to paint pictures. Education should include a full study of medicine for the child—not grammar or French or History—to the extent that they are taught. Students today finish high school and know nothing about life or even their own bodies.

So human beings can be good and evil. And all people who wish to try and use the drug of their choice to "expand their consciousness," "learn further truths," or even just "feel good" —should have the right to ask someone's help (a physician) or to obtain and use the drug themselves or give them a simple test such as is given to get an auto license. I have seen bad drivers get licenses, but no good driver has failed to receive his license to drive (to my knowledge). He who will misuse his license will—but it will all be on his own head—and if he harms others he would have done so anyway and there is no point in punishing the many because of the few. They will use the drugs anyway—for it is a life need that they have discovered and if they had not discovered it their lives would be so tortured and suffering as to belie description.

Society must eventually become charitable to dissident groups and allow them the same rights it allows others. The laws against hashish should be repealed and those who are transgressors against the public good should be punished just as disorderly conduct by an alcoholic or even an ordinary citizen is. Those who will work will and there is more good and honest and really productive work forthcoming from a satisfied person—satisfied according to his own individual, personal needs, whatever they may be. The good and decent want these needs fulfilled, the evil do not see the variety in human beings and wish limitations. To be good is to be nice —to be nice is to let people have their own way if you can. To be evil is to be nasty—to insist on your own way being the only correct way. He who is most intelligent perceives as if by giant antennae the intense variety in people and thus cannot limit them if he can help it for he sees their various needs intently. Others of less intelligence do not perceive this and think they themselves correct, thereby tending to inhibit the freedom of others around them. The world is at the cross-roads now and either the limitations will win and a structured pigeon-hole society will form, or it will open up into a truly freedom-loving happy society both for the limited and the unlimited. I have no argument with those who wish to be limited. I only argue with those who wish to limit me and others of the good who wish no limitations on their goodness.

A crime occurs where one person interferes with the free will of the other who causes no harm or interference with any others. In the case of smoking hashish no crime is committed by the smoker, but a crime is committed by those who have sponsored and legislated and supported actively or by assent and inactively have allowed a situation to come about that inhibits the non-outward harming activity of hashish smoking. Society here participates in the crime, and if I did not speak up on this subject and attempt to change it I too would be committing a crime—against humanity, and I may be accused and even suffer the indignity of imprisonment for having smoked hashish or having written this piece and would be and am a criminal in the eyes of the local laws. But I obey a higher law and would be a criminal to support a wrong by inactivity. I do not accuse those who are unaware, but I would accuse myself if I did not take all conceivable action towards remedying a bad situation.

BOOK THREE

Scientific Papers

CHAPTER ONE

THE MARIHUANA PROBLEM
IN THE CITY OF NEW YORK

Mayor LaGuardia's Committee
on Marihuana

The year was 1938 and the city was New York, but it could have been Los Angeles, New Orleans, Chicago—or for that matter any other large American city in the late thirties. The nation's press was having a field day with lurid marihuana headlines: in New York City pushers were reported selling marihuana to thousands of innocent school children, and the city administration was under fire.

Most American officials demagogically played along with The Marihuana Myths rather than question their scientific validity. The Marihuana Tax Act of 1937 had just been passed and the Draconian Regulations No. 1 came sharp on its heels. Police raids—which sensation-hungry newspapers provoked and dramatically featured—were commonplace, and thousands of marihuana users, as well as sellers, were arrested and jailed. Against this background of American officialdom's knuckling under to the marihuana myths, the incorruptible figure of Fiorello H. LaGuardia stands in welcome bas-relief. Instead of yielding to the panic on September 13, 1938, New York's most popular mayor asked the world-renowned New York Academy of Medicine to make a scientific and sociological study of the reported use of the drug in the City of New York. In response to the Mayor's request, the Academy appointed a special scientific team (known as The Mayor's Committee) which comprised thirty-one eminent physicians, psychiatrists, clinical psychologists, pharmacologists, chemists, and sociologists. This impressive scientific body was charged with the responsibility of conducting a painstaking, two-part scientific study. The Academy of Medicine delineated the scope of the study as follows:

(1) a sociological study dealing with the extent of marihuana smoking and the methods by which the drug is obtained; in what districts and among what races, classes, or types of persons the use is most prevalent; whether certain social conditions are factors in its use; and what relation there is between its use and criminal or antisocial acts; and

(2) a clinical study to determine by means of controlled experiments the physiological and psychological effects of marihuana on different types of persons; the question as to whether it causes physical or mental deterioration; and its possible therapeutic effects in the treatment of disease or of other drug addictions.

The Mayor's Committee received the full cooperation of the New York City Police Department: six police officers, four men and two women, were trained as social investigators by the Committee to assist it on a full-time basis in obtaining sociological data. In addition, the entire medical staff of New York's prison hospital on Riker's Island actively assisted the thirty-one members of the Committee in the study. Also, the Goldwater Memorial Hospital provided the Committee with two wards, office space, and a staffed laboratory to conduct experiments.

Never before or since has so thorough and meticulous a scientific study been made on marihuana. Issued in 1944, the Mayor's Report still remains the most impressive collection of factual finding in the whole body of scientific literature on marihuana—a literature that goes back thousands of years. Mayor LaGuardia was sharply aware of the value and scientific impact of the Report. In his foreword he wrote:

The report of the present investigations covers every phase of the problem and is of practical value not only to our own city but to communities throughout the country. It is a basic contribution to medicine and pharmacology.

N.B. for the sake of brevity, and bearing in mind the general interest of the lay reader, several lengthy technical sections of the Report (relating to a detailed breakdown and analysis of methods and procedures employed in the study) have been eliminated. The editor has in no way, however, added to or altered any of the original wording of the text, nor have any of the findings and conclusions been omitted.

SOCIOLOGICAL, MEDICAL, PSYCHOLOGICAL AND PHARMACOLOGICAL STUDIES

by the Mayor's Committee on Marihuana

GEORGE B. WALLACE, MD, *Chairman*
E. H. L. CORWIN, PhD, *Secretary*
MCKEEN CATTELL, MD
LEON H. CORNWALL, MD
ROBERT F. LOEB, MD
CURRIER MCEWEN, MD
BERNARD S. OPPENHEIMER, MD
CHARLES DILLER RYAN, MD
DUDLEY D. SHOENFELD, MD

Ex Officio

PETER F. AMOROSO, MD
KARL M. BOWMAN, MD
S. S. GOLDWATER, MD
JOHN L. RICE, MD

Special Advisers for Clinical Study

KARL M. BOWMAN, MD
DAVID WECHSLER, PhD

Supervisors of Clinical Study

J. MURRAY STEELE, MD
S. BERNARD WORTIS, MD

FOREWORD

As Mayor of the City of New York, it is my duty to foresee and take steps to prevent the development of hazards to the health, safety, and welfare of our citizens. When rumors were recently circulated concerning the smoking of marihuana by large segments of our population and even by school children, I sought advice from The New York Academy of Medicine, as is my custom when confronted with problems of medical import. On the Academy's recommendation I appointed a special committee to make a thorough sociological and scientific investigation, and secured funds from three Foundations with which to finance these studies.

My own interest in marihuana goes back many years, to the time when I was a member of the House of Representatives and, in that capacity, heard of the use of marihuana by soldiers stationed in Panama. I was impressed at that time with the report of an Army Board of Inquiry which emphasized the relative harmlessness of the drug and the fact that it played a very little role, if any, in problems of delinquency and crime in the Canal Zone.

The report of the present investigations covers every phase of the problem and is of practical value not only to our own city but to communities throughout the country. It is a basic contribution to medicine and pharmacology.

I am glad that the sociological, psychological, and medical ills commonly attributed to marihuana have been found to be exaggerated insofar as the City of New York is concerned. I hasten to point out, however, that the findings are to be interpreted only as a reassuring report of progress and not as encouragement to indulgence, for I shall continue to enforce the laws prohibiting the use of marihuana until and if complete findings may justify an amendment to existing laws. The scientific part of the research will be continued in the hope that the drug may prove to possess therapeutic value for the control of drug addiction.

I take this occasion to express my appreciation and gratitude to the members of my committee, to The New York Academy of Medicine, and to the Commonwealth Fund, the Friedsam Foundation, and the New York Foundation which supported these important investigations so generously.

F. H. LaGuardia
Mayor

INTRODUCTION

E. H. L. Corwin, PhD, *Secretary*

On September 13, 1938, The New York Academy of Medicine was informed of Mayor LaGuardia's concern about the marihuana problem and of his desire "that some impartial body such as The New York Academy of Medicine make a survey of existing knowledge on this subject and carry out any observations required to determine the pertinent facts regarding this form of drug addiction and the necessity for its control." The Mayor's request was referred to the Committee on Public Health Relations of the Academy, which Committee on October 17, 1938, authorized the appointment of a special subcommittee to study the Mayor's request.

This Subcommittee, consisting of Dr. George B. Wallace, Chairman, Dr. E. H. L. Corwin, Secretary, and Drs. McKeen Cattell, Leon H. Cornwall, Robert F. Loeb, Currier McEwen, B. S. Oppenheimer, Charles Diller Ryan, and Dudley D. Shoenfeld, reviewed the existing literature on the subject. On the basis of this review, the Subcommittee could come to no conclusion regarding the effect of marihuana upon the psychological and physiological functions of the human being. Nor were attempts to learn the extent of the use of marihuana in New York City any more successful. A conference with representatives of the Police Department, the Department of Education, the Department of Correction, the Psychiatric Division of the Department of Hospitals, the Court of Domestic Relations, the District Attorney's office, and the Citizens Committee on the Control of Crime served to emphasize the existing differences of opinion regarding the extent of the use of marihuana in this city and its relationship to crime.

The Subcommittee therefore came to the conclusion that, in view of the possibility that marihuana smoking might constitute an important social problem, it was time that a study of its effects be made based upon well-established evidence, and prepared an outline of methods of procedure for the study of the problem. It recommended that such a study should be divided into two parts: (1) a sociological study dealing with the extent of marihuana smoking and the methods by which the drug is obtained; in what districts and among what races, classes or types of persons the use is most prevalent; whether certain social conditions are factors in its use, and what relation there is between its use and criminal or antisocial acts; and (2) a clinical study to determine by means of controlled experiments the physiological and psychological effects of marihuana on different types of persons; the question as to whether it causes physical or mental deterioration; and its possible therapeutic effects in the treatment of disease or of other drug addictions.

The Committee on Public Health Relations adopted the report of its Subcommittee and recommended to Mayor LaGuardia that he appoint a special committee to carry out the proposed study. Accordingly in January 1939 he appointed the Mayor's Committee on Marihuana, composed of the members of the Subcommittee of the Committee on Public Health Relations which recommended the study and four ex-officio members: Dr. Peter F. Amoroso, First Deputy Commissioner (later Commissioner) of Correction; Dr. Karl M. Bowman, Director of the Psychiatric Division of the Department of Hospitals; Dr. S. S. Goldwater, Commissioner of Hospitals; and Dr. John L. Rich, Commissioner of Health. Upon his accession to the commissionership of the Department of Hospitals, Dr. Willard C. Rappleye succeeded Dr. Goldwater as a member of this Committee.

This Committee studied the broad outlines of the proposed plans for about a year before work was actually begun. At its first meeting in March 1939 two subcommittees were appointed; one, consisting of Drs. Shoenfeld, Ryan, and Corwin, to plan the sociological study, and the other, composed of Drs. Cattell, Bowman, Cornwall, and Loeb, to work out the details of the clinical study. Drs. Bowman and Wechsler were appointed as special advisers for the clinical study and Dr. J. Murray Steele and Dr. S. Bernard Wortis as the supervisors of this study.

The studies were made possible by the financial support of three Foundations, the Friedsam Foundation, the New York Foundation, and the Commonwealth Fund, each of which donated $7,500. The whole amounts granted by the Friedsam Foundation and the Commonwealth Fund and $5,000 of the New York Foundation's grant were to be applied to the clinical study; the remaining $2,500 given by the New York Foundation was earmarked for the sociological study. The Research Council of the Department of Hospitals undertook the financial supervision of the clinical study and The New York Academy of Medicine that of the sociological study.

The sociological study proceeded under the active direction of Dr. Dudley D. Shoenfeld and was carried out by six police officers who were trained by Dr. Shoenfeld as social investigators. In acknowledgment of the great help rendered to the Committee by these officers, the Committee passed the following resolution at its meeting on March 18, 1941.

Now that the sociological study of the marihuana problem in New York City has been completed, the Mayor's Committee on Marihuana wishes to record its appreciation of the Mayor's interest in this problem and his placing at the disposal of the Committee the services of the Narcotic Squad Division of the Police Department.

Without the cooperation of Commissioner Valentine, Inspector Curtayne, Lieutenant Cooper, Sergeant Boylan, and Detective Loures, this study would have been impossible. They helped in planning it and assigned to the Committee six members of the Force, four men and two women, whose intelligence, interest in the work, and desire to obtain the facts of the situation were of invaluable aid in obtaining the information on which the sociological report is based. The four men and two women assigned to us made painstaking observations and reports, acted as investigators and social workers and not as police officers, and brought to the performance of this task a native intelligence, specialized training, and civic interest. The thanks of the Committee are due to them and through them to their superiors.

The clinical study consisted of two parts—the medical, including psychiatric, and the psychological. Dr. Karl M. Bowman directed the medical and psychiatric part of this study and Dr. David Wechsler the psychological part. The members of the Committee closely supervised the work during the course of the study. The staff of the clinical study included:

Samuel Allentuck, MD, Psychiatrist, who was in charge.

Louis Gitzelter, MD
Frank Anker, MD } Assistant Physicians

Robert S. Morrow, PhD
Florence Halpern, MA } Psychologists
Adolph G. Woltmann, MA

Miss Rose Horowitz, who was the secretary-stenographer and bookkeeper.

The Committee is indebted to the Department of Hospitals for making available two small wards and office space in the Welfare Hospital (now known as the Goldwater Memorial Hospital), to Dr. Chrisman G. Scheri, the Superintendent of the hospital, and to the laboratory staff of the Third Medical Division for their assistance in the conduct of laboratory experiments. Acknowledgment should also be made of the services of Dr. Robert C. Batterman who interpreted the electrocardiograms and Dr. Hans Strauss for the electroencephalographic work. Professor Walter R. Miles of Yale University assisted in the planning of the psychological part of the study.

This whole undertaking would have been impossible without the help and cooperation of Dr. Peter F. Amoroso, of the Department of Correction, who, aside from his services as a member of the Committee, was responsible for arrangements for volunteers from among the prisoners of the Riker's Island Penitentiary. Thanks are due also to the medical staff of the Riker's Island Hospital for their assistance in the narcotic addiction study.

At the suggestion of Dr. Cattell a pharmacological study was done in the Department of Pharmacology of Cornell Medical School by Dr. S. Loewe. Dr. W. Modell collaborated in this work. We are indebted to Dr. Roger Adams, Professor of Chemistry at the University of Illinois, and to Dr. H. J.

Wollner, Consulting Chemist of the United States Treasury Department, who supplied some of the active principles of marihuana which were used in the study.

The names of those who conducted the investigations are given under the different chapters. Those sections of the report for which no author is indicated have been written by the Chairman of the Committee.

The tremendous task of compiling, editing, and revising the reports was undertaken by Dr. George B. Wallace, the chairman of the Committee, and Miss Elizabeth V. Cunningham of the staff of the Committee on Public Health Relations of The New York Academy of Medicine. They had the assistance of Dr. Dudley D. Shoenfeld, who prepared the sociological report; Dr. David Wechsler, who revised the psychological reports, and Dr. McKeen Cattell, who edited the pharmacological report.

In the judgment of the Committee, this painstaking study should be of considerable value from a scientific and social viewpoint.

THE SOCIOLOGICAL STUDY

Dudley D. Shoenfeld, MD

Introduction

In order to understand fully the purpose and scope of this particular part of the survey conducted by the Mayor's Committee on Marihuana, a brief digest of the history of the growth and usage of this drug is essential.

Indian hemp, from which marihuana (the American synonym for hashish) is obtained, has been known to man for more than three thousand years. This plant, although originally indigenous to Central Asia, is now found in practically every section of the world, growing either wild or cultivated, legally or illegally.

When originally discovered, the use to which this plant was principally put was the conversion of its fiber for commerical purposes in the production of cord, twine and textiles. Shortly thereafter its pharmaceutical properties were employed in the practice of medicine and surgery. Authoritative proof is available that the Chinese found it valuable as an effective anesthetic in surgery as far back as two thousand years. It was not until approximately the tenth century that the peoples of Africa and Asia began to use it in a rather indiscriminate manner for its intoxicating effects.

Very shortly after its usage became popular, this drug engaged the attention of the various African and Asian governments, as well as of lay persons interested in medical, religious and sociological problems. Some of these very early investigators propounded the theory that physical and mental deterioration was the direct result of smoking hashish. Others extolled its benefits, deeming it actually essential to life, and urged people to indulge in it.

During this early period, the peoples of Europe were aware of the use of hashish in Africa and Asia, and considered it a vice particularly common to the peoples of those continents. In the nineteenth century their interest was raised to a high pitch because of the fictional reports of the smoking of hashish given by the romanticists of that period.

These individuals, who had the power of the pen, experimentally indulged in the smoking of hashish, and described in an expansive, subjective manner the effects the drug had upon them. A review of the fanciful literature reveals that in most instances these writings referred to the authors' experiences with toxic doses. Summed up, the conclusions were that hashish could cause psychotic episodes and even death and that prolonged use would result in physical and mental deterioration. The exalted position held by these romanticists tended to influence the Europeans to accept their conclusions as scientific monographs on the subject of hashish, so that the smoking of hashish did not become popular with them. However, in recent years there has been a fairly wide participation on the part of Europeans in smoking hashish or marihuana, but it is referred to as an American vice. This allows one to infer that whereas the knowledge pertaining to this habit was very early recognized in Europe, at the present time participation in it is from their point of view the direct result of its introduction into Europe not from Africa and Asia, but from America.

In America, Indian hemp was planted in the New England colonies, solely for commercial purposes, as early as the seventeenth century. At the present time it can be found growing either wild or cultivated, legally or illegally, in practically all our states. Lawful cultivation is confined principally to the states of Kentucky, Illinois, Minnesota, and Wisconsin. It has been estimated that not more than ten thousand acres are devoted to its legal production. It is of value commercially in the manufacture of rope, twine, and textiles. The seed is used for bird-food, and the oil extracted from the seed is occasionally used as a substitute for linseed oil in the preparation of artists' paints. A rosin extracted from the plant is used in the production of pharmaceutical preparations.

Since the history of hemp cultivation in America dates back to the seventeenth century, it is exceedingly interesting, but difficult to explain, that the smoking of marihuana did not become a problem in our country until approximately twenty years ago, and that it has become an acute problem associated with a great deal of publicity only in the past ten years.

The origin of the word "marihuana" is in doubt. Some authorities are of the opinion that it is derived from the Portuguese word "mariguano," meaning intoxicant. Others are of the opinion that it has its derivation in the Mexican words for "Mary and Jane." The introduction into the United States of the practice of smoking marihuana has been the subject of a great deal of speculation. The most tenable hypothesis at the present time is that it was introduced by Mexicans entering our country.

It is accepted that in Mexico marihuana smoking is an old, established practice. Therefore, it would appear logical to assume that Mexican laborers crossing our border into the Southwest carried this practice with them. Having used marihuana in their native land, they found it natural to continue smoking it in the new country, and planted it for personal consumption. Once available, it was soon made use of by our citizens. At the present time, the smoking of marihuana is widespread in this nation.

Believing that marihuana smoking might be deleterious, and knowing it to be widespread, federal and municipal governments, private individuals, and such agencies as the Opium Advisory Association, the International Narcotic Education Association, and others investigated the subject. These investigative organizations have contributed a great deal of data and pertinent information to the knowledge of the use of marihuana.

The mass of information so obtained when untangled can be summed up with the general statement that a majority of investigators are of the opinion that marihuana smoking is deleterious, although a minority maintain that it is innocuous. The majority believe that marihuana smoking is widespread among school children; that the dispensers of the drug are organized to such an extent that they encourage the use of marihuana in order to create an ever-increasing market; that juvenile delinquency is directly related to the effects of the drug; that it is a causative factor in a large percentage of our major crimes and sexual offenses; and that physical and mental deterioration are the direct result of the prolonged habit of smoking marihuana.

As a result of these official and semi-official conclusions in regard to the disastrous effects produced by this habit, the newspapers and magazines of our country have given it wide publicity. At this point it may be profitable to give the conclusions of some of the investigators and quote the publicity associated with it.

In a pamphlet "Marihuana or Indian Hemp and Its Preparations" issued by the International Narcotic Education Association, one finds:

Marihuana is a most virile and powerful stimulant. The physiological effect of this drug produces a peculiar psychic exaltation and derangement of the central nervous system. The stage of exaltation and confusion, more marked in some addicts than in others, is generally followed by a stage of depression.

Sometimes the subject passes into a semi-conscious state, experiencing vivid and extravagant dreams which vary according to the individual character and mentality. In some the stage is one of self-satisfaction and well-being. In others, it is alarming, presenting the fear of some imminent and indefinite danger or of impending death. Later the dreams are sometimes followed by a state of complete unconsciousness. Sometimes convulsive attacks and acute mania are developed.

The narcotic content in marihuana decreases the rate of heart beat and causes irregularity of the pulse. Death may result from the effect upon the heart.

Prolonged use of marihuana frequently develops a delirious rage which sometimes leads to high crimes, such as assault and murder. Hence marihuana has been called the "killer drug." The habitual use of this narcotic poison always causes a very marked mental deterioration and sometimes produces insanity. Hence marihuana is frequently called "loco weed." (Loco is the Spanish word for crazy.)

While the marihuana habit leads to physical wreckage and mental decay, its effects upon character and morality are even more devastating. The victim frequently undergoes such degeneracy that he will lie and steal without scruple; he becomes utterly untrustworthy and often drifts into the underworld where, with his degenerate companions, he commits high crimes and misdemeanors. Marihuana sometimes gives man the lust to kill unreasonably and without motive. Many cases of assault, rape, robbery, and murder are traced to the use of marihuana.[1]

1 International Narcotic Education Association. "Marihuana or Indian Hemp and Its Preparations." Los Angeles, 1936.

In an article published in the *New York Daily Worker,* New York, Saturday, December 28, 1940, there appeared under the column headed "HEALTH ADVICE":

A DRUG AND INSANITY.

Bill Wilson was strolling by his favorite soda joint on the way home from high school when he heard a familiar voice whisper loudly, "Hey, Bill, c'mere." Behind the Texaco billboard, he found his side-kick Jim, who said excitedly, "I got some reefers!" "Reefers, what're they?" Mysteriously, Jim reached into his pocket and pulled out two large cigarettes. "Marihuana!" Jim's pupils dilated. "Come on over to the club and we'll smoke 'em. Boy, that's fun!"

Bill is only one of thousands of new marihuana smokers created yearly among boys and girls of high school age. What is this drug? It is a narcotic in the same class as opium and is derived from a plant, which grows wild, extensively in some parts. For this reason, it is hard to control and the drug is easy to obtain at very little cost.

Smoking of the weed is habit-forming. It destroys the willpower, releases restraints, and promotes insane reactions. Continued use causes the face to become bloated, the eyes bloodshot, the limbs weak and trembling, and the mind sinks into insanity. Robberies, thrill murders, sex crimes and other offenses result.

When the habit is first started, the symptoms are milder, yet powerful enough. The smoker loses all sense of time and space so that he can't judge distances, he loses his self-control, and his imagination receives considerable stimulation.

The habit can be cured only by the most severe methods. The addict must be put into an institution, where the drug is gradually withdrawn, his general health is built up, and he is kept there until he has enough willpower to withstand the temptation to again take to the weed.

The spread of this terrible fad can be stopped only when the unscrupulous criminals trafficking in the drug are rooted out.

Dr. Robert P. Walton, Professor of Pharmacology of the School of Medicine of the University of Mississippi, has written a most comprehensive book on the subject of marihuana, embodying in detail pharmacological and social studies.[2] A chapter on the "Present Status of the Marihuana Vice in the United States" was prepared by Dr. Frank R. Gomila, Commissioner of Public Safety of New Orleans, and C. G. Lambou,

2 Walton, R. P. *Marihuana: America's New Drug Problem.* J. B. Lippincott Co., Philadelphia, 1938.

Assistant City Chemist. They refer to New Orleans as being possibly the first large city in the United States where the drug habit became widely established among the native population, and they therefore believe that the authorities in this city had a decided opportunity to observe the progress of the smoking of marihuana as a social problem. Referring specifically to the use of marihuana among school children, they state that reporters in New Orleans not only heard about but observed large numbers of boys of school age actually buying and smoking marihuana cigarettes. One peddler was so brazen as to keep his stock under the street stairs to a girls' high school.

Inquiries further revealed that school children of forty-four schools in New Orleans (only a few of these were high schools) smoked marihuana. As a result of exposure and widespread agitation,

> Verifications came in by the hundreds from harassed parents, teachers, neighborhood pastors, priests, welfare workers and club women. Warrington House for boys was full of children who had become habituated to the use of cannabis. The superintendent of the Children's Bureau reported that there were many problem children there who had come under the influence and two who had run away because they couldn't get their "muggles" at the Bureau. The Director of Kingsley House for boys received many pleas from fathers of boys who had come under the influence and were charged with petty crimes. After personally seeing these boys in an hysterical condition or on the well-known "laughing jags," the director termed the situation decidedly grave. The Waif's Home, at this time, was reputedly full of children, both white and colored, who had been brought in under the influence of the drug. Marihuana cigarettes could be bought almost as readily as sandwiches. Their cost was two for a quarter. The children solved the problem of cost by pooling pennies among the members of a group and then passing the cigarettes from one to another, all the puffs being carefully counted. . . .
>
> The result of these investigations ended in a wholesale arrest of more than 150 persons. Approximately one hundred underworld dives, soft-drink establishments, night clubs, grocery stores, and private homes were searched in the police raid. Addicts, hardened criminals, gangsters, women of the streets, sailors of all nationalities, bootleggers, boys and girls—many flashily dressed in silks and furs, others in working clothes—all were rounded up in the net which Captain Smith and his squad had set.
>
> . . . Notwithstanding the thoroughness with which this police roundup was carried out, it did not entirely eradicate in one stroke a vice which had already become so well estab-

lished. During the next few years New Orleans experienced a crime wave which unquestionably was greatly aggravated by the influence of this drug habit. Payroll and bank guards were doubled, but this did not prevent some of the most spectacular holdups in the history of the city. Youngsters known to be "muggle-heads" fortified themselves with the narcotic and proceeded to shoot down police, bank clerks and casual bystanders. Mr. Eugene Stanley, at that time District Attorney, declared that many of the crimes in New Orleans and the South were thus committed by criminals who relied on the drug to give them a false courage and freedom from restraint. Dr. George Roeling, Coroner, reported that of 450 prisoners investigated, 125 were confirmed users of marihuana. Dr. W. B. Graham, State Narcotic Officer, declared in 1936 that 60 per cent of the crimes committed in New Orleans were by marihuana users.[3]

The Mayor's Committee on Marihuana decided to confine its investigations to a limited area. For a number of reasons the Borough of Manhattan seemed to be the most profitable section of the city in which to concentrate. In order to crystallize our particular project we deemed it advisable to direct our efforts to finding answers to the following questions:

1. To what extent is marihuana used?
2. What is the method of retail distribution?
3. What is the general attitude of the marihuana smoker toward society and toward the use of the drug?
4. What is the relationship between marihuana and eroticism?
5. What is the relationship between marihuana and crime?
6. What is the relationship between marihuana and juvenile delinquency?

In the course of our investigations, we have made extensive use of subjective data obtained from those who were actual smokers of marihuana and directly acquainted with its effects and those who were not smokers, but, because of residence, occupation or other interests, were acquainted with the general subject.

Organization of Staff

In October 1939 Police Commissioner Lewis J. Valentine designated Deputy Chief Inspector Daniel Curtayne, Lieutenant Edward Cooper, Sergeant Bernard Boylan and Detective

3 *Ibid.*

Joseph Loures of the Narcotic Squad of the Police Department of the City of New York to cooperate with the Mayor's Committee on Marihuana. These police officials submitted a list of intelligent young officers with a suitable background. From this list, six officers were selected: two policewomen, and four policemen, one of whom was a Negro. They were: Mr. James Coen, Mr. William Connolly, Mr. Benjamin Weissner, Mr. John Hughes, Miss Adelaide Knowles and Miss Olive Cregan. These police officers were encouraged to read literature on the subject of marihuana and to familiarize themselves with some of the characteristics of the plant, as well as of marihuana cigarettes. They became expert in detecting the aroma of burning marihuana, and were thus able to recognize it and to identify its use in a social gathering.

Regular assignments were made by the director of the survey. At intervals each officer dictated a general report on his activities and findings to a stenographer engaged by the Committee. Frequent conferences were held in the office of the director of the survey, at which time individual reports were discussed in detail and evaluated. An attempt was made to give the "marihuana squad" a psychological approach to the performance of their duties.

At no time were these officers permitted to make known their activity to other members of the police force, or to make arrests. This arrangement was considered essential in order that they might maintain an effective role of investigator without being in any respect recognized as police officers. Although they were members of the police force and constantly in contact with violators of law, their immediate superiors cooperated to an extreme degree by allowing the "marihuana squad" to report directly to the director of the survey.

While on duty the squad actually "lived" in the environment in which marihuana smoking or peddling was suspected. They frequented poolrooms, bars and grills, dime-a-dance halls, other dance halls to which they took their own partners, theatres—backstage and in the audience—roller-skating rinks, subways, public toilets, parks and docks. They consorted with the habitués of these places, chance acquaintances on the street, loiterers around schools, subways and bus terminals. They posed as "suckers" from out of town and as students in colleges and high schools.

We highly commend these officers individually for their exceptionally good performances. The aid given by Deputy Chief Inspector Daniel Curtayne, Lieutenant Edward Cooper, Sergeant Bernard Boylan and Detective Joseph Loures throughout deserves mention and appreciation. At times we must have been a source of annoyance to them, but our requests were always cheerfully met and assistance heartily extended.

Method of Retail Distribution

In general, marihuana is used in the form of a cigarette. Occasionally some individuals chew the "weed" and seem to get the same effect as do others through smoking. The common names for the cigarettes are: muggles, reefers, Indian hemp, weed, tea, gage and sticks. Cigarettes made of marihuana differ in size as do cigarettes made of tobacco: they are long, short, thick or thin.

The price varies in accordance with the accepted opinion as to the potency of the marihuana used in the cigarettes, and this appears to be determined by the place of origin. The cheapest brand is known as "sass-fras," and retails for approximately three for 50 cents. It is made of the marihuana that is grown in the United States. Smokers do not consider such marihuana very potent. They have found that they must consume a greater number of cigarettes in order to obtain the desired effect colloquially termed as "high." This opinion, expressed by smokers in the Borough of Manhattan, is at variance with that of some authorities who believe that marihuana grown in the United States is as potent as the marihuana grown in other countries.

The "panatella" cigarette, occasionally referred to as "meserole," is considered to be more potent than the "sass-fras" and usually retails for approximately 25 cents each. The hemp from which the "panatella" is made comes from Central and South America.

"Gungeon" is considered by the marihuana smoker as the highest grade of marihuana. It retails for about one dollar per cigarette. The "kick" resulting from the use of this cigarette is reached more quickly than from the use of "sass-fras" or "panatella." It appears to be the consensus that the marihuana used to make the "gungeon" comes from Africa. The sale of this cigarette is restricted to a clientele whose economic status is of a higher level than the majority of marihuana smokers.

A confirmed marihuana user can readily distinguish the quality and potency of various brands, just as the habitual cigarette or cigar smoker is able to differentiate between the qualities of tobacco. Foreign-made cigarette paper is often used in order to convince the buyer that the "tea is right from the boat."

There are two channels for the distribution of marihuana cigarettes—the independent peddler and the "tea-pad." From general observations, conversations with "pad" owners, and discussions with peddlers, the investigators estimated that there were about 500 "tea-pads" in Harlem and at least 500 peddlers.

A "tea-pad" is a room or an apartment in which people gather to smoke marihuana. The majority of such places are located in the Harlem district. It is our impression that the landlord, the agent, the superintendent or the janitor is aware of the purposes for which the premises are rented.

The "tea-pad" is furnished according to the clientele it expects to serve. Usually, each "tea-pad" has comfortable furniture, a radio, victrola or, as in most instances, a rented nickelodeon. The lighting is more or less uniformly dim, with blue predominating. An incense is considered part of the furnishings. The walls are frequently decorated with pictures of nude subjects suggestive of perverted sexual practices. The furnishings, as described, are believed to be essential as a setting for those participating in smoking marihuana.

Most "tea-pads" have their trade restricted to the sale of marihuana. Some places did sell marihuana and whisky, and a few places also served as houses of prostitution. Only one "tea-pad" was found which served as a house of prostitution, and in which one could buy marihuana, whisky, and opium.

The marihuana smoker derives greater satisfaction if he is smoking in the presence of others. His attitude in the "tea-pad" is that of a relaxed individual, free from the anxieties and cares of the realities of life. The "tea-pad" takes on the atmosphere of a very congenial social club. The smoker readily engages in conversation with strangers, discussing freely his pleasant reactions to the drug and philosophizing on subjects pertaining to life in a manner which, at times, appears to be out of keeping with his intellectual level. A constant observation was the extreme willingness to share and puff on each other's cigarettes. A boisterous, rowdy atmosphere did not prevail and on the rare occasions when there appeared signs indicative of a belligerent attitude on the part of a smoker, he was ejected or forced to become more tolerant and quiescent. One of the most interesting setups of a "tea-pad," which was clearly not along orthodox lines from the business point of view, was a series of pup tents arranged on a roof-top in Harlem. Those present proceeded to smoke their cigarettes in the tents. When the desired effect of the drug had been obtained they all merged into the open and engaged in a discussion of their admiration of the stars and the beauties of nature.

Because of the possibility of spreading disease, note should be taken of what seems to be a custom known as "pick-up" smoking. It is an established practice whereby a marihuana cigarette is lit and after one or two inhalations is passed on to the next person. This procedure is repeated until all present have had an opportunity to take a puff or two on the cigarette.

Occasionally a "tea-pad" owner may have peddlers who sell their wares in other localities and at the same time serve as procurers for those who wish to smoke marihuana on the premises.

One also finds other methods of retail distribution. After proper introduction, one may be able to purchase the cigarette in certain places. This is not an easy procedure, but it can be accomplished. In some bar-and-grills, restaurants, and bars our investigators were able to establish contact with someone who, in turn, would introduce them to a peddler who apparently made regular rounds of these places in order to sell cigarettes. It appears that the owners of such places are not aware of this practice, and in many instances they would discharge any employee known to be directly or indirectly associated with the sale of marihuana.

On rare occasions public guides, if properly approached would refer one to a place where the "reefer" could be bought. There was no evidence that the guide received money when acting as go-between. Terminal porters, mainly Negroes, appeared to be more directly connected with the traffic of marihuana. They were more conversant with the subject and it was easier for them to establish contact between purchaser and peddler.

Marihuana smoking is very common in the theatres of Harlem according to the observations of the investigators. We have reason to believe that in some instances, perhaps few in number, employees actually sold cigarettes on the premises. In the Harlem dance halls smoking was frequently observed either in the lavatories or on the main floor. The patrons as well as the musicians were seen in the act of smoking. There was no evidence of sales being made by employees on the premises, or that there was any gain on the part of the owners or employees in permitting this practice. Whereas the smoking of marihuana was not encouraged, nothing was done to prohibit such practice.

There are specific sections in the Borough of Manhattan where the sale of marihuana cigarettes appears to be localized: 1) the Harlem district; 2) the Broadway area, a little east and west of Broadway and extending from 42nd Street to 59th Street. While it is true that one may buy the cigarette in other districts, it is not as easily obtainable as in the two localities mentioned.

The Mental Attitude of the Marihuana Smoker Toward Society and Marihuana

Most of the smokers of marihuana coming within the scope of our survey were unemployed, and of the others most had part-time employment.

Occasional, as well as confirmed, users were all aware of the laws pertaining to the illegal use of the drug. They did not indulge in its use with a spirit of braggadocio or as a challenge to law as has been reported by some investigators in other districts. They did not express remorse concerning their use of marihuana, nor did they blame this habit as a causative factor in the production of special difficulties in their personal lives. Except for musicians there appeared to be no attempt at secretiveness on the part of the habitual smoker. This attitude is in marked contrast to that usually taken by those addicted to morphine, cocaine, or heroin.

The consensus of marihuana users is that the drug is not harmful and that infrequent or constant use of marihuana does not result in physical or mental deterioration.

In describing the most common reaction to the drug they always stated that it made them feel "high." Elaboration of just what the smoker meant by "high" varied with the individual. However, there was common agreement that a feeling of adequacy and efficiency was induced by the use of marihuana and that current mental conflicts were allayed. Organic illness was not given as a cause for smoking "reefers."

A person may be a confirmed smoker for a prolonged period, and give up the drug voluntarily without experiencing any craving for it or exhibiting withdrawal symptoms. He may, at some time later on, go back to its use. Others may remain infrequent users of the cigarette, taking one or two a week, or only when the "social setting" calls for participation. From time to time we had one of our investigators associate with a marihuana user. The investigator would bring up the subject of smoking. This would invariably lead to the suggestion that they obtain some marihuana cigarettes. They would seek a "tea-pad," and if it was closed the smoker and our investigator would calmly resume their previous activity, such as the discussion of life in general or the playing of pool. There were apparently no signs indicative of frustration in the smoker at not being able to gratify the desire for the drug. We consider this point highly significant since it is so contrary to the experience of users of other narcotics. A similar situation occurring in one addicted to the use of morphine, cocaine, or heroin would result in a compulsive attitude on the part of the addict to obtain the drug.

If unable to secure it, there would be obvious physical and mental manifestations of frustration. This may be considered presumptive evidence that there is no true addiction in the medical sense associated with the use of marihuana.

The confirmed marihuana smoker consumes perhaps from six to ten cigarettes per day. He appears to be quite conscious of the quantity he requires to reach the effect called "high." Once the desired effect is obtained he cannot be persuaded to consume more. He knows when he has had enough. The smoker determines for himself the point of being "high," and is ever-conscious of preventing himself from becoming "too high." This fear of being "too high" must be associated with some form of anxiety which causes the smoker, should he accidentally reach that point, immediately to institute measures so that he can "come down." It has been found that the use of such beverages as beer, or a sweet soda pop, is an effective measure. Smokers insist that "it does something to the stomach" and that it is always associated with "belching." A cold shower will also have the effect of bringing the person "down."

Smokers have repeatedly stated that the consumption of whisky while smoking negates the potency of the drug. They find it is very difficult to get "high" while drinking whisky, and because of that smokers will not drink whisky while using the "weed." They do, however, consume large quantities of sweet wines. It is their contention that this mild alcoholic beverage aids the drug in producing the desired effect. Most marihuana smokers insist that the appetite is increased as the result of smoking.

We have been unable to confirm the opinion expressed by some investigators that marihuana smoking is the first step in the use of such drugs as cocaine, morphine, and heroin. The instances are extremely rare where the habit of marihuana smoking is associated with addiction to these other narcotics.

Marihuana and Eroticism

In the popular agitation against the use of marihuana, its erotic effects have been stressed repeatedly. As previously stated in this report, our investigators visited many "tea-pads" in the Borough of Manhattan. It is true that lewd pictures decorated the walls but they did not find that they were attracting attention or comment among the clientele. In fact one of the investigators who was concentrating his attention on the relation between marihuana and eroticism stated in his report that he found himself embarrassed in that he was the only one who examined the pictures on the wall.

Numerous conversations with smokers of marihuana revealed only occasional instances in which there was any relation between the drug and eroticism. At one time one of our investigators attended a very intimate social gathering in an apartment in Harlem, having succeeded in securing the position of doorman for the occasion. There was a great deal of drinking, and the dancing was of the most modern, abandoned, "jitter-bug" type. This form of dancing is highly suggestive and appears to be associated with erotic activity. The investigator made careful observation of those who were dancing, and found that there was no difference between the ones who were and the ones who were not smoking "reefers." Similar impressions were received after careful observations in public dance halls, places where they knew that some persons were under the influence of marihuana.

Visits to brothels which occasionally also served as "tea-pads" revealed that the use of marihuana was not linked to sexuality. These observations allow us to come to the conclusion that in the main marihuana was not used for direct sexual stimulation.

Crime

One of the most important causes of the widespread publicity which marihuana smoking has received is the belief that this practice is directly responsible for the commission of crimes.

During our investigation many law enforcement officers, representing various federal, state and local police bureaus, were interviewed and asked for a confidential expression of opinion on the general question of crime and marihuana. In most instances they unhesitatingly stated that there is no proof that major crimes are associated with the practice of smoking marihuana. They did state that many marihuana smokers are guilty of petty crimes, but that the criminal career usually existed prior to the time the individual smoked his first marihuana cigarette. These officers further stated that a criminal generally termed as a "real" or "professional" criminal will not associate with marihuana smokers. He considers such a person inferior and unreliable and will not allow him to participate in the commission of a major crime.

In the period beginning October 1939 and ending November 1940, the Police Department made 167 arrests for the possession and use of marihuana. Classified according to race they were: white, 33 men, 4 women; Latin-American, 26 men, 2 women; Negro, 83 men, 6 women; Latin-American (colored)

9 men, 1 woman; British East Indies 1; Filipino 1; Chinese 1.

Classified according to age, 12 per cent were between the ages of 16 and 20, 58 per cent between the ages of 21 and 30, 24 per cent between the ages of 31 and 40, and 6 per cent between the ages of 41 and 50.

During the period under discussion, the Police Department confiscated approximately 3,000 pounds of marihuana.

The sale and use of marihuana is a problem engaging the vigilance of the New York Police Department. However, the number of officers available for such duty is limited. Officers specifically assigned to the Narcotics Division of the Police Department are acquainted with the problem, but the majority of the officers are fundamentally without authoritative knowledge regarding this subject.

The relation between marihuana smoking and the commission of crimes of violence in the city of New York is described by Dr. Walter Bromberg, psychiatrist-in-charge of the Psychiatric Clinic of the Court of General Sessions, in an article published in the *Journal of the American Medical Association:*

In the south of this country (New Orleans) the incidence of marihuana addicts among major criminals is admittedly high. Sporadic reports from elsewhere in the country of murders and assaults due to marihuana appear in the press frequently. It is difficult to evaluate these statements, because of their uncritical nature. The bulletin prepared by the Foreign Policy Association lists ten cases "culled at random from the files of the U.S. Bureau of Narcotics" of murder and atrocious assault in which marihuana was directly responsible for the crime. Among the ten patients, the second, J. O., was described as having confessed how he murdered a friend and put his body in a trunk while under the influence of marihuana.

J. O. was examined in this clinic; although he was a psychopathic liar and possibly homosexual, there was no indication in the examination or history of the use of any drug. The investigation by the probation department failed to indicate use of the drug marihuana. The deceased, however, was addicted to heroin.

Our observations with respect to marihuana and crime were made in the Court of General Sessions over a period of five and a half years. The material in that court is limited as to residence to New York County, although it must be remembered that the offenders come from many sections of the country and are of many racial types. This is important, because the British investigators have noted in India that cannabis does not bring out the motor excitement or hysterical symptoms in Anglo-Saxon users that occur in natives. There are several other difficulties in collecting reliable material, one being the complete dependence on the history and statements of the prisoners without an opportunity for objective tests or other corroborative check, as in the case of other drugs, e.g., heroin or morphine. During routine interviews of some 17,000 offenders in six and a half years, several hundred have been found who had direct experience with marihuana. Their testimony checks with experimental results and clinical experiences with regard to the symptoms of intoxication, the absence of true addiction, and the negative connection with major crime. Especially is this noteworthy among sexual offenders and in cases of assault or murder. The extravagant claims of defense attorneys and the press that crime is caused by addiction to marihuana demands careful scrutiny, at least in this jurisdiction. . . .

Most of the narcotic cases in New York County are heard in the Court of Special Sessions, where misdemeanants are handled and where indictments on charges of the possession of drugs for use are returned. In the Court of Special Sessions in the same six-year period, of approximately 75,000 indictments for all crimes, 6,000 resulted in convictions for the possession and use of drugs. Since neither the law, the district attorney nor the police department makes any distinction between the several kinds of narcotics in arraignments or indictments, there were no figures from which to estimate the number of users of marihuana as distinguished from the number of users of other drugs. A system of sampling the 6,000 cases was therefore adopted in order to furnish an approximate estimate of the total number of marihuana users who came into conflict with the law.

In this sampling the records of 1,500 offenders, or 25 per cent of the 6,000, were examined. Of these, 135 were charged in connection with marihuana. From this fact it was estimated that about 540 offenders, or 9 per cent of all drug offenders coming to the Court of Special Sessions in six years, were users of marihuana. In analyzing this sample of 135 cases, it was found that 93 offenders had no previous record, the previous charges or charges of 8 concerned only drugs, 5 had records including drug charges and 29 had records not including drug charges. Among those with longer records, that is, from four to seven previous arrests, none showed progression from the use of drugs to other crimes.

As measured by the succession of arrests and convictions in the Court of General Sessions (the only method of estimation) it can be said that drugs generally do not initiate criminal careers. Similarly, in the Court of Special Sessions, only 8 per cent of the offenders had previous charges of using drugs and 3.7 per cent had previous charges of drugs and other petty crimes. In the vast majority of cases in this group of 135, then, the earlier use of marihuana apparently did not predispose to crime, even that of using other drugs. Whether the first offenders charged with the use of marihuana go on to major crime is a matter of speculation. The expectancy of major crimes following the use of cannabis in New York County is small, according to these experiences.[4]

Marihuana and School Children

One of the most serious accusations leveled against marihuana by special feature writers has been that it is widely used by the school children of this nation. These authors have claimed that it has so detrimental an effect on development that it is a major factor in juvenile delinquency. This phase of the marihuana problem was deemed serious enough to merit primary consideration in our study of the marihuana problem in New York City—specifically in the Borough of Manhattan. We decided to attack this aspect of the problem along the following lines:

1. To observe schools in order to see if pupils bought marihuana cigarettes from any peddlers operating in the neighborhood.

2. To investigate thoroughly complaints made by parents to school and police authorities relative to marihuana and its use by school children.

3. To interview principals, assistant principals, and teachers of many of the schools in New York City with reference to our project.

4. To gather relevant statistics from various city bureaus and private agencies.

Unknown to the school authorities, our investigators had under surveillance many of the schools in the Borough of Manhattan. They would observe a particular school for a number of consecutive days, watch loiterers and suspicious characters in the locality, and, under certain circumstances, follow some of the children. This procedure was repeated at varying intervals in different localities. From time to time the investigators would return to some of the schools which they previously had kept under surveillance. Attention was naturally concentrated upon those schools from which emanated the most numerous complaints and which were located

4 Bromberg, W. "Marihuana: a psychiatric study." *J.A.M.A. 113:* 4, 1939.

in suspected neighborhoods. We must admit that it would have been possible for such sales to have taken place during the time that our investigators were not on duty, but we came to the conclusion that there was no organized traffic on the part of peddlers in selling marihuana cigarettes to the children of the schools we observed.

Certain of the school authorities deserve special commendation for their alertness in singling out suspicious characters loitering in the vicinity of their schools. While investigating one of the suspected schools, our investigators who were loitering in the neighborhood were suspected and treated as "suspicious characters" by the school authorities.

During the period of this survey the Police Department, while engaged in an entirely separate criminal investigation, received a lead indicating the sale of marihuana to children in a certain high school. As a result, one pupil was arrested and convicted for selling cigarettes to his classmates.

In the Harlem district we discovered a few places where school children gathered during and after school hours for the purpose of indulging in smoking ordinary cigarettes, drinking alcoholic beverages, and engaging in homosexual and heterosexual activities. One of our investigators, having gained entrance to such a place, ostentatiously displayed marihuana cigarettes which he had with him. The madam of the place promptly cautioned him against using the "weed" and insisted that at no time did she permit any person to smoke it on her premises.

A surprising number of school children smoking ordinary cigarettes were noted. A checkup revealed that these cigarettes were being illicitly sold by men on the street and in candy stores in the "loose" form. It is possible that this trade in ordinary cigarettes is occasionally misinterpreted as trade in "reefers."

Interviews with school authorities were very significant, and it is of value to summarize briefly some of the statements actually made by them. The locations of the schools and the names of the persons quoted are in our official files.

1) High School. Predominantly white. The principal stated, "The school has never had any connection with marihuana, not even a rumor."

2) High School. Predominantly white. The principal at first appeared to be evasive and did not readily volunteer information, but after repeatedly being pressed with the question stated that the school "had not had any difficulty with the subject of marihuana."

3) High School. Predominantly white. The principal em-

phatically stated, "I have had no trouble with marihuana in my school."

4) A vocational school in the Borough of Queens. Mixed. "I have never heard the slightest thing about marihuana in connection with this school."

5) High School. Queens. Mixed. "We never had the slightest connection with marihuana in any way."

6) Junior High School. Harlem. Predominantly Negro and Latin-American. The principal stated that there had been a few marihuana cases among the boys about eighteen months ago. His assistant volunteered the information that there had been some boys in the school who had "reefers" in their possession. On other occasions some of the boys appeared to be intoxicated and when examined confessed to having smoked "reefers." He further stated, "It was difficult to be sure if sleepy, perspiring, pallid-looking boys were feeling the effects of marihuana or were just recovering from too much 'partying' or drinking." He volunteered the opinion that since marihuana was an acute problem among the adult population in that particular district, it could be assumed that marihuana could occasionally become a problem in the school.

7) Junior High School. White and Latin-American. On the fringe of Harlem. Principal and assistant principal stated that they have never had the slightest difficulty arising from marihuana.

8) Junior High School. White and Negro. Bordering on Harlem. The principal, because of his short tenure of office, was unable to express his opinion on the subject. The chief clerk stated that marihuana had never been a problem in the school. She was certain, however, that it was sold in the neighborhood.

9) Junior High School. White, with a high percentage of Negro and Latin-American. The principal stated, "As yet we have had no contact with marihuana although, considering the neighborhood, it would not be unlikely."

10) Junior High School. Latin-American, Negro, and some white. The principal stated, "We have had no trouble with marihuana." He was of the opinion that because of the locality it would be possible for some older boys to smoke it without anybody being cognizant of it. He added that he would let us know if any boys were detected smoking. During the period of the survey no such report was made.

11) Junior High School. Latin-American predominating. The principal stated that she had not had any trouble with marihuana.

12) Junior High School. White predominating. The prin-

cipal stated, "I have had no contact with it." However, due to the location of the school, which was near Harlem, she stated she would notify the Juvenile Aid Bureau if such a problem arose. During the period of the survey no such report was received.

13) Junior High School. White. The principal stated that no information concerning the use of any narcotics had ever come to his attention and was equally insistent that teachers would have reported any such information to him.

14) Junior High School. White. The principal stated that she had never found anything to indicate the use of any drug in the school.

15) Junior High School. White and mixed. The principal stated that last year he had suspected that a group of chronic truants were using marihuana but he was unable to obtain any direct evidence.

16) Junior High School. White. The principal and his assistant stated that they had no real evidence of any marihuana problem in the school, and they do not believe that the drug is used to any extent.

17) Junior High School. White. The principal stated that although she had no tangible evidence of marihuana smoking among the students, she has problem groups that gather in premises where she is inclined to think that marihuana could be obtained if they wished to get it. She is certain no marihuana is used in the school itself. We investigated thoroughly the suggestions made by the principal as to premises where marihuana might be sold but we were unable to gather any evidence of its sale.

18) Junior High School. White. The acting principal and a teacher in the school who had been there for a number of years stated that there had never been any evidence of the use of marihuana or any other drugs in the school.

19) Junior High School. White. The health director of this school stated that any evidence concerning the use of narcotics by pupils would have been called to his attention, but none had been.

20) Junior High School. White. The authorities stated that there had been no traces of marihuana smoking.

21) Junior High School. White. The authorities stated that there had never been the slightest suggestion of marihuana smoking in the school.

22) Junior High School. White. The assistant principal stated that he knew of no marihuana problem in the school.

23) Junior High School. White. The principal stated that because of the publicity given to marihuana smoking she had

been on the alert to discover indications of its use in her school but had found no evidence of marihuana in the school or of anything that would lead her to believe that any one of her students used marihuana outside of the school.

24) Junior High School. White. The principal stated that nothing pertaining to the use of narcotics had been reported to him in all the years he had been there.

25) High School. Predominantly white. Authorities, including the medical department, stated that no student had ever been reported for being under the influence of marihuana.

26) High School. Predominantly white. The principal stated, "There is no indication of a marihuana problem in the school."

27) Grammar School. The principal stated that anonymous letters had been received from time to time from pupils in the school in reference to marihuana. One letter was actually signed by a pupil of the school, who reported the sale of marihuana in a candy store in the vicinity. The principal withheld the name of the pupil but requested us to investigate the report. We kept this school, the immediate neighborhood, and all candy stores in the vicinity under strict surveillance, but were unable to gather any evidence which would indicate that the pupils of this school were obtaining marihuana.

28) Junior High School. Negro. Queens. The assistant principal stated that he had never heard anything about marihuana being a problem in his school. We had received a complaint about this school and one of our investigators had an informal chat with one of the teachers of this school who, because of her interest in the school children, appeared to be more conversant than anyone else with general problems at the school. She stated that she was certain marihuana was used by some of the students. She elaborated on the subject and recalled that a few months prior to the interview she had sent home five students (three Negroes and two Italians) whom she had noticed acting "dopey" in the classroom after the noon recess. She was not positive they were under the influence of marihuana but was fairly certain that they were under the influence of some drug. A student had told her that these boys used "reefers" and, noticing their stupor, she had concluded that they were under the influence of marihuana. Superficial examination showed her that their condition was not due to drinking whisky or any alcoholic beverage.

In this school it was not necessary to notify the principal if a student was sent home. The teacher did so on her own account, arriving at a diagnosis without informing the principal of the condition. There was no doctor or nurse to examine the students.

29) Grammar School. Negro. The principal and the social worker attached to this school stated that some time prior to the interview they had heard that cigarettes were being sold to children in Harlem. We were told of a certain man who was suspected of selling them to the children. The social worker was certain that a year before the interview marihuana cigarettes were sold on a certain street in Harlem to school children, but she had no knowledge as to whether the condition existed at the time of our investigation.

While working on another part of the survey, we interviewed a young Negress, approximately 20 years of age, who was a marihuana smoker. She stated that she and another girl started to smoke marihuana cigarettes while attending this particular school.

30) High School. Mixed, predominantly white. The principal stated that he was positive that there was no marihuana problem in his school.

31) High School. Predominantly white. A student was arrested for selling marihuana cigarettes to other pupils. We kept this school under surveillance after the arrest. Although we heard rumors that the sale of marihuana would start again, we were unable to gather any evidence of this. Our investigators attended the dance of the graduating class of this school at one of the hotels in the city. The dance was well conducted and had a large attendance. There was no evidence of smoking at this affair. The principal was cooperating with the Juvenile Aid Bureau of the Police Department in conducting the investigation of the marihuana problem in his school.

32) High School. White and Negro. Although rumor is widespread that "reefer" smoking is common at this school, thorough investigation did not produce evidence of it at the time of our investigation. We did obtain information, which we consider authoritative, that in 1935 a man was offered the concession to sell marihuana cigarettes to the students of this school. He refused the offer. The principal of this school stated that there had never been any trouble as a result of marihuana smoking and he knew of no actual cases.

33) High School. White, Negro, and Latin-American. The director of health education, who was conversant with the subject, stated that the school had no problem with regard to marihuana smoking on the premises but that a Puerto Rican student who lived in Harlem had informed him that he could obtain marihuana cigarettes in his locality.

34) College. White, some Negroes and Latin-Americans. We did not interview the authorities. Observation of the be-

havior of and conversation with students did not reveal any marihuana problem.

35) College. White, some Negroes and Latin-Americans. This college is located near one of the famous "tea-pads" of Harlem. Many of the students pass the house regularly. Continued observation did not reveal any student attendance.

36) Junior High School. Negro. Most of the boys of this school were familiar with the subject of marihuana. The pupils of the school are incessant smokers of ordinary cigarettes. We were unable to obtain any information which would indicate that they used "reefers." Some students were observed entering a house in which there was a "tea-pad," but we never found any of the occupants of this "tea-pad" to be pupils of the school. The counselor at the school stated that during the previous term there were suspicions regarding the use of marihuana.

37) Junior High School. Negro. The principal, who is considered qualified to discuss this subject, stated that for the three months prior to the interview there had been no marihuana problem. She ventured the opinion that a few cases do arise in the spring and summer. Observation of this school reveals that practically every day young boys between the ages of 18 and 20 loitered near the gates of the schoolyard at the close of the session. Some of these boys were known to our investigators as "reefer" smokers, and they associated with the girls of the school. Two young girls known by our investigators to be "reefer" smokers stated that they started to smoke marihuana while at that school.

38) High School. White, many Negroes and Latin-Americans. Many students smoked ordinary tobacco cigarettes. Numerous complaints and rumors were associated with this school. The principal stated that in 1934 they had an acute marihuana problem but that at the present time they did not think it existed. They are constantly on guard, especially at the beginning of a term, because they get many new students from the Harlem district. We are of the opinion that there are definite signs indicating that there is some marihuana smoking in the school.

39) High School. Negro and white. The principal of this school stated that they did not have a marihuana problem. We are certain, however, that this school does to some extent present an acute problem for we have observed a few students smoking "reefers" away from the school. We have reason to believe that some of them smoke it while at school. The girls attending this high school have a very low moral standard.

On the basis of the above statements and findings, we feel justified in concluding that although marihuana smoking may be indulged in by small numbers of students in certain schools of New York City, it is apparently not a widespread or large-scale practice.

In the belief that actual facts concerning the role played by marihuana in the production of juvenile delinquency could best be revealed in the records of the Children's Court of New York City, we interviewed the proper authorities on this subject. On the basis of the Children's Court records for 1939, marihuana is not an important factor in the development of delinquency.

Conclusions

From the foregoing study the following conclusions are drawn:

1. Marihuana is used extensively in the Borough of Manhattan but the problem is not as acute as it is reported to be in other sections of the United States.

2. The introduction of marihuana into this area is recent as compared to other localities.

3. The cost of marihuana is low and therefore within the purchasing power of most persons.

4. The distribution and use of marihuana is centered in Harlem.

5. The majority of marihuana smokers are Negroes and Latin-Americans.

6. The consensus among marihuana smokers is that the use of the drug creates a definite feeling of adequacy.

7. The practice of smoking marihuana does not lead to addiction in the medical sense of the word.

8. The sale and distribution of marihuana is not under the control of any single organized group.

9. The use of marihuana does not lead to morphine or heroin or cocaine addiction and no effort is made to create a market for these narcotics by stimulating the practice of marihuana smoking.

10. Marihuana is not the determining factor in the commission of major crimes.

11. Marihuana smoking is not widespread among school children.

12. Juvenile delinquency is not associated with the practice of smoking marihuana.

13. The publicity concerning the catastrophic effects of marihuana smoking in New York City is unfounded.

THE CLINICAL STUDY

PLAN AND SCOPE

Interest in the effects of marihuana on the human subject follows two main lines: first, concerning what may be called pleasurable effects which account for its widespread use; and second, regarding undesirable effects, including those leading to criminal and other antisocial acts.

In his monograph on marihuana, Walton has reviewed at length the literature on hashish experience. He has grouped these descriptions as retrospective accounts by professional writers and physicians who have taken the drug through curiosity or scientific interest, reports by physicians concerning patients who have taken excessive doses, and observations by psychiatrists on subjects under marihuana influence. In all of these instances a dose toxic to the individual had been taken and the effects described correspond to psychotic episodes of greater or less degree.

In the literature there are commonly described two basic types of effect, one of excitation, psychic exaltation, and inner joyousness, with divorcement from the external world; the other a state of anxiety with fear of consequences, such as death or insanity. Either one of these types of reaction may be experienced alone, but usually both are present during the intoxication. They occur in no regular sequence but replace each other in rapid succession. The euphoric and anxiety states are generally accompanied by mental confusion, a rapid flow of dissociated ideas, and a feeling of prolongation of time and spatial distortion. Sexual desires or phantasies may also occur.

The detailed descriptions of the experience vary. Those given by trained writers, such as Ludlow and Bayard Taylor, are vivid and dramatic, embodying sensual, visual, and auditory illusions—phantasies of overpowering splendor and beauty, on the one hand, and intense suffering and horror on the other. The authors, familiar with stories of hashish effects and gifted with strong imaginative powers, undoubtedly were expectant of much that happened. The account given by the eminent Philadelphia physician, H. C. Wood, while following the same general pattern, has much less embellishment. He describes a feeling of well-being and inner joyousness and buoyancy and the performance of antics which he knew to be foolish but was unable to control. He was able to recall no illusions or hallucinations. Later a state of anxiety came on, developing into an overpowering fear of death.

A number of studies by psychiatrists on selected subjects have been reported. An excellent example is that of Kant and Krapf. Each acted as subject for the other and the effects of marihuana are described and analyzed at length. In general, the objective in such studies is the interpretation of the reactions in terms of disturbances in psychological processes and functionings.

The descriptions referred to have been given by persons of a higher social class, well educated and accustomed by training to act in conformity with conventional social behavior. Although a state of irritability may occur and threats of suicide be made by individuals of this type under toxic doses of marihuana, it is noteworthy that in none of the descriptions is there found an expression of antagonism or antisocial behavior which led to acts of violence or what would be called criminal conduct.

Of more direct interest are the publications of Walter Bromberg, psychiatrist, Bellevue Hospital, Psychiatrist-in-Charge, Psychiatric Clinic, Court of General Sessions of New York County. Marihuana users who are brought before the court or admitted to the hospital come under his observation and he has reported at length on the psychiatric observations of 29 of these who showed psychotic reactions. He describes two types of reactions, one an acute marihuana intoxication with a psychotic syndrome, the other a toxic psychosis. Acute intoxication occurs in any individual if the marihuana is taken in sufficiently large doses. It comes on promptly and passes off some hours later. In marihuana psychosis, the symptoms are much more severe and of longer duration. He describes a number of cases in which the psychotic state continued for a number of days and required hospitalization.

The toxic psychosis seen in marihuana users occurs at any time and is of indefinite duration. Bromberg states that the relationship between cannabis and the onset of a functional psychotic state is not always clear. The personality factor is of undoubted importance and other toxic agents, such as alcohol and other drugs, as well as endogenous elements, may be involved. The symptoms, except for the longer duration, resemble those observed in persons under marihuana intoxication, but often take on the characteristics seen in schizophrenic or manic-depressive psychosis.

A description of 11 cases admitted to Bellevue Hospital is given for illustration. The marihuana was taken in the form of cigarettes. In this group were 5 Negroes, 2 of whom were women, 1 Puerto Rican, and 5 whites, one of whom was a Mexican and another a boy of 16. Except for one of the whites, a homosexual, they were all of a low intellectual and social order. One of the Negroes was arrested for following women in Central Park. The others were admitted at their own request, or were sent in by the police or family. Three of the group had definite sexual stimulation but in none was there an outburst in the form of an attack on women. The Puerto Rican became confused and excited and began chasing people with an ice pick. Shortly after his discharge he was readmitted to the hospital, was diagnosed as definitely psychotic, and was transferred to a state hospital as a schizophrenic. The majority of the group, 8 in fact, had psychopathic personalities and 3 of these were transferred to state institutions for further care. The group as a whole is representative of those who come into the hands of the police because of abnormal conduct and who are the source of the sensational newspaper and magazine stories.

Bromberg's findings concerning the lack of a positive relationship between marihuana and crime are described in the sociological section of this study.

In marihuana literature, the action of the drug is usually described from retrospective observation of the effects on a single individual. Relationship to varying dosage, to the subject's personality and background, to environmental conditions when the drug was taken, is given little if any attention. It is the lack of information concerning these and other factors involved in marihuana reaction which has given rise to the present confusion regarding its effects.

The clinical study here described was designed to afford information not found in marihuana literature but necessary for any comprehensive view of marihuana action. For obtaining this information there were these requisites: an adequate number of subjects for the study, a clear understanding of the mental and physical make-up of each subject, a uniformity of environmental factors, accurately graded dosage of marihuana, and standardized methods of obtaining and recording marihuana effects. In addition to defining the usual and unusual effects of marihuana, as shown by subjective and objective symptoms and alterations in behavior and in physical reaction, the study was expected to answer questions which must arise in consideration of the problem as a whole. Of special importance are these: Do marihuana users show fundamental traits differentiating them from non-users? Do users present evidence of psychological or physical damage directly attributable to the drug? What are the pleasurable effects which account for the widespread usage of marihuana? To what extent does it lead to antisocial or dangerous behavior?

The sections covering the clinical study are under the following headings:

A. Medical Aspects
   1. Symptoms and Behavior
   2. Organic and Systemic Functions
B. Psychological Aspects
   1. Psychophysical and Other Functions
   2. Intellectual Functioning
   3. Emotional Reactions and General Personality Structure
   4. Family and Community Ideologies
C. Comparison Between Users and Non-Users from the Standpoint of Mental and Physical Deterioration
D. Addiction and Tolerance
E. Possible Therapeutic Applications

Organization for the Study

The clinical studies were carried out at the Welfare Hospital,[1] a New York City hospital for chronic diseases on Welfare Island. The quarters assigned to the study consisted of a ward of eight beds for the group to be studied at any one period, an adjoining ward of two beds for the study of individuals of the group, three additional rooms with equipment for special examinations, and a diet kitchen for the preparation of the subjects' meals.

Four female nurses were employed and the subjects in the larger ward were under constant supervision. In addition to routine records, each nurse reported the behavior of the subjects while she was on duty. Guards were assigned from the Department of Correction and the New York City Police Force for the subjects drawn from the Riker's and Hart Island penitentiaries and the House of Detention for Women.

The facilities of the Third Medical Division laboratory were used for general clinical laboratory examinations and for more detailed study of organ functioning. For measurement of psychological reactions, special apparatus was provided. A description of equipment used for each division of the study is given under its proper section.

Subjects Selected for the Study

For the purpose of establishing a uniform plan of procedure to be followed throughout the study, a test group of 5 individuals who had had no previous experience with marihuana

1 Now named the Goldwater Memorial Hospital.

was selected. These were volunteers who were paid for their services. They were of a low socio-economic level, but classified as of better than average intelligence. Only one of the group came within the range of what is considered normal personality. They represented the type of person who would readily take to marihuana were the opportunity offered.

The main group, 72 subjects, was drawn from the inmates of the penitentiaries at Riker's and Hart Islands and the House of Detention for Women, all of which are under the supervision of the Department of Correction of New York City. There were two advantages in selecting subjects from this particular group; first, they could be kept under continuous observation throughout the period desired, and second, they constituted an excellent sample of the class in New York City from which the marihuana user comes. The subjects all volunteered for the study after having its purpose and the part they were to take in it fully explained to them.

Race, Sex and Age. Of the group, 65 were males and 7 were females; 35 were white, 26 were Negroes, and 11 were Puerto Ricans. The ages ranged from 21 to 37 years except for one who was 45 and another who was 43. Of the women, 6 had been opium addicts for a number of years.

Previous Experience with Marihuana. Forty-eight of the group, including 6 of the women, gave a history of marihuana smoking. The extent of the usage was variable; for some it was occasional, while others had indulged in the habit fairly steadily over a period of years. Of the 48 users, those who were sellers of marihuana were probably the most consistent smokers, as in carrying on the traffic they would endeavor to keep a stock on hand. But in any instance, the number of cigarettes smoked during any stated period would vary according to circumstance. Thus one user stated that he smoked from 2 to 6 marihuana cigarettes a day, another from 10 to 15 a day, another 3 or 4 a week, and another 5 or 6 a month. Those who smoked daily are here classified as steady users,

TABLE 1

Previous experience with marihuana of 48 subjects

Years of Use	Number of Steady Users	Number of Occasional Users
1–5	13	4
6–10	16	4
over 10	9	2
Total	38	10

those who smoked when opportunity was offered but not daily, as occasional users.

The users had all been deprived of marihuana from the time of their arrest, the shortest period being two weeks, the longest, one year and ten months. They all stated that the habit had often been interrupted voluntarily and the enforced discontinuation of it had caused no discomfort.

Health Record. The subjects were individually selected by Dr. Allentuck as suitable for the study. A physical and neurological examination at the hospital showed no evidence of disease. However, the Wassermann and Kline tests gave positive results for 6 subjects and the Kline test alone was positive for 2 and doubtful for 2. These figures are consistent with those of the population from which the group was selected. Of the 12,000 inmates of the Riker's Island Penitentiary in 1940 and the 8,000 in 1941, 10 per cent reacted positively to serological tests.

Intelligence Record. Sixty subjects (40 users and 20 non-users) to whom the Bellevue Adult Intelligence Test was given had an average I.Q. of 99.3, range 70 to 124. The average I.Q. of the user group was 96.7, range 70 to 124, while that for the non-user group was 104.5, range 93 to 114. When analyzed according to racial distribution, the two groups were even better equated intellectually than the total results indicate. Of the 28 white subjects examined, the average I.Q. of the 13 users was 106.1, range 77 to 124, and that of the 15 non-users was 106.3, range 96 to 114. The 19 Negro users had an average I.Q. of 92.6, range 70 to 112, and the 5 Negro non-users averaged 98.8, range 93 to 101. Although in the colored group the non-users averaged 6.2 points higher than the users, it must be taken into account that the number of Negro non-users tested was small. The average I.Q. of the 8 Puerto Rican users was 91.0, range 72 to 100; that is, they were very similar in mental ability to the Negro users. From the results obtained from the Bellevue Adult Intelligence Test, one may conclude that neither the users nor the non-users were inferior in intelligence to the general population.

Marihuana Used

The marihuana that was used for oral administration was supplied by Dr. H. J. Wollner, Consulting Chemist of the United States Treasury Department. It was in the form of an alcohol fluid concentrate, the alcohol content ranging from 55 to 67.3 per cent and the content of solids from 22.9 to 33.6 Gm. per 100 cc. According to the bio-assay made by

Dr. S. Loewe of the Department of Pharmacology of the Cornell University Medical School, the strength of the fluid concentrate was found to be from 71 to 90 per cent of that of the U.S.P. fluid extract for cannabis marketed by Parke, Davis and Company. The fluid extract was not miscible with water and had a characteristic, disagreeable taste which made it easily recognized. For these reasons the concentrate was evaporated to a viscid consistency and made into pill form, with glycyrrhiza as the excipient. Each pill was equivalent to 1 cc. of the concentrate. For controls, glycyrrhiza pills without marihuana were used.

Several products prepared by Dr. Roger Adams in his investigation of the chemistry of marihuana were used. A comparison of their action with that of the concentrate will be found below.

In addition to the concentrate, marihuana cigarettes were used. These were obtained from supplies confiscated by the New York City Police. Each contained approximately from .4 to .8 Gm. of marihuana. As the quality of the marihuana varied and the amount of active principles taken in with the smoke was unknown, there was no exactness in dosage. In general, however, it appeared that smoking 2 cigarettes was equivalent to taking 1 pill.

The minimal dose of the concentrate which produced clearcut effects was 2 cc. During the repeated observations on each member of the group larger doses were given, commonly up to around 8 cc. and in one instance up to 22 cc. For smoking, from one to as many as eleven cigarettes were used.

The Active Principles. Determination of relative potencies of drugs having similar action can be made on human beings to a limited extent only. The comparison is based on easily measurable effects on some organ or system on which the drug has a highly selective action, but the existing state of the system influences greatly the ensuing result. Marihuana effects come mainly from action on the central nervous system. The type and degree of response of this system to stimuli of various origins vary in different individuals and in the same individual at different times. When marihuana is given the pre-existing state cannot be classified but it has influence in determining the response, and the same dose of marihuana does not produce identical effects in different subjects or in one subject at different times. In general, however, when the dose given is definitely effective the responses are of a fairly uniform character.

For this reason the relative potency of the active principles supplied by Dr. Roger Adams could be determined only approximately. The principles used were the natural tetrahydro-cannabinol, the synthetic isomer, and the synthetic hexylhy-drocannabinol. These all brought on effects similar to those of the marihuana concentrate. The estimate of their relative potency is as follows: 1 cc. of the concentrate, representing the extraction from 1 Gm. of marihuana, had as its equivalent 15 mg. of the natural tetrahydrocannabinol, 60 mg. of the synthetic hexylhydrocannabinol, and 120 mg. of the synthetic tetra compound. In explaining the differences in the estimated potencies, the rates of absorption must be taken into account since the action of marihuana depends on the amount of active principle absorbed and its concentration in the brain at a certain time.

The main conclusion is that the action of the marihuana concentrate is dependent on its tetrahydrocannabinol content and that the synthetic compounds retain the action of the natural principle.

Procedure

The procedure for examining the main group of subjects was adopted in the light of the experience gained from the preliminary study.

The subjects were brought to the hospital in groups of from six to ten, and they stayed there from four to six weeks.

Each subject had his history taken and was given a physical, neurological, and psychiatric examination on the day of admission. Since it has been shown that pulse variation is the most constant index of marihuana action, the pulse rate was recorded every half hour during the day with the subjects at rest for five minutes before each reading.

During the following days, through careful observation by the Director, the general make-up of the subject, his personality, the character of his responsiveness, and his behavior in new surroundings were determined both before and while he was under the influence of marihuana. Additional information came through the nurses' reports.

In addition, each subject was given a series of tests before and after the administration of marihuana in order that the changes brought about by the drug might be measured. Included among these tests were psychological tests for mental functioning and emotional reactions, psychomotor tests for both simple and complex psychophysical functions, tests to determine such abilities as musical aptitude and the perception of time and space, and laboratory examinations to test the functioning of the various organs and systems of the body.

Medical Aspects

SYMPTOMS AND BEHAVIOR

Samuel Allentuck, MD

IN PRELIMINARY GROUP

The preliminary study of the 5 volunteer subjects had for its purpose the establishment of methods of procedures to be followed for the main group, and the obtaining of a general picture of the physical and mental effects induced by the drug. Having no knowledge of the safe limits of marihuana dosage, the dosage given to this group was restricted to from 1 to 4 cc. of the concentrate, and for smoking from 1 to 3 cigarettes.

When ingested, 1 cc. of marihuana was slightly effective, the multiples of this more so. There was noted in all subjects some increase in pulse rate and in blood pressure, dilated and sluggish pupils, dryness of the mouth and throat, ataxia, and some clumsiness and incoordination of movement. Symptoms distinctly disagreeable were dizziness in 3 subjects, a sense of heaviness of the extremities in 2, nausea in 2 and faintness in 2. Three showed motor restlessness. A state classed as euphoria, characterized by laughter, witticisms, loquaciousness, and lowering of inhibitions occurred in 3 subjects. This was not sustained but alternated with periods during which disagreeable symptoms were dominant. In one of the subjects (V.C.) there was no euphoric state, but a feeling of discomfort and depression throughout. Finally in one of the 5 (A.V.) with 2 cc. there was a state of depression with anxiety and with 4 cc. a psychotic episode with fear of death.

With the exception of the one individual during his psychotic episode, the subjects gave no evidence of abnormal mental content at any stage of the drug action, the only change noted being a delay in focusing attention on questions asked and difficulty in sustaining mental concentration. While there was objection at times to carrying out repetitive tests, there was no definite refusal. There was no sexual stimulation giving rise to overt expression.

With the cigarette smoking, ataxia and charges in the pulse rate, blood pressure, and pupils corresponded to those following oral administration. In only one of the subjects, however, was there definite euphoria. The common symptoms were dizziness and drowsiness. Two of the subjects found it difficult to concentrate.

The duration of the effects of marihuana was variable. When it was ingested, the effects usually passed off in from two to four hours, but in one instance persisted for seven hours and in another for fourteen hours. After smoking, the duration of effects was from one to three hours.

IN MAIN GROUP

The evidence of the effects of marihuana was obtained by the subject's statement of symptoms and sensations, by the nurses' reports and by the examiner's observations and interpretation of changes in the subject's mental state and behavior.

The dosage of the marihuana concentrate ranged from 2 to 22 cc. and in each subject the effects of more than one dose were studied. Dosage ranging from 2 to 5 cc. was used for the largest number of subjects, and that from 14 to 21 cc. on only seven occasions. It is known that marihuana intoxication may bring about a comatose state, but no attempt was made to determine the dosage required for this. The number receiving each of the selected doses is shown in Table 2.

TABLE 2

Dosage of marihuana

Dosage	Number of Subjects	Dosage	Number of Subjects	Dosage	Number of Subjects
2 cc.	37	8 cc.	4	14 cc.	1
3 cc.	6	9 cc.	6	15 cc.	2
4 cc.	20	10 cc.	8	17 cc.	1
5 cc.	16	11 cc.	5	18 cc.	1
6 cc.	8	12 cc.	5	19 cc.	1
7 cc.	7	13 cc.	4	22 cc.	1

While the duration of action and its intensity tended to increase with dosage, this was not always the case and equal doses did not bring about uniform effects in all those receiving them. Thus, 3 cc. produced a striking effect in one individual, much less in another; in still another, 10 cc. produced less effect than 5 cc. Such variations are to be explained by differences in the mental make-up of the subject, and the particular state of his responsiveness at the time when marihuana is taken.

The number of cigarettes smoked ranged from one to eleven. The smoking of a single cigarette took about ten minutes and up to eight could be smoked in an hour. In smoking, increasing the number of cigarettes usually increased the sensation described as "high," but here also there was no uniformity in individuals or groups.

When marihuana was ingested, in dosages from 2 cc. up, its actions became evident in from one half to one hour. The maximum effects were seen in from two to three hours. These subsided gradually, but the time of disappearance was variable, usually three to five hours, in some instances twelve hours or more.

When marihuana cigarettes were used the effects appeared almost immediately. After one cigarette, these had usually disappeared in an hour. After several cigarettes had been smoked the effects increased progressively in intensity and reached a maximum in about an hour. In most instances they disappeared in from three or four hours.

The Concentrate

Behavior Symptoms. The effects on the general behavior of the subjects taking the concentrate were variable. If left undisturbed some remained quietly sitting or lying, showing little interest in their surroundings. Others were restless and talkative. Under the heading "Euphoria" there are listed those marihuana effects which give rise to pleasurable sensations or experiences. These are a sense of well-being and contentment, cheerfulness and gaiety, talkativeness, bursts of singing and dancing, daydreaming, a pleasant drowsiness, joking, and performing amusing antics. The drowsiness, daydreaming and unawareness of surroundings were present when the subject was left alone. Other euphoric expressions required an audience and there was much contagiousness of laughing and joking where several of the subjects under marihuana were congregated. The occurrence of a euphoric state, in one or another form, was noted in most of the subjects. But except for those who were allowed to pass the time undisturbed, the pleasurable effects were interrupted from time to time by disagreeable sensations.

Quite commonly seen, as with the preliminary group, was a difficulty in focusing and sustaining mental concentration. Thus, there would occur a delay in the subject's answers to questions and at times some confusion as to their meaning. There was, however, except in a few isolated instances, no abnormal mental content evident and the responses brought out by the examiner were not different from those in the pre-marihuana state.

Altered mental behavior which would give rise to more concern was seen in a relatively small number of subjects. In some this took the form of irritation at questioning, refusal to comply with simple requests and antagonism to certain of the examiners. There was, however, only verbal and no active opposition in any of these behaviors, caused by the subject's desire to be left undisturbed and his disinclination to carry out certain tests which in his pre-marihuana period he had considered tiresome and meaningless. With this came antipathy to those conducting the tests.

The occurrence of the disagreeable physical symptoms accompanying marihuana action would naturally lead to a feeling of disquietude and some alarm as to significance and consequences. This, however, was a prominent feature in relatively few instances. A pronounced state of anxiety reaching a panic stage, associated usually with fear of death or of insanity, was observed only in those subjects experiencing psychotic episodes and here the anxiety state led to pleas for escape and not to acts of aggression. Even in the psychotic states there were no uncontrollable outbursts of rage or acts of violence.

Some evidence of eroticism was reported in about 10 per cent of the 150 instances in which marihuana was administered to the group. The presence of nurses, attendants and other women associated with the study gave opportunity for frank expression of sexual stimulation, had this been marked. There was no such expression even during the psychotic episodes.

In some isolated instances there was evidence of marked lowering of inhibitions such as loud discharge of flatus, urinating on the floor instead of in the vessels supplied, and in one instance frank exhibitionism. In the last instance the subject, who was not a regular marihuana user, had been arrested on three occasions for indecent exposure.

The frequency with which significant changes in behavior occurred is indicated in Table 3.

TABLE. 3

Effects of varying doses of marihuana on behavior of users and non-users

	2–5 cc.		6–10 cc.		11–22 cc.	
	Per cent affected		Per cent affected		Per cent affected	
Symptoms	Users (41 trials)	Non-users (43 trials)	Users (25 trials)	Non-users (12 trials)	Users (17 trials)	Non-users (3 trials)
Euphoria	92		92		100	
Excitement	19	32	8	41	24	33
Antagonism	7	11	0	16	6	0
Anxiety	7	27	4	41	6	33
Eroticism	4	11	4	16	12	0

As used in Table 3, anxiety means the subject's expressed worry concerning what might happen to him. Excitement, shown by physical restlessness, mucular twitchings and jerky movements, and loud talking, and some degree of antagonism are known to be expressions of an "alarm" or "fear" state.

It is seen from this table that, except for euphoria, the effect of marihuana was definitely more pronounced on the non-users. This might be taken as evidence of a persisting tolerance to the drug in the user group, but, on the other hand, it may have as its basis a feeling of greater apprehension in the non-users. Such a feeling would undoubtedly arise among those who have had no previous experience with marihuana and are in a state of uncertainty as to its possible harmful effects.

Physical Symptoms. Of the subjective symptoms, a feeling described as lightness, heaviness, or pressure in the head, often with dizziness, was one of the earliest and occurred in practically all subjects, irrespective of dose. Dryness of the mouth and throat were reported by over half of the subjects as was also a floating sensation. Unsteadiness in movement and a feeling of heaviness in the extremities were commonly experienced as was a feeling of hunger and a desire for sweets especially. Less commonly noted were nausea, vomiting, sensations of warmth of the head or body, burning of the eyes and blurring of vision, tightness of the chest, cardiac palpitation, ringing or pressure in the ears, and an urge to urinate or defecate.

From observation by the examiner, tremor and ataxia were present in varying degrees in practically all instances and in all dosages used, as were also dilatation of the pupils and sluggish response to light. These effects were often present on the day following marihuana administration.

The frequency of the more common subjective symptoms and their relation to dosage is shown in Table 4. The figures are taken from the subject's reports.

There is a tendency for the symptoms to be more frequent in the non-users than in the users but the differences are variable and in general not striking.

The Cigarette

Smoking. When marihuana is smoked, there is, as has been stated, no such accuracy in dosage as is the case when it is ingested. The marihuana user acquires a technique or art in smoking "reefers." This involves special preparation of the cigarette and regulation of the frequency and depth of inhalations. In a group of smokers, a cigarette circulates from one to another, each in turn taking one or more puffs. The performance is a slow and deliberate one and the cigarette, held in a forked match stick, is smoked to its end.

When the smoke comes in contact with the respiratory

mucous membrane, the absorption of the active principle is rapid and the effects are recognized promptly by the subject. He soon learns to distinguish the amount of smoking which will give pleasant effects from the amount which will give unpleasant ones and so regulates his dosages. Providing there are no disturbing factors, as is the case in gatherings of small friendly groups or parties in "tea-pads," the regulated smoking produces a euphoric state, which accounts for continued indulgence.

TABLE 4

Physical symptoms produced in users and non-users by varying doses of marihuana

Symptoms	2–5 cc.		6–10 cc.		11–12 cc.	
	Per cent affected		Per cent affected		Per cent affected	
	Users (41 trials)	Non-users (43 trials)	Users (25 trials)	Non-users (12 trials)	Users (17 trials)	Non-users (3 trials)
Lightness in head, dizziness	83	97	80	85	100	100
Dryness of throat	69	72	48	67	76	100
Heaviness of extremities ...	46	51	32	41	41	67
Unsteadiness ..	41	39	20	33	41	33
Hunger, thirst .	44	35	48	41	70	33
High floating sensation	60	63	72	66	64	33

The effect from smoking marihuana cigarettes was studied in 32 subjects. Of these, 20 were classed as users, that is, prior to their arrest they had had more or less extensive experience in smoking. In the study the smoking was repeated by each subject several times, the number of cigarettes smoked within an hour ranging from one to eight.

In all of the user group the smoking produced a euphoric state with its feeling of well-being, contentment, sociability, mental and physical relaxation, which usually ended in a feeling of drowsiness. Talkativeness and laughing and the sensation of floating in the air were common occurrences. These effects were of short duration, from one to three or four hours after the smoking was concluded. In none of these subjects was there an expression of antagonism or antisocial behavior.

In the non-user group the effects were similar except that in one subject a state of mental confusion occurred and in another the main effect was a feeling of dizziness, unsteadiness, and muscular weakness. Finally one subject showed effects entirely different from the others. He smoked one cigarette and became restless, agitated, dizzy, fearful of his surroundings, afraid of death. He had three short attacks of unconsciousness. At one period he had visions of angels, and for a few minutes a euphoric state. The entire episode lasted a little over an hour, after which he went to sleep. This subject had a similar psychotic episode after taking 120 mg. of tetrahydrocannabinol. On seven other occasions he had been given the marihuana concentrate or tetrahydrocannabinol with no unusual effects.

Of the physical symptoms occurring with smoking, dryness of the mouth and throat, dizziness, and a sensation of hunger were the most common. None of these or other symptoms seemed to lessen materially the pleasurable effects.

The effect of smoking on the 7 females, 6 of whom were classed as users, corresponded to that on the male group. All showed euphoric effects. One of the subjects was nauseated and another was restless, irritable, and contrary. These effects were observed in both of the subjects when marihuana was taken by stomach. One of the users, euphoric after smoking 6 and 10 cigarettes, had a psychotic episode after 8 cc. of marihuana concentrate.

Tea-Pad Parties.[1] In addition to the quantitative data regularly obtained from the subject during the course of the testing program, the examiner had opportunity to make diverse observations of the subject's global reactions, which threw interesting light on the general effect of the drug on the individual personality.

When the subject became "high," his inclination was to laugh, talk, sing, listen to music, or sleep, but the requirement that he solve problems, answer questions, or remember drawings created an artificial situation, tending to bring him "down" and spoil his pleasure. In order, therefore, that the influence of the drug might be observed in less formal circumstances and in a set-up more nearly like the customary "tea-pad," two groups of men were given "parties" on the last night of their hospital sojourn. The men were consulted beforehand, and the stage was set according to their desires. They requested that nothing be done until it was really dark outside. They brought the radio into the room where the smoking took place and turned it to soft dance music. Only one shaded light burned, leaving the greater part of the room shadowy. The suggestion was made that easy chairs or floor cushions be procured but the party progressed without these.

The men were allowed as many cigarettes as they wanted.

1 This section on "Tea-Pad Parties" was prepared by Mrs. Halpern.

When the "reefers" were passed out they crowded around with their hands outstretched like little children begging for candy. The number of cigarettes the men smoked varied, the range being from two to twelve or thirteen. There were both users and non-users in these two groups. The users of course were highly elated at the prospect of getting much free "tea," and some of the non-users also smoked with genuine enjoyment.

In the beginning the men broke up into little groups of twos and threes to do their smoking, or in some instances went off by themselves. Smoke soon filled the atmosphere and added to the general shadowy effect. After the initial smoking there was some moving about; some men laughed and joked, some became argumentative, while some just stared out of the window. The arguments never seemed to get anywhere, although they often dealt with important problems, and the illogical reasoning used was never recognized or refuted by the person to whom it was addressed. Gradually, as though attracted by some force, all restlessness and activity ceased, and the men sat in a circle about the radio. Occasionally they whispered to one another, laughed a little, or swayed to the music, but in general they relaxed quietly in their chairs. A feeling of contentment seemed to pervade, and when one man suddenly got a "laughing jag" they were annoyed at the interruption.

In general, they gave the impression of adolescent boys doing something which was forbidden and thereby adding spice to the indulgence. Many of the adolescent personality patterns as they appear in group activities were clearly observable here. There was the eternal "wisecracker," the domineering "important" individual who tried to tell everyone what to do, the silly, giggling adolescent and the shy, withdrawn introvert. One forgot that these were actually adults with all the usual adult responsibilities. One could not help drawing the conclusion that they too had forgotten this for the time being.

Although urged to smoke more, no subject could be persuaded to take more than he knew or felt he could handle. After about an hour and half of smoking, the men were given coffee and bread and jam and the party broke up. They all went to bed and reported the next day that they had slept very well.

Another attempt at evaluating the effect of marihuana in less formal situations was made in the following manner. The examiner, one of the police officers and the subjects listened to Jack Benny on the Jello Program at 7 o'clock Sunday evening. The police officer noted the number of times the audience laughed, and the length of time the laughter lasted. The examiner checked these items for the subjects. The first time this was done without marihuana; the following week the subjects were given several "reefers" about fifteen minutes before the radio program started. The results were as follows: Without drug, the subjects laughed 42 times as against 72 laughs in the radio audience. The total time for all laughs was 63 seconds as compared with 139 seconds for the radio audience. With cigarettes the subjects laughed 43 times as compared with 47 laughs in the audience, the total laugh time being 129 seconds as compared with 173 seconds of laughter in the audience. Without drug, the subjects laughed, roughly speaking, only half as often and as long as the audience; while under the drug they laughed almost as often and the laugh time was about 75 per cent that of the audience.

It is obvious that under marihuana the subject laughs more readily and for longer time intervals. This is probably due both to the fact that things seem funnier to him and because when under the influence of the drug he is less inhibited.

Differences Between Concentrate and Cigarette

When marihuana was ingested, it was in the form of the concentrate, containing all the active principles which are soluble in the menstruum used. The relative proportions of the principles present are unknown, and the effects can be assumed to give a composite picture of different actions, the dominating one being that of tetrahydrocannabinol. There is no information available concerning the principles present in marihuana smoke, and it is possible that some of those found in the concentrate have been destroyed by the heat of combustion. The effects from smoking correspond to those induced by tetrahydrocannabinol taken by stomach, so it may be assumed that this principle is present in the smoke. The rapidity with which effects occur after smoking demonstrates the quick absorption of the cannabinol from the respiratory tract and the short duration of these effects indicates its prompt excretion or detoxification. When the concentrate is taken, the absorption from the intestinal tract is slower and more prolonged. For these reasons it is not possible to make a precise comparison between the effects of the two forms of administration.

In general the subject's consciousness of unpleasant symptoms is more marked when the concentrate is taken and this may interrupt or obscure the pleasant effects. The long duration of action and the inability of the subject to stop it serve to accentuate the physical symptoms and to cause apprehension concerning what may happen. The result of all this readily accounts for the irritability, negativism and antagonism oc-

curring. The lessening of inhibitions is not peculiar to marihuana, for in a few subjects who were given alcohol in intoxicating doses the behavior corresponded to that induced by
marihuana.

After smoking the main effect was of a euphoric type. Some
dizziness and dryness of the mouth were generally present,
but were not pronounced enough to distract from the pleasant
sensations. The condition described as "high" came on promptly and increased with the number of cigarettes smoked, but
it was not alarming or definitely disagreeable, and did not
give rise to antisocial behavior. On the contrary it prompted
sociability. The marihuana was under the subject's control,
and once the euphoric state was present, which might come
from only one cigarette, he had no inclination to increase it
by more smoking. When a considerable number of cigarettes
were smoked, the effect was usually one of drowsiness and
fatigue.

The description of the "tea-pad parties" brings out clearly
the convivial effect on the groups and the absence of any rough
or antagonistic behavior.

Psychotic Episodes

What has been referred to as psychotic episodes occurred
in 9 subjects, 7 men and 2 women. A description of the hap-
penings in each instance is given.[2]

A.V. Male. Non-user. Given 4 cc. of marihuana concentrate.
About three hours later he became restless, tremulous, agitated, fearful of harmful effects, suspicious of examiners. For
short periods he was euphoric. At one time he had visual hallucinations of figures making gestures suggesting harm. He
talked continuously, mainly expressing fear. His answers to
questions were delayed but intelligent.

W.P. Male. Occasional user. Given 3 cc., repeated two hours
later. At first there was a euphoric state; later he became
resistant and negativistic. He showed antagonism to the examiner, demanding to be left alone. He vomited twice.
Throughout he was highly excited and talked to himself. The
effects in general resembled those seen in a maniacal state. He
returned to his normal state in about three hours after the
second dose.

F.D. Male. Occasional user. Given 4 cc. Five hours later
he became confused, disoriented and slow in answering ques-

2 Throughout this section fictitious initials are used to avoid any dis-
closure of the subjects' identities.

tions. There were periods of elation and depression with laughter and weeping. The effects passed off in six hours.

R.W. Male. Non-user. Given 5 cc. Three hours later he became disoriented with continued talkativeness and rapid shifting of thought. He had fits of laughter and weeping, grandiose ideas, some paranoid trends. He answered questions clearly but without perseveration. He returned to normal after six hours.

I.N. Female. Occasional user. Also heroin addict for many years. Given 8 cc. Three hours later she became confused and anxious with periods of laughing and weeping. There were several short episodes resembling hysterical attacks and dyspnea, pallor and rapid pulse during which she felt that she was dying and screamed for the doctor and for a priest. Throughout, her response to questioning was intelligent but delayed. There was a return to her normal state in three hours.

E.C. Male. Non-user. Given 6 cc. Two hours later he developed a marked state of anxiety accompanied by a sensation of difficulty in breathing. This began during a basal metabolism test. In the Sanborn equipment used there is a nose clip occluding nasal breathing and a rubber mouthpiece through which the air is inspired and expired. During the test the subject became confused, panicky and disoriented as to time. The anxiety over breathing continued for four hours but could be interrupted by distraction. He was then given 4 cc. more. The breathing difficulty lasted five hours more.

The condition here had features seen in claustrophobia. Before the episode, the subject had taken marihuana on five occasions in 2, 4, 5, 5, and 2 cc. dosage, without any symptoms of respiratory distress. However, after the episode he took marihuana on three occasions in 2, 5, and 6 cc. dosage and each time the respiratory symptoms occurred. A certain degree of nervousness was present but there was no mental confusion. The subject realized that there was no physical obstruction to his breathing and had learned that by concentrating his thought on other lines he could keep his respiratory difficulties in abeyance and would not suffer from real anxiety. Smoking up to as many as thirteen marihuana cigarettes did not bring about the respiratory effect. It appeared then that the respiratory symptoms were precipitated by the wearing of the apparatus while under the influence of marihuana, and through suggestibility there resulted a conditioning to the marihuana concentrate which was given subsequently.

The description of these six psychotic episodes fits in with many others found in marihuana literature. They are examples of acute marihuana intoxication in susceptible individuals which comes on shortly after the drug has been taken and persists for several hours. The main features of the poisoning are the restlessness and mental excitement of a delirious nature with intermittent periods of euphoric and an overhanging state of anxiety and dread.

Three other subjects presented the features of marihuana psychosis.

R.H. Male. White. Age 23. Non-user. In prison for the offense of living on prostitution. The family history was bad. His father never supported his wife or family and there was continual discord at home. When the subject was 9 years old the father deserted the family. Three brothers received court sentences, one for stealing a taxi, one for rape, and one for striking a teacher. R.H. was a problem child at school and on account of truancy and waywardness he was sent to the Flushing Parental School. He ran away from this school several times and was transferred to the House of Refuge on Randall's Island. At the age of 16 he was discharged. Since that time he had had two jobs, one for three months in a factory, the other for four and one-half months in the W.P.A. When he was 16 he was run over by a truck and was unconscious for a time. After his return to the Riker's Island Penitentiary from Welfare Hospital further questioning concerning his past revealed that he was subject to "fits" occurring once or twice every two months. During the attacks his body became rigid and his mouth felt stiff.

The subject was admitted to Welfare Hospital for the marihuana study on February 20th. After the usual program of examinations he was given 2 cc. of the concentrate on February 27th and February 28th. These doses brought on the symptoms of dizziness and tremor and heaviness of the head and the state called "high" which is characterized by periods of laughter and talkativeness. These effects passed off in a few hours and were followed by drowsiness and a sense of fatigue. On March 1st at 1 p.m. he smoked one marihuana cigarette. Immediately afterwards he became agitated and restless and suddenly lost consciousness. He recovered quickly and stated that he had had visions of angels and had heard choirs singing. Later he had a second short period of unconsciousness. During the afternoon he continued to be agitated and restless and had periods of laughing and weeping. After he was given phenobarbital he went to sleep. On the next day his only complaint was that he felt dizzy. Following this episode he was given 4 cc. of marihuana concentrate on March 3rd and 2 cc. on March 10th and 2 cc. of tetrahydrocannabinol on March 5th and 4 cc. on March 8th. The effects corresponded to those seen after the earlier administrations of 2 cc. doses of the concentrate.

On March 11th R.H. was given 5 cc. (75 mg.) of the tetrahydrocannabinol at 11 a.m. and 3 cc. at 2 p.m. No unusual effects were noted during the afternoon and he ate his supper with appetite at 4:30 p.m. At 6 p.m. he became restless, apprehensive and somewhat belligerent. He felt that something had happened to his mother, that everybody was acting queerly and picking on him. He continued to be agitated and fearful, refused medication and slept poorly. This condition persisted and on March 13th he was returned to Riker's Island. After four days there he became quiet and composed. The psychotic state cleared up completely. The resident psychiatrist's report was: Impression 1. Psychosis due to drugs. (Marihuana experimentally administered.) Acute delirium, recovered. 2. Convulsive disorder, idiopathic epilepsy. Petit mal on history.

H.W. Female. White. Age 28. Non-user. Drug peddler, serving three years' indefinite sentence for unlawfully possessing a drug. Her parents died when she was about 10 years old and she was raised in an orphanage. At the age of 19 she entered a training school for nurses, but gave this up after four months and supported herself by prostitution. Her sister and her sister's husband were drug addicts and through them she began taking morphine and heroin, being, according to her account, depressed and dissatisfied at the time. She continued using these drugs up to the time of her arrest, a period of eight years. In 1938 she married a man who was also a drug addict, and engaged in the drug traffic.

On May 7th she was given 2 cc. of marihuana. Aside from a headache and a feeling of muscular weakness and incoordination, the effect was to make the subject feel gay and very good-natured. On May 8th she was given 3 cc. of the concentrate and became somewhat confused and unsteady, irritated and upset at carrying out tests, and greatly worried about the physical symptoms. Five hours after she had taken the drug the effects had largely passed off. Six hours later, however, she became restless and agitated, moving about constantly, and worried about past conduct. This state continued for a few hours. On other occasions the subject was given marihuana in doses of 2, 3, and 4 cc. Twice after the administration of 3 cc. the general effect was of a euphoric type, and after 4 cc. had been given a state of sadness set in on two occasions and one of euphoria on a third. Toward the end of her stay the subject became depressed and moody, constantly dwelling on the belief that she had committed unpardonable sins.

She was returned to the House of Detention on June 2nd, transferred to the Psychiatric Division of Bellevue Hospital on June 9th, and from there was sent to Matteawan State Hospital on July 10th. On admission to the State Hospital she appeared confused, retarded, apprehensive, and depressed. She had a marked feeling of guilt. She began to improve in September and was discharged, cured, in January. Since her return to New York she reports at frequent intervals to the parole officer. She has secured employment in a food shop and is to be promoted to the position of manager of the shop.

The diagnosis made at the State Hospital was: Psychosis, due to drugs and other exogenous poisons (morphine and heroin).

D.P. Male. Colored. Age 23. Occasional user. Sentenced for unlawful possession of drugs. Since graduation from high school at the age of 16 he had had no occupation. His criminal record dated from his graduation. He was arrested in 1934 for disorderly conduct and in the same year sentenced to Elmira Reformatory for five years for second-degree assault. He was paroled in 1936, but during the same and the following year was arrested three times for assault or robbery. He was returned to Elmira where he remained until his discharge in 1940. In August 1940 he was arrested for the possession of drugs and sentenced to a three-year indefinite term. He had served eight months of this sentence when he was admitted to Welfare Hospital as a subject for the marihuana study.

During his stay at Welfare Hospital, D.P. was given marihuana in the form of a concentrate and as cigarettes on numerous occasions. His symptoms and behavior corresponded to those usually seen, lasting a few hours with no after-effects. When the time came for his return to Riker's Island he urged that he be allowed to stay at the hospital and assist in the study. Two weeks after his return to the penitentiary he developed a psychosis characteristic of schizophrenia. He was transferred to Matteawan where the diagnosis made was: Psychosis with psychopathic personality.

These three cases are of special interest from the standpoint of the relationship of marihuana to the psychosis. The first subject, R.H., had a definite history of epileptic attacks. After smoking one marihuana cigarette he experienced an acute confusional state which lasted a few hours. In the second episode which lasted six days there was a more prolonged confusional state. Epileptics are subject to such attacks, epileptic or epileptic equivalents, which may be brought on by any number of upsetting circumstances. In this case marihuana is the only known factor which precipitated the attack.

The second subject, H.W., was a heroin addict of long standing. During her stay in the hospital, in her retrospective reports on her marihuana experiences there were usually included expressions of worry and remorse at her failure to answer questions or perform tests honestly, informing on the other women in her group, and denials concerning a syphilitic infection she thought she had had. Prior to this incarceration she had had no prison experience. The mental picture developed from the study at the hospital and at Matteawan and the subject's subsequent history represent a fairly typical example of what is termed a prison psychosis.

The third subject, D.P., did not develop his psychosis until two weeks after he had been returned to the Riker's Island Penitentiary. He had shown no unexpected effects from marihuana and had hoped to be allowed to stay on at the hospital instead of going back to prison to complete more than two years of an unexpired sentence. At Matteawan this subject was considered to have an underlying psychopathic personality. His case also may be taken as an example of prison psychosis. With both the second and third subjects, the exact role of marihuana in relation to the psychosis cannot be stated.

Dr. Peter F. Amoroso, Commissioner of Correction of the city of New York, has given us information concerning the prisoners sentenced to the penitentiary at Riker's Island from whom our subjects were drawn. During the year beginning July 1, 1941, and ending June 30, 1942, there were 1,756 inmates in this institution. They had received an indeterminate sentence, that is, from a minimum of a few months to a maximum of three years. Of this group, 175 were subjected to intensive study by the psychiatrist because they were considered possible psychotic cases, 117 were sex offenders, and 200 were miscellaneous cases referred for mental observation, making a total of 492. Twenty-seven of these cases were committed to state institutions for the criminal insane, namely, 25 to Matteawan and 2 to Dannemora.

Commissioner Amoroso, after reviewing these cases, writes as follows: "The prison atmosphere may place a most severe strain on those who are physically or mentally abnormal upon commitment . . . Emotionally unstable persons find themselves during incarceration denied the assertion and enjoyment of the basic human urges and impulses and it is natural to expect, therefore, that prison life may result in various types of explosions, such as psychoses, neuroses, sex perversion, and even physical and moral deterioration.

"I am indeed surprised that we had so little trouble with our volunteers upon completion of their study and sojourn at Welfare Hospital, and the few psychotic episodes that occurred are exactly what we would expect in the whole group without considering the administration and effects of excessive doses of marihuana."

Summary

In the study of the actions of marihuana in respect to subjective and objective symptoms and behavior, the marihuana was given a number of times to each of the subjects in the form of the concentrate taken by stomach. The amount given ranged from 2 to 22 cc., in most cases from 2 to 5 cc. After marihuana was taken, the systematic action became evident in from one-half to one hour and the maximum effects were seen in from two to three hours. They passed off gradually, usually in from three to five hours, although in some instances they did not completely disappear until twelve or more hours.

Of the symptoms occurring, a feeling of lightness in the head with some dizziness, a sensation of floating in the air, dryness of the throat, hunger and thirst, unsteadiness and heaviness in the extremities were the most frequent. Tremor and ataxia, dilation of the pupils and sluggishness in responsiveness to light were observed in all subjects.

From observations on the behavior and responses of the subjects, it was found that a mixture of euphoria and apprehension was generally present. If the subjects were undisturbed there was a state of quiet and drowsiness, and unawareness of surroundings, with some difficulty in focusing and sustaining mental concentration. If they were in company, restlessness, talkativeness, laughter and joking were commonly seen. A feeling of apprehension, based on uncertainty regarding the possible effects of the drug and strengthened by any disagreeable sensations present, alternated with the euphoria. If the apprehension developed into a state of real anxiety, a spirit of antagonism was shown. However, any resistance to requests made to the subjects was passive and not physical and there was no aggressiveness or violent behavior observed. Erotic ideas or sensations when present took no active expression.

Six of the subjects developed toxic episodes characteristic of acute marihuana intoxication. The dosage varied from 4 to 8 cc. of the concentrate, and the episodes lasted from three to six hours, in one instance ten hours. The effects were mixtures of euphoric and anxiety states, laughter, elation, excitement, disorientation and mental confusion.

The doses given were toxic to the individuals in question but not to others taking the same or larger ones. Once the drug had been taken the effects were beyond the subject's control. The actions described took unusual expression because for the particular subject at a particular time the dose was unusually effective. A corresponding toxicity did not occur from cigarettes for here the effects came on promptly and on the appearance of any untoward effects, the smoking was stopped.

In three of the subjects a definite psychotic state occurred, in two shortly after marihuana ingestion, in one after a two-week interval. Of the first two, one was an epileptic and the other had a history of heroin addiction and a prepsychotic personality. The third was considered a case of prison psychosis. The conclusion seems warranted that given the potential personality make-up and the right time and environment, marihuana may bring on a true psychotic state.

ORGANIC AND SYSTEMIC FUNCTIONS

Samuel Allentuck, MD

The functions of the body organs and systems were studied in the manner common to hospital practice according to the methods and with the equipment in use at Welfare Hospital. The study was designed to show not only the effects of varying doses of marihuana but also whether subjects who had long been users of the drug gave evidence of organic damage. The tests were made before the drug was administered, during its action, and often in the after period. The heart and circulation, blood composition, kidney, liver and gastro-intestinal function, and basal metabolism received special consideration.

SUMMARY

The most consistent effect of marihuana observed in this division of the study was an increase in pulse rate which began shortly after the taking of the drug, reached a peak in about two hours, and gradually disappeared. In a few instances a temporary sinus tachycardia or sinus bradycardia was noted, but except for these there were no abnormalities in rhythm. The increase in pulse rate was usually accompanied by a rise in blood pressure.

There was in general an increase in the blood sugar level and in the basal metabolic rate, quite marked in some subjects, but in the majority the levels reached did not exceed the high normal limits.

An increase in the frequency of urination was often observed. There was, however, no appreciable increase in the total amount of urine passed during the drug action.

Hunger and an increase in appetite, particularly for sweets, was noted in the majority of the subjects, and the taking of candy or sweetened drinks brought down a "too high" effect of the drug. Nausea and vomiting occurred in a number of instances, diarrhea only during psychotic episodes.

On the other hand, the blood showed no changes in cell count, hemoglobin per cent, or the urea nitrogen, calcium, and phosphorus figures. The figures for the circulation rate and vital capacity and the results of the phenolsulfonphthalein test for kidney infection and the bromsulfalein test for liver function were not different from those of the control period. The electrocardiograms showed no abnormalties which could be attributed to a direct action on the heart. In the few observations on gastric motility and secretion no evidence of marihuana action on these functions was obtained.

The positive results observed, increase in pulse rate and blood pressure, increase in blood sugar and metabolic rate, urge to urinate, increased appetite, nausea and vomiting, and diarrhea, were not intensified by an increase in dosage, for they could occur in an equal degree after the administration of any of the effective doses within the range used. All the effects described are known to be expressions of forms of cerebral excitation, the impulses from this being transmitted through the autonomic system. The alterations in the functions of the organs studied come from the effects of the drug on the central nervous system and are proportional to these effects. A direct action on the organs themselves was not seen.

Psychological Aspects

PSYCHOPHYSICAL AND OTHER FUNCTIONS

Robert S. Morrow, Ph.D.

In this phase of the study an effort was made to determine the effect of marihuana on various psychomotor and some special mental abilities. Appraisal of these effects was made wherever possible through the use of standardized tests. A number of different tests were originally tried under varying experimental conditions on the group of 5 volunteer subjects who had never before taken marihuana. Only those tests were retained which, in the course of this preliminary investigation, demonstrated the greatest potentialities. With the tests finally selected it was hoped to measure the effect of marihuana on the following functions.

FUNCTIONS AND CAPACITIES TESTED

Static Equilibrium

This was measured by means of the Miles Ataxiameter, which is an instrument for recording body sway. The subject remains stationary in the ataxiameter with his hands at his sides and his feet together while a system of pulleys attached to a helmet on his head records the direction and degree of movement. The subject's score is the cumulative sway in all directions measured in millimeters. This test was applied to each subject for two minutes with his eyes open and two minutes with his eyes closed. Each trial was followed by a rest period of five minutes.

Hand Steadiness

Hand steadiness was measured by means of the Whipple Steadiness Tester which consists of a metal disk with a hole $\frac{3}{16}$ of an inch in diameter, connected in series with dry cells, an electric counter, and a stylus. The subject was instructed to hold the stylus in the hole for two minutes without touching the metal sides. Each contact with the side of the hole was recorded and the total number of contacts gave an index of unsteadiness of hand.

Speed of Tapping

Speed of tapping was measured in somewhat the same manner as was hand steadiness. The Whipple Apparatus was used, the tapping board replacing the steadiness disk and a thicker and heavier stylus replacing the steadiness stylus. The subject tapped repeatedly on the metal plate for two minutes and the total number of taps was recorded on the counter, thereby giving a measure of motor speed.

Strength of Grip

The Collins Dynamometer was used to measure the subject's strength of grip. Three trials were made for each hand and the scores averaged.

Simple and Complex Hand and Foot Reaction Time

Special apparatus was constructed to measure simple and complex hand and foot reaction time. To measure simple hand reaction time, the subject was instructed to press down on a telegraph key and remove his hand as quickly as possible when a red light appeared on the board which stood directly before him. A Cenco counter recorded the reaction time, that is, the time which elapsed between the presentation of the stimulus and the response.

For the measurement of simple foot reaction time, the subject pressed down on a pedal with his foot, removing it as quickly as possible when the red light appeared.

For the measurement of complex (choice or discrimination) hand and foot reaction time either a red or a blue light served as a stimulus. The subject had no advance knowledge as to which color light would appear. For measuring the response with the hand, the subject pressed down on the telegraph key with the right hand and, at the sight of the red light, moved the peg from the red compartment into the center (neutral) compartment with the left hand, then removed the right hand from the key; at the appearance of the blue light, he moved the peg from the blue to the neutral compartment. For measuring complex foot reaction time, the procedure was similar to that for estimating the hand reaction time except that the right foot and the pedal were substituted for the right hand and the telegraph key.

Each subject made fifteen trials for each of the four variations.

Musical Aptitude

Musical aptitude was determined by means of the Kwalwasser-Dykema Music Tests. The eight tests administered were the tonal memory test, the quality discrimination test, the intensity discrimination test, the tonal movement test, the time discrimination test, the rhythm discrimination test, the pitch discrimination test, and the melodic taste test. The sum of the scores for these separate tests was used to give a total score for musical aptitude.

Auditory Acuity

By means of the Galton Whistle, the subjects' limits of auditory acuity were gauged for both ascending and descending frequencies. The final score was the average of the results of three trials in each direction.

Perception of Time

An attempt was made to appraise the subject's facility in estimating time by asking him to state when, after a given signal, he thought the following intervals had elapsed—fifteen seconds, one minute, and five minutes. Several trials were given for each time interval and the average of the results of the trials was taken as the final score.

Perception of Length

Subjects were asked to estimate the length of lines which were 3 inches, 5 inches, and 8 inches in length and to draw lines of 3 inches and 7 inches.

The Subjects

Fifty-four subjects were used in this part of the experiment, 36 marihuana users and 18 non-users. The two groups were equated approximately for the following factors: age, height, weight, years of formal education, and number of arrests. The age range for the user group was from 21 to 45 years with 27.9 years as an average; the age range for the non-user group was from 22 to 43 years with 29.8 years as an average. The range in height for the users was from 54 to 75 inches with a mean of 67.5 inches; for the non-users the range was from 60 to 71 inches with a mean of 66.8 inches. Range in weight for the users was from 123 to 178 pounds with 151.3 pounds as the mean, for the non-users from 115 to 180 pounds with 149.5 pounds as the mean. The schooling of the user group ranged from no education at all to 10 years with a mean of 7.1 years; that of the non-users varied from 6 to 12 years with a mean of 8.3 years. As regards the number of arrests, the range for users was from 1 to 20 with a mean of 5.1 and for the non-users from 1 to 15 with a mean of 5.3.

The two groups differed radically with respect to race. Of the 36 marihuana users, 11 (31 per cent) were white, 18 (50 per cent) were Negroes, and 7 (19 percent) were Puerto Ricans. Of the 18 non-users, 12 (67 per cent) were white, 6 (33 per cent) were Negroes, and none were Puerto Rican.

In addition, the user group was analyzed with respect to the age when the marihuana habit was begun, the duration of the habit, the number of marihuana cigarettes generally smoked per day, and the period of deprivation. The variation of the habit as already described for the entire group of users applies to the 36 subjects studied here.

Procedure

The tests were first administered to the subjects before they had taken marihuana, then about a week later when they were under the influence of 2 cc. of marihuana, and finally another week later after 5 cc.[1] of marihuana had been administered. On each occasion the psychomotor tests for static equilibrium, hand steadiness, tapping, strength of grip, and reaction time were repeated at hourly intervals for eight successive hours in order that the time-effects of marihuana might be determined.[2] The other tests, that is, those measuring musical ability, auditory acuity, visual memory, and perception of time and length were given to the subjects while in the undrugged condition and from three to four hours after the drug had been administered. The music tests were given under normal conditions and after 5 cc. of marihuana had been administered, but not under 2 cc. dosage.

In almost all instances the marihuana was given in the morning shortly after breakfast and generally after a day when no drug had been taken in order that "hangover" effects might be avoided. For the most part the subjects rested and did little or nothing except the prescribed tests on days when marihuana was taken.

The equilibrium, steadiness, tapping and strength of grip tests were given together on one day and the different forms of the reaction-time test on another day. Ordinarily four or five days elapsed between retests.

In addition to being tested after standard doses of the marihuana concentrate had been ingested, 11 users and 9 non-users were tested after smoking marihuana cigarettes.[3] The cigarettes weighed from 4 to 8 grains each. Most of the subjects smoked

1 A dose of 5 cc. of marihuana proved "too much" for many non-user subjects in the sense that ingestion of this amount was often followed by nausea and general symptoms of malaise which interfered with further testing. For this reason the higher dose for non-users was sometimes reduced to 3 cc. or 4 cc. In all, only 6 of the non-user subjects took the 5 cc. dose. Accordingly, although the higher dosage is referred to as 5 cc. it should be noted that the actual amount used varied from 3 cc. to 5 cc.

2 The scores for the first 25 users and 6 non-users were obtained every half hour, but since there was little difference between the half-hourly and hourly results it was decided to record hourly scores only, except for the first half hour.

3 A short experiment in which placebos were employed was also tried on these subjects. An attempt was made to have the placebos simulate the marihuana as much as possible but unfortunately the placebo pills had a distinctive taste which rendered them easily identifiable. The subjects referred to them as the "licorice" pills or the "blanks." While the experiment was completed and resulted in some interesting findings, the factors which might have invalidated the results were so serious that these experiments are not reported at this time.

five cigarettes, two non-users smoked only three, and one non-user smoked four. The tests with cigarettes were given at quarter-hour, half-hour and hour intervals.

Summary and Conclusions

1. The effect of marihuana on the psychomotor functions depends primarily on the complexity of the function tested. Simpler functions like speed of tapping and simple reaction time are affected only slightly by large doses (5 cc.) and negligibly, if at all, by smaller doses (2 cc.). On the other hand, the more complex functions like static equilibrium, hand steadiness, and complex reaction time may be affected adversely to a considerable degree by the administration of both large and small doses of marihuana.

2. The function most severely affected is body steadiness and hand steadiness. The ataxia is general in all directions rather than predominant in any particular axis.

3. The effects produced by larger doses (5 cc.) are systematically, though not necessarily proportionately, greater than those brought about by small doses.

4. The time required by the drug to exert its maximum effect varies somewhat with the function and size of dose, but, on the whole, time curves for both functions and dosages have similarity of form. The effect of the drug begins from one to two hours after ingestion and reaches its peak at the fourth hour, after which it declines so that by the eighth hour most of it is dissipated.

5. When marihuana is taken in cigarette form the psychomotor effects are similar in character and trend to those observed after the ingestion of the drug but they occur much sooner and taper off more quickly.

6. The effects seem to be essentially the same for women as for men, except that women are sometimes affected maximally at the second or third hour after the drug is administered. In women the return to the normal condition is in some instances quicker and more abrupt than it is in the men.

7. Non-users generally seem to be more affected by the drug when it is ingested than are users.

8. Auditory acuity is not affected by marihuana.

9. There is no evidence that musical ability, of non-musicians at least, is improved by marihuana.

10. The ability to estimate short periods of time and short linear distances is not measurably affected by the ingestion of marihuana.

INTELLECTUAL FUNCTIONING

Florence Halpern, MA

In this phase of the study investigation was directed primarily toward establishing the effect of marihuana on the subject's intellectual functioning. An attempt was made to determine what changes in mental ability occur under different amounts of the drug, what direction these changes take, when they are first measurable, and how long they persist.

TESTS

Bellevue Adult Intelligence Test

This test was used to measure the general mental level of all the subjects. It was chosen in preference to other available scales because it is the only individual test of intelligence which has been standardized on an adult population, takes into account both verbal and performance abilities, and compares the individual with standards established for his particular age group. It consists of ten tests, five verbal and five performance. The verbal tests cover the fields of general information and general comprehension, draw on the individual's capacity for abstract reasoning and test his arithmetical ability and his rote memory. The performance tests also evaluate the subject's comprehension of social situations, but here the results are independent of language. There are also tests of the individual's ability to carry out a routine task, to organize parts into a meaningful whole, to distinguish between essential and unessential details, and to analyze and synthesize.

Army Alpha (Bregman Revision, Forms A, B, 5, 7 and Bellevue Revision)

This is a group test first used in the United States Army in 1917 and 1918 when it was given to more than a million recruits. It consists of eight tests: test 1, a direction test which was not used in this study since the item does not appear on all forms; test 2, a test of arithmetical reasoning; test 3, a test of common sense in which the subject indicates which he considers the best of three possible responses to a given question; test 4, a modified vocabulary test; test 5, in which the subject must mentally reorganize disarranged sentences and then indicate whether the resultant statement is true or false; test 6, a test of numerical relations in which the subject must supply the last two numbers in a numerical series on the basis of the relationship between the first six numbers; test 7, a test of analogies in which the subject determines the relationship between two given words and then underlines one of four words which is related to a third word in the same way; and test 8, which on Forms A and B and on the Bellevue Revision is a test of general information in which the subject is given a choice of five answers to a question. On Forms 5 and 7, this test is a test of directions.

Because this test has five alternate forms which are roughly of equivalent difficulty it could be repeated many times within a short time interval. It was therefore used to establish a curve showing at what time following ingestion the marihuana has an effect on general intelligence and on individual higher mental processes.

Pyle's Digit Symbol Test

In this test each number from 1 through 9 is associated with a specific symbol, as, for example, number 1 is associated with a square and number 2 with an asterisk. The numbers and their associated symbols appear at the top of the sheet of paper. Below the sample are rows of symbols, five symbols to a row, followed by five blank squares. The subject is expected to fill in each square with the number associated with the respective symbol. With practice the association bond between the number and the symbol becomes stronger and the subject depends less and less on the model at the top of the sheet. He is therefore able to work faster and his learning rate is reflected in the increased number of squares filled.

Cancellation Test

The subject is required to cross out a specific geometric form wherever it appears on a sheet which is covered with rows of geometric figures. This measures the individual's capacity for carrying out a routine task.

Form Board Test

The measurement of the ability to manipulate concrete material in contrast to the verbal or abstract ability determined by the Army Alpha test required the introduction of certain form board tests. These were the Seguin Form Board, the Two Figure Board, the Casuist Board, the Five Figure Board, Healy A, Triangle Test, Diagonal Test, all administered and scored according to the Pintner-Patterson Performance Series. The Seguin Form Board has ten blocks of various geometric forms, to be put in their appropriate places as rapidly as possible. Three trials are given. The Two Figure Board has nine pieces which, when placed correctly, form a large cross and a large square. Time and the number of moves are recorded. The Casuist Board has twelve pieces which, when correctly placed, form three circles and an oval. Time and errors are recorded. The Five Figure Board has five geometrical figures which are formed by the correct placement of two or three pieces for each figure. Time and errors are recorded. Healy A has five small rectangular pieces which, when placed correctly, form a large rectangle. Time and the number of moves are recorded. The Triangle Test consists of four triangular pieces which are fitted together in a board. Time and errors are recorded. The Diagonal Test has five pieces of various shapes which must be fitted together in a rectangular frame. Time and moves are recorded.

Kohs Block Design Test

This is a performance test which is less a test of manual dexterity and more dependent on abstract intelligence than are the form board tests. It correlates more highly with intelligence than do most performance items and yet it is entirely independent of language. Therefore, the individual who cannot express himself well or who suffers from a language handicap is not penalized as he is on verbal scales.

The test consists of sixteen cubes each with a red, a white, a blue, a yellow, a red-and-white, and a blue-and-yellow side. A colored design which can be reproduced with the cubes is placed before the subject and he is expected to make it. Results are rated numerically, depending upon the time consumed in execution. In this experiment two sets of designs of equivalent difficulty were required; Designs IV, VI, and XIV were selected for one series and V, VII, and XII for the other.

Memory Tests

Although memory in itself cannot be considered a measure of intelligence, it is essential to any intelligent functioning and must therefore be included in any estimate of intelligence. Three aspects of memory, namely rote memory, the ability to recall presented objects, and visual memory were tested. The rote memory test requires the repetition of digits in forward and reverse order as given on the Bellevue Intelligence Test.

Object memory was tested by exposing ten small objects for three seconds and recording the number of articles the subject was able to recall. Visual memory or the ability to reproduce designs after a ten-second exposure was estimated by using the designs and scoring technique from the Army Performance Test.

PROCEDURE

The Bellevue Adult Intelligence Test

Each subject was given the Bellevue Adult Intelligence test within two or three days after his admission to the hospital and before any marihuana had been administered.

The Army Alpha, Pyle's Digit Symbol, and Cancellation Tests

These tests were given as group tests to a total of 20 subjects. The Army Alpha and Pyle's Digit Symbol tests were given every half-hour, beginning a half-hour after drug ingestion. The Army Alpha was continued for seven hours and Digit Symbol for five hours. The Cancellation test was given every hour for six hours, beginning one hour after drug administration. Eleven users and 9 non-users took the Army Alpha and the Digit Symbol tests, while 9 users and 11 non-users took the Cancellation test.

Tests 2 through 8 of the Army Alpha require twenty and a half minutes for actual performance while such preparations as the distribution of papers and the reading of directions consume almost ten minutes more, so that had the entire Alpha been given at each half-hourly session, the subjects would have gone from test to test with no intermittent rest period. For this reason the tests were divided and the following schedule arranged:

	First Day			*Second Day*	
Test 2	5 minutes		Test 6	3 minutes	
Test 3	1½ minutes		Test 7	3 minutes	
Test 4	2* minutes		Test 8	4 minutes	
Test 5	2 minutes		Cancellation	1½ minutes	
Digit Symbol	2 minutes			11½ minutes	
	12½ minutes				

Each subject took three test series, one without the drug, one with 2 cc. and one with 3, 4, 5, or 6 cc., depending on indi-

---

* Although one and a half minutes is the usual time allotment for this test, two minutes were used for it in this study.

vidual tolerance. A test series consisted of fourteen half-hour sessions for the Alpha, ten half-hour sessions for the Digit Symbol and seven hourly sessions for the Cancellation tests. Because of the time factor, a series required two days for its completion.

The halves of a series were given on successive days, and the different series a week apart. Thus for example, a subject might take his first test series with 2 cc. on Monday and Tuesday of one week; the following Monday and Tuesday the series would be repeated with the subject in a different drug state (no drug or 5 cc.); and a final series would be given the third week with the subject in still another drug condition.

An effort was made to obviate practice effect by giving the first test series to one third of the subjects without drug, to one third with 2 cc., and to one third with 3, 4, or 5 cc. However, because of the necessity of increasing dosage gradually this ideal presentation was not actually obtained. The following gives the amount of drug administered to users and non-users at each test series.

| USERS | | NON-USERS | |
No. of cases	Size of dose (in cc.)	No. of cases	Size of dose (in cc.)
3	0, 2, 5*	3	0, 2, 5
3	2, 5, 0	2	2, 5, 0
2	5, 0, 2	1	-, 5, 0†
1	5, 0, -**	2	2, 0, 5
2	5, 2, 0	1	2, 0, -‡

1st Trial	2nd Trial	3rd Trial	1st Trial	2nd Trial	3rd Trial
0 cc. - 3	0 cc. - 3	0 cc. - 5	0 cc. - 3	0 cc. - 3	0 cc. - 3
2 cc. - 3	2 cc. - 5	2 cc. - 2	2 cc. - 5	2 cc. - 3	2 cc. - 0
5 cc. - 5	5 cc. - 3	5 cc. - 3	5 cc. - 0	5 cc. - 3	5 cc. - 5

Since the various forms of the Army Alpha are not absolutely equivalent in difficulty, their order of presentation for any one group had to be identical in each of the three drug states. However, for each of the three groups tested the order of presentation was different so that all the difficult forms did not come at the same interval, as is shown on the following page.

* 5 cc. is used to indicate large doses although the amount ranged from 3 cc. to 6 cc. depending on individual tolerance. In the non-user group no maximum dose for this test was more than 4 cc.
** Entered experiment too late to take more than two series.
† Patient took initial series with 5 cc. but became so ill test was discontinued and only two subsequent series given.
‡ Patient discharged from experiment before third series was given.

Kohs Block Design, Form Board, and Memory Tests

Administration of these tests differed markedly from those discussed above in that no attempt was made to give them at regular successive time intervals. Rather, they formed part of a battery of individual tests given to various subjects under specific drug conditions. For example, 5 cc. of marihuana would be ordered for a patient for 8:00 A.M., and testing began as soon thereafter as the patient appeared "high," the state of "highness" being judged by the subject's own statement, his pulse rate, the condition of his pupils and other physiological signs.

Time	Group I	Group II	Group III
9:30	A	5	Bellevue
10:00	5	B	7
10:30	B	A	5
11:00	7	7	A
11:30	A	Bellevue	B
12:00	5	5	Bellevue
12:30	B	B	7
1:00	7	A	5
1:30	A	7	A
2:00	5	Bellevue	B
2:30	B	5	Bellevue
3:00	7	B	7
3:30	A	A	5
4:00	5	7	A

Kohs Block Design was given to each subject twice, once without the drug and once with 5 cc. The test was taken by a total of 21 subjects, 10 users and 11 non-users. Five users took the test first without the drug, 5 had their first trial with 5 cc. Of the non-user group 8 had their first trial without marihuana, 3 with 4 cc. The average time at which the test was given to the user group was three and a half hours after drug administration, with range from two to five and a half hours. For the non-user group, the average time of administration of the test was also three and a half hours after the drug was given, range two and half to five and a half hours.

The two series of designs (one series being Designs IV, VI and XIV, the other V, VII and XII) were presented in such manner that half of the subjects were tested on one series and half on the other series while they were under the influence of marihuana. Thus any difference in degree of difficulty between the two sets of designs was cancelled out. The weighted scores given on the Arthur Point scale were used in evaluating the results.

Form Board Tests were divided into three batteries, each battery consisting of the Seguin Form Board, one of the three larger boards (Two Figure, Five Figure, or Casuist) and one of the three smaller boards. Various combinations of boards were used under various drug conditions in order to make the results as comparable as possible. The following indicates the number of times the various boards were used with different dosages of marihuana.

From the results it appears that Gwyn Triangle was used too often with 5 cc. and Healy A was not used often enough.

	0 cc.	2 cc.	5 cc.	Total
Casuist	8	6	6	20
Two Figure	5	7	6	18
Five Figure	6	5	6	17
Diagonal	6	5	8	19
Triangle	7	4	9	20
Healy A	6	7	3	16

Aside from the Triangle and the Healy A, the distribution of boards in different drug stages was such as to obviate any differences in degree of difficulty. Nineteen subjects, 10 users and 9 non-users, took this test. The results were scored for time and errors according to the Pintner-Patterson Performance series.

Memory tests. The first digit span test was always given before marihuana had been administered, since the Bellevue Scale was given each patient during the first two or three days of the study. The trials under 2 cc. and 5 cc. were alternated. In all, 28 subjects, 17 users and 11 non-users, took this test before and after the ingestion of marihuana. The final score equaled the number of digits recalled.

To test Object Memory, ten small articles such as a key, a ring, a pill box, and a crayon were placed on a flat, neutral surface and exposed for three seconds. An attempt was made to vary some of the articles at each presentation so that six or seven were the same and three or four were different. Twenty-six subjects, 11 users and 15 non-users, took this test. They were so divided that 10 of them took the test the first time without drug, 10 with 2 cc., and 6 with 5 cc.

To test Visual Memory, Army designs were given each subject three times, once prior to the administration of marihuana, once under 2 cc., and once under 5 cc. The test was given to a total of 28 subjects, 16 users and 12 non-users.

Because there is no alternative form for this test, results were definitely influenced by practice. Here, therefore, more than with any other test, it became important to arrange the order of administration. The following indicates the dosage of marihuana at the first test.

	0 cc.	2 cc.	5 cc.
User	6	5	5
Non-User	5	4	3
Total	11	9	8

It is obvious that the initial examination was given slightly more often when the subjects were not under the influence of the drug. Improvement derived from practice is therefore more of a factor in the tests which were performed under marihuana.

FINDINGS

Bellevue Adult Intelligence Test

General Intelligence. The results of the Bellevue Adult Intelligence Test which was administered to 60 subjects, 40 users and 20 non-users, are shown in Table 5. As has been pointed out elsewhere, these findings indicate that both the user and the non-user groups may be classified as of average intelligence.

TABLE 5

I.Q. as determined by the Bellevue Intelligence Test and age of sixty subjects

Subjects	Age (in years)		Verbal I.Q.		Performance I.Q.		Total I.Q.	
	Average	Range	Average	Range	Average	Range	Average	Range
White								
13 Users	27.7	21–34	105.6	79–125	105.7	78–129	106.1	77–124
15 Non-users	28.3	22–43	105.5	80–117	106.3	81–116	106.3	96–114
Negro								
19 Users	27.8	22–45	93.1	77–118	93.2	67–112	92.6	70–112
5 Non-users	30.8	25–37	100.0	88–106	96.8	84–105	98.8	93–101
Puerto Rican								
8 Users	29.0	24–34	91.5	73–100	92.2	74–108	91.0	72–100
Total								
40 Users	28.5	21–45	96.9	73–125	97.1	74–129	96.7	70–124
20 Non-users	28.9	22–43	104.1	80–118	103.9	81–116	104.5	93–114

Mental Deterioration. Studies of mental deterioration due to toxic, organic or psychotic factors, as given in the literature, reveal that in such cases the subtest scores on the Bellevue

Adult Intelligence Test show marked irregularity, depending upon the functions involved in the deteriorative process. As a group, the marihuana users tested show very even functioning, and what little irregularity occurred can be explained on the basis of language and racial factors.[4] From this we may conclude that the marihuana users had suffered no mental deterioration as a result of their use of the drug.

Army Alpha Test

Total Mental Functioning. The total scores obtained from this test at the successive testing periods are shown in Table 6. Those recorded before the administration of the drug give a picture like that seen in any learning curve, that is, there is a gradual increment in test scores at each testing interval, interspersed with plateau periods. Thus, without drug the test score for the second testing interval showed a 2 per cent gain over the initial score, the score for the third testing interval showed a 4 per cent gain over the initial score, and so on up to the last testing period when there was a 13 per cent gain over the initial test score.

Between two and a half and three hours after ingestion of 2 cc. of the drug there appeared to be a possible very slight falling off in mental ability. Otherwise the results paralleled the findings obtained in the undrugged condition except that toward the end of the day the increments were larger than those which occurred when the subjects were undrugged. This may be due to complications in the experimental procedure or may be an indication of accelerated mental functioning resulting from drug ingestion. This point is discussed more fully when the effect on different mental functions is considered.

Deleterious effects were apparent an hour after the ingestion of 5 cc. of marihuana. There was a 3 per cent drop from the initial score at this one-hour period and this first attainment is not surpassed until four and a half hours after drug ingestion. From the four-and-a-half-hour period on to the end of the testing there were gradual increments in score.

Different Mental Functions. A very elaborate study was made of the scores made on the subtest (Table 7). Some irregularities occurred even in the undrugged state, and these may be attributed primarily to chance factors, as, for example, the difference in difficulty of the various test forms. On the whole, the findings were in line with those which one would

4 The age factor does not affect the result since the groups were well equated in this respect.

expect in any situation where constant repetition increases efficiency.

The effects of 2 cc. of marihuana on the different mental functions were variable. Tests involving number concepts gave clear-cut, consistent findings and revealed that impairment occurred an hour after the drug was taken and continued for from two and a half to three hours after ingestion. Results of other tests showed that there was little if any loss in ability, and some of them, especially those done toward the end of the day, showed gains which exceeded the ones made in the undrugged state. It is not possible on the basis of the present data to ascertain whether these large increments indicate that small amounts of the drug serve as stimulants in situations dependent primarily upon verbal facility or whether they are due to certain complications in the test technique. The former theory coincides with the increased verbosity noted on other tests as well as with the clinical impression, but the latter also cannot be overlooked. Further investigation of this point is definitely indicated.

The effect of the 5 cc. dosage on each function was in line with that reported for total scores, that is, there was a falling off in efficiency one hour after the drug was taken and this impairment continued for anywhere from three and a half to six and a half hours after ingestion. Here too the scores on tests involving number concepts were most severely affected, recovery for them taking place from six to six and a half hours after drug administration.

Degree and Duration of Drug Effect. In general it may be stated that marihuana has a deleterious effect on mental functioning, the extent, time of onset, and duration of the impairment being related to the amount of drug taken.

The adverse effect of the 2 cc. dosage on global intelligence was slight (about 3 per cent to 4 per cent impairment in efficiency) and of sort duration, occurring at about two and a half hours after ingestion and lasting little longer than a half-hour or an hour. Certain mental functions, especially those dealing with number concepts, appear to have been affected much earlier than others, the effect on the number test scores being measurable as early as one hour after ingestion and continuing until two and a half hours after ingestion. For other functions, in particular those involving verbal facility, the results were variable, in some instances showing no adverse effect and even a slight acceleration.

The effect of 5 cc. of marihuana on global intellectual functioning was apparent within an hour from the time the drug was taken and was operative until four and a half hours

TABLE 6

Effect of marihuana on mental functioning as shown by total scores on Army Alpha Tests made by twenty subjects

MEASUREMENTS OF TOTAL SCORES MADE BY TWENTY SUBJECTS UNDER DOSES OF

Time after ingestion (in hours)	0 cc.					2 cc.					5 cc.				
	Average	S.D.	Range	*Smoothed average	Change over initial score (in %)	Average	S.D.	Range	*Smoothed average	Change over initial score (in %)	Average	S.D.	Range	*Smoothed average	Change over initial score (in %)
½	107.1	43.97	20–179	108.1		89.5	36.17	32–167	92.4		114.3	35.47	61–181	113.5	
1	109.1	48.32	26–192	110.1	2	95.3	37.88	48–186	95.7	4	112.6	37.39	58–180	110.2	—3
1½	111.1	44.46	28–185	112.9	4	96.0	38.15	36–181	99.4	8	107.8	34.81	54–161	108.5	—4
2	114.6	47.28	34–188	111.7	3	102.8	37.54	28–179	99.4	8	109.1	36.82	50–163	107.8	—5
2½	108.7	44.91	39–186	112.7	4	95.9	36.57	33–176	96.3	4	106.5	34.79	52–158	110.8	—2
3	116.7	44.75	38–184	117.7	9	96.6	35.03	48–182	98.6	7	115.0	35.73	60–172	113.3	0
3½	118.7	43.09	41–193	118.8	10	100.5	35.65	46–186	100.9	9	111.6	38.62	52–165	113.0	0
4	118.8	41.34	49–184	120.1	11	101.3	35.25	56–185	102.5	11	114.3	39.15	57–174	117.1	3
4½	121.3	40.77	51–190	118.6	11	103.7	35.19	41–184	102.5	11	119.8	35.19	66–177	118.9	5
5	115.8	43.57	41–191	117.2	8	101.3	33.59	36–184	105.0	14	118.0	34.22	65–169	120.2	6
5½	118.5	41.44	36–188	121.2	12	108.7	31.67	52–180	111.0	20	122.4	36.02	61–179	122.0	7
6	123.8	39.57	53–194	121.6	14	113.3	34.49	61–190	114.7	24	121.6	38.90	59–180	122.9	8
6½	123.3	40.29	56–187	123.6	13	116.1	33.18	66–183	115.7	25	124.2	36.17	70–179	125.5	11
7	120.8	44.06	43–191	122.1		115.2	36.24	51–189			126.7	35.01	71–174		

* Smoothed average is obtained by averaging scores of successive intervals.

after ingestion. All mental functions showed this early impairment but for some of them recovery from the adverse effect was earlier than for others. Those most severely impaired from point of view of duration were the ones dealing with number concepts.

The testing program was continued for only seven hours after the drug was taken and, therefore, any estimate of the effect of marihuana after this time is purely a subjective one. However, both the subject and the examiner felt that the drug produced a "hang-over" which in most cases continued into the following day. The subject complained of being headachy, sleepy, and unable to work at his usual level, and the examiner also noted that the subject did not work as well or as quickly when called upon to do something on a day following marihuana ingestion.

The impairment reported here is not entirely representative of the maximum impairment which occurs under the influence of marihuana. Two opposing variables account for the results obtained in the drugged condition. One variable is practice effect which tends to increase test scores with each succeeding trial. The other variable, the drug, tends to lower test scores. In the earlier sessions there was evidence that the marihuana, especially when given in large doses, is the more potent force, as seen by the continuing downward trend of the curve during the first few hours. In these earlier phases, in spite of repetition, results were lower with each succeeding trial, or if there was no actual loss, the increments made were never comparable to those made in the undrugged state. Three or four hours after drug administration there was a general trend toward rising scores. Some of this gain must be attributed to increased practice effect which was counteracting, in part at least, the deleterious effect of the marihuana. For this reason it is not certain that the drug was less effective at later points in the curve than it was at the moment of seemingly greatest impairment. This seems particularly plausible because, beginning with the third hour, the subject was no longer working on new tasks but was actually repeating identical tasks that he performed earlier in the day. Thus, at the third hour the test form used was the same as the one given at the initial session; at the end of the three-and-a-half-hour period the form was the same as the one-hour examination, and so on. What is shown in the curves is the effect of marihuana on intellectual tasks with which the subject has become very familiar. For practical purposes the test situation has the advantage of being comparable with daily living since the tasks performed in daily routine are usually relatively familiar ones.

TABLE 7

Effect of marihuana on individual mental functions as shown by Army Alpha Subtests on twenty subjects

Time after ingestion (in hours)	Arithmetical reasoning			Common sense			Same-opposite			Mixed sentences			Numerical relations			Analogies		
	0 cc.	Dose 2 cc.	5 cc.	0 cc.	Dose 2 cc.	5 cc.	0 cc.	Dose 2 cc.	5 cc.	0 cc.	Dose 2 cc.	5 cc.	0 cc.	Dose 2 cc.	5 cc.	0 cc.	Dose 2 cc.	5 cc.
1¼	3	1	−5	−3	−6	−6	0	13	−1	3	2	−2	2	−1	−2	2	6	−1
1¾	5	0	−9	3	0	−6	5	22	2	7	11	1	3	−6	−5	7	11	−4
2¼	7	0	−9	7	7	−1	−3	14	−7	3	7	−3	6	−1	−5	7	13	−5
2¾	9	2	−5	13	13	6	−7	10	−9	4	1	−6	10	0	−5	5	13	−7
3¼	10	8	−3	16	13	7	3	13	−4	9	8	−1	11	1	−6	10	18	−3
3¾	9	5	−4	15	16	3	4	11	−4	13	13	0	11	5	−2	12	14	11
4¼	9	3	−4	17	16	9	5	12	−2	15	19	1	11	8	−7	16	15	11
4¾	12	5	−3	20	14	6	0	4	−1	6	15	4	13	10	−6	16	19	10
5¼	12	9	−2	20	19	15	−3	5	6	−1	13	−7	14	11	−4	12	18	14
5¾	12	9	−1	23	25	18	3	19	4	4	19	1	12	8	−4	18	31	14
6¼	12	10	1	19	29	21	1	26	−5	9	24	8	13	8	10	25	41	17
6¾	12	11	1	23	30	20	−3	23	−4	13	32	8	13	10	10	24	41	22

AVERAGE INCREASE (IN PER CENT) OVER INITIAL SCORE* IN SUBTESTS FOR

* Using smoothed curve.

Speed Versus Power. Intellectual impairment under the influence of marihuana resulted from a loss in both speed and efficiency. There was a slowing up in output indicated by the difference in the number of items done before and after the administration of the drug. On the whole the number of test items attempted tended to increase at each succeeding examination period even when the subject was under the influence of marihuana, but the percentage of increase in the drugged state practically never equaled that attained for the corresponding time interval when the subject had not ingested the drug. The findings for the number of items done in the drugged and undrugged condition follow very closely the findings in respect to the number of items correctly done. From this it may be concluded that under the influence of marihuana an individual functions less rapidly and also less efficiently than when he has had no drug.

Careful analysis of what causes the loss in efficiency reveals that certain factors not necessarily related to mental ability per se were accountable for the reduced scores in the drugged state. For example, under the influence of the drug the subject felt dizzy, had blurred vision, or exhibited other handicapping physiological disturbances. These impeded his efficiency in putting his answer on the correct line, or marking a cross in the right box. Men were observed running their fingers across the page in an effort to keep their place. On the other hand, much of the intellectual loss can be ascribed to an impairment in the thinking processes, and there seemed to be a general confusion of ideas and inability to maintain a fixed goal. Some subjects reported that the reason they accomplished so little was that, by the time they had finished reading a question, they no longer remembered what their purpose in reading it had been. Occasionally perseveration of a form of response specific to one test was found in a subsequent test. For example, some forms of the Same-Opposite test require the subject to mark the answer S or O. In a later test requiring a plus or minus response occasional irrelevant S's or O's appeared.

Comparison of the Effect of Marihuana on User and Non-User. When the group is divided into marihuana users and non-users certain interesting and suggestive differences are revealed (Table 8). Although the general findings for total intelligence scores for the two groups follow similar curves, the deleterious effects were not as great on the user as on the non-user. Thus under 2 cc. of marihuana the user showed no real intellectual impairment except for a very short interval beginning about two and a half hours after ingestion and lasting for an hour or an hour and a half. In contrast to this he made gains both at the beginning of the testing and toward the end of the day which exceeded those made in the undrugged state. The non-user who had ingested 2 cc. of marihuana showed a definite drop in score beginning about two and a half hours after ingestion, and for a period from one and a half to two and a half hours after this time he did not make increments comparable to those which he made in the undrugged state. Following this, during the last two hours of testing he, like the user, obtained scores which showed an acceleration not paralleled in the undrugged state.

TABLE 8

Comparison of the effect of marihuana on the mental functioning of users and non-users as shown by total scores made on Army Alpha Tests

Time after ingestion (in hours)	PER CENT INCREASE OVER INITIAL SCORE° MADE UNDER DOSES OF					
	0 cc.		2 cc.		5 cc.	
	11 users	9 non-users	11 users	9 non-users	11 users	9 non-users
1¼	−1	6	1	6	−3	− 3
1¾	1	8	7	9	−1	− 7
2¼	4	3	10	3	2	−12
2¾	4	4	9	−1	3	− 7
3¼	5	12	8	6	2	− 2
3¾	6	14	9	10	1	− 2
4¼	9	14	14	8	7	0
4¾	9	11	17	4	11	− 1
5¼	7	10	15	12	12	0
5¾	11	13	17	24	11	4
6¼	12	17	20	29	11	6
6¾	9	18	22	29	14	7

° Using smoothed averages.

Under 5 cc. of marihuana both the user and the non-user showed a 3 per cent loss in efficiency within an hour of the time that the drug was taken. Although recovery was slow for both groups, the user was less severely affected, as is indicated by the fact that at the next testing interval his score was only 1 per cent below his initial score as compared with a 7 per cent loss on the part of the non-user. The disparity in the degree of impairment for the two groups continued for several hours. The more marked drug effect in the case of the non-user was further evidenced by the fact that the user showed recovery four or four and a half hours after ingestion (as measured by the time when his scores approach those made when in the undrugged state) while the non-user, even at the end of seven hours of testing, did not approximate his undrugged performances.

No simple explanation of this difference is available. The most probable reason seems to be that previous use of the drug in some way serves to ameliorate that anxiety and inevitable disorganization which the use of any drug may have on an individual who has never taken it before. Another explanation may lie in possible physiological adaptation to the drug which, though not identical with tolerance in the ordinary pharmacological sense, seems to act in the same direction.

Variability. The results reported here are all in terms of averages. A study of individual scores indicates that there was marked variability in the effect of the drug on different subjects. In one case the drug action came early and soon disappeared. Another subject experienced no reaction until after he had eaten his lunch, at which time a very definite effect was apparent. A third subject showed impairment late in the day when the drug effect on almost all the other subjects had worn off. There were some hardy souls who did not appear to be affected by even large quantities of marihuana, while a few (mainly non-users) became so ill that they could not continue with the examinations.

Pyle's Digit Symbol Test

Comparison of the results obtained on this test when the subject was in the undrugged condition and when he had had 2 cc. of marihuana reveals that small amounts of the drug did not interfere with his ability to carry out the appointed task (Table 9). In fact, as was noted above for certain other tests, the improvement in score at the end of two and a half or three hours was greater after the ingestion of 2 cc. of marihuana than it was when no drug had been administered, and at the end of the five-hour testing period there was a 32 per cent increase in score as against a 22 per cent increase in the undrugged condition.

Under the influence of 5 cc. of marihuana, however, there was a decrease in ability occuring within an hour after the time the drug was administered. Although the scores show no actual loss as compared with the initial score, the increments did not equal those made in the undrugged condition until from four to four and a half hours after ingestion.

It may therefore be concluded that certain types of learning ability are not affected by small amounts (2 cc.) of mari-

TABLE 9

Effect of marihuana on learning ability as measured by Pyle's Digit Symbol Test

Time after ingestion (in hours)	MARIHUANA DOSAGE					
	0 cc. (20 subjects)		2 cc. (18 subjects)		4.5 cc. (19 subjects)	
	Average score* (smoothed)	Increase over initial score (in %)	Average score* (smoothed)	Increase over initial score (in %)	Average score* (smoothed)	Increase over initial score (in %)
¾	78.6	—	60.8	—	75.4	—
1¼	82.8	5	63.8	5	77.5	3
1¾	85.9	9	66.3	9	77.7	3
2¼	88.4	12	71.1	17	78.6	4
2¾	91.9	17	75.5	24	79.0	5
3¼	92.6	18	73.9	22	80.6	7
3¾	92.9	18	74.9	23	85.2	13
4¼	93.7	19	78.1	28	91.3	21
4¾	95.7	22	80.3	32	95.8	27

* Score = number of right answers — number of wrong answers.

huana, but are impaired when larger amounts (5 cc.) are ingested.

Cancelling a Geometric Form

The results of this test are shown in Table 10.

With 2 cc. of marihuana, there was a slight falling off in

TABLE 10

Effect of marihuana on the ability to carry out a routine task as measured by the cancelling of geometric figures by twenty subjects

Time after ingestion (in hours)	MARIHUANA DOSAGE					
	0 cc.		2 cc.		4.5 cc.	
	Average score*	Increase over initial score (in %)	Average score*	Increase over initial score (in %)	Average score*	Increase over initial score (in %)
1	59.2	—	50.5	—	52.1	—
2	65.0	10	56.5	12	54.4	4
3	65.9	11	55.1	9	55.2	6
4	67.2	14	57.0	13	54.9	5
5	66.5	12	58.3	15	57.9	11
6	74.0	25	62.3	23	64.8	24

* Score = number of right answers — number of wrong answers.

the subject's efficiency occurring about three hours after drug ingestion. At that time he was 3 per cent less efficient than he had been an hour previous. With 5 cc. of marihuana there was a slowing up in the subject's ability to carry out the appointed task, which was apparent two hours after drug ingestion (and possibly earlier). At that time there was only a 4 per cent increment over his initial score as compared with a 10 per cent increment in the undrugged state and a 12 per cent increment when the 2 cc. dosage had been administered. He improved only slightly at the three- and four-hour testing interval, and only at the five-hour interval did he show an appreciable improvement.

Apparently, the carrying out of a simple routine task is adversely affected to a slight degree and for a short period of time as the result of the ingestion of 2 cc. of marihuana, while the ingestion of 5 cc. of the drug produces adverse effects which are more severe and more lasting.

Performance Tests

Seguin Form Board. For adults of average intelligence this test is primarily one involving speed of reaction time. The average time taken by the subjects when they were not under the influence of marihuana was 12.8 seconds. This was increased to 14.0 and 14.1 seconds under doses of 2 cc. and 5 cc. respectively. Thus, ingestion of marihuana in 2 cc. and 5 cc. doses caused a 9 per cent delay in performance time.

Form Boards. The time scores for this test remained practically the same whether no drug, 2 cc. or 5 cc. of marihuana had been administered, the average scores in terms of mental age being respectively 11.7, 11.7 and 11.9 years. The error scores also showed little change as a result of drug ingestion, the averages in terms of mental age being 9.7 years (no marihuana), 9.9 years (2 cc.) and 10.2 years (5 cc.), and what change occurred was in a positive direction, that is, there was a very slight improvement in the subject's performance when he was under the influence of marihuana.

Kohs Block Design. This test correlates more highly with abstract intelligence than do any of the other performance tests. Here the drug had a definitely deleterious effect when it was administered in large amounts. The average score was 17.6 when the subjects were not under the influence of marihuana and 14.8 after they had ingested the drug; that is, under 5 cc. of marihuana there was a 16 per cent loss in score as compared with undrugged results.

In general it appears that those functions most closely associated with higher intellectual processes are more impaired by the drug than are the simpler functions.

Memory Tests

Rote Memory. As measured by the ability to repeat digits forward there were no changes in rote memory as a result of drug ingestion, the average scores under no drug, 2 cc. of marihuana, and 5 cc. of marihuana being in each case 7.1.

Digits Reversed. Although the giving of digits in reverse order is always grouped with memory tests, this task actually requires something over and above mere recall. It demands a mental control not necessary in tests dependent purely upon rote memory. Although simple rote memory, as measured by the ability to repeat digits forward, was not affected by the ingestion of marihuana, the repetition of digits reversed was affected adversely. In the undrugged state the average for the group was 5.4, with 2 cc. the average was 5.0, and with 5 cc. it was 4.8. The impairment was comparatively small but it seems to have been related to the amount of drug taken.

Object Memory. The average scores under no drug, 2 cc. of marihuana, and 5 cc. of marihuana were respectively 6.2, 5.6, and 5.9; that is, there was a loss of about 9 per cent in the subject's ability to recall objects which had been exposed to his vision for three seconds when he took the test under the influence of 2 cc. of marihuana, while after the ingestion of 5 cc. the impairment was less, being only about 5 per cent. This seemingly contradictory result is probably due to the fact that by the time the subjects took the test under the influence of 5 cc. most of them had already had it two times previously. The loss in terms of absolute number of remembered articles was slight.

Visual Memory. In this test as in the case of digits reversed something over and above simple memory function is involved. A capacity for analysis and synthesis which correlates well with intelligence is required for the successful execution of this task, and it is this function which is adversely affected by the ingestion of marihuana. The average scores were 10.3 (no drug), 9.7 (2 cc.) and 7.8 (5 cc.); that is, after the ingestion of 2 cc. of marihuana there was a 6 per cent drop in score, while under 5 cc. there was a 24 per cent drop.

In general one may conclude that simple memory functions are not affected by the administration of marihuana while the more complex memory functions are affected adversely, the extent of the impairment being related to the amount of drug taken.

Throughout the examination of subjects on individual tests, the same difference was observed in intensity of the effect upon user and non-user as was noted in group tests.

Experiments with Marihuana Cigarettes

In addition to the tests made to determine the effect of the ingestion of marihuana on various intellectual functions, several experiments were tried with marihuana cigarettes. The tests used in this part of the study were the Bellevue Adult Intelligence Test; the Woody McCall Mixed Fundamentals Test, Form I, which consists of thirty-five examples requiring addition, subtraction, multiplication or division; a cancellation test in which the subject is required to cross out a specific number (in this instance the number 8) wherever it appears on a sheet covered with rows of numbers; the Kohs Block Design Test; and the test for rote, object, and visual memory.

The subjects took the test series and individual tests twice, once without the drug and once after having smoked marihuana cigarettes. They were not given a specific number of cigarettes but were told to smoke until they felt "high." The number of cigarettes smoked to produce this effect ranged from two to seven.

The Mixed Fundamentals and cancellation tests were given as group tests and were repeated at half-hour intervals for two and a half hours. In the series given when the subjects were "high," the first test was taken as soon as the cigarettes had been smoked. Time limit on each test was one and a half minutes.

The Bellevue Adult, Kohs, and memory tests were given as individual tests and were administered only twice, once before the subject had smoked marihuana cigarettes and once after he had become "high" from smoking them. If during the course of the examination he wanted another cigarette or the examiner had reason to suspect that he was no longer under the influence of the drug, more cigarettes were smoked. The number of cigarettes used during a three-hour testing period ranged from six to twelve.

In the cancellation, Kohs, and memory tests the subjects were so divided that half took the tests for the first time before they had smoked and half after they had smoked. In the Woody McCall Mixed Fundamentals Test more non-users had their first tests before they had smoked. The Bellevue Adult Intelligence Test was always given first without the drug during the two or three days immediately following the subject's admission. Four weeks later the test was repeated on

10 subjects while they were under the influence of marihuana cigarettes.

Bellevue Adult Intelligence Test

Ten subjects, 5 users and 5 non-users, repeated this test under the influence of marihuana. The results are shown in Table 11.

TABLE 11

Effect of marihuana cigarettes on I. Q. of ten subjects as measured by the Bellevue Adult Intelligence Test

Dose	Verbal I.Q. Average	Range	Performance I.Q. Average	Range	Total I.Q. Average	Range
Without Cigarettes ..	100.7	88-118	102.3	81-129	101.6	89-124
With Cigarettes ...	101.8	90-119	106.5	91-135	104.4	94-126

Since the test taken when the subject was "high" was always his second experience with it, some allowance must be made for practice effect. Without drug the average I.Q. of these subjects was 101.6, while after they had smoked cigarettes it was 104.4. This increase of only 2.8 points is smaller than one would probably get with repetition occurring after such a short time interval. It may be concluded, therefore, that smoking marihuana cigarettes has some negative effect on intellectual functioning, in that the subject benefits less from previous experiences than he would if he had not smoked.

Woody McCall Mixed Fundamentals Test, Form 1

This test was given to 24 subjects, 10 users and 14 non-users. From the results which are shown in Table 12 it may be concluded that when the subject was "high" after smoking marihuana cigarettes there was a slowing up in his ability to do simple arithmetic calculations. This lag occurred within the first half-hour after smoking and continued for at least an hour. The deleterious effect was not such as to cause an actual loss in ability but the increments resulting from repeated practice were never as great in the drugged as in the undrugged state. Thus, the initial increment was 10 per cent in the test given before smoking and only 4 per cent in the one administered after the subject had become "high." The final increment at the end of two and a half hours was 20 per cent without drug, 13 per cent with drug.

This test measures the subject's ability to use acquired

knowledge. Under the influence of marihuana cigarettes the capacity for using such an acquired skill is not lost but is slowed down. The adverse effect of smoking marihuana in cigarette form occurs almost immediately in contrast to the delayed action of the pills.

TABLE 12

Effect of marihuana cigarettes on the ability to use acquired knowledge as measured by the Woody McCall Mixed Fundamentals Test on twenty-four subjects

Time after smoking (in hours)	BEFORE SMOKING		AFTER SMOKING	
	Average score*	Increase over initial score (in per cent)	Average score*	Increase over initial score (in per cent)
0	15.0	—	15.9	—
½	16.5	10	16.6	4
1	16.8	12	17.2	8
1½	16.8	12	17.9	13
2	17.9	19	18.8	18
2½	18.0	20	17.8	12

* Score = number of right answers.

Cancelling 8's

Sixteen subjects, 8 users and 8 non-users, took this test, the results of which are shown in Table 13. As a result of smoking marihuana cigarettes the subject worked a little slower in his execution of a routine task than he did when he had not smoked. The increment over the initial score in the test

TABLE 13

Effect of marihuana cigarettes on the ability to carry out a routine task as measured by the cancelling of 8's by sixteen subjects

Time after smoking (in hours)	BEFORE SMOKING		AFTER SMOKING	
	Average score*	Increase over initial score (in per cent)	Average score*	Increase over initial score (in per cent)
0	50.0	—	48.4	—
½	54.7	9	51.6	7
1	55.3	11	49.7	3
1½	57.2	14	56.2	16
2	54.0	8	51.6	7
2½	57.2	14	58.1	20

* Score = number of right answers — number of wrong answers.

score made a half-hour after he became "high" was only 7 per cent as against an increment of 9 per cent when the cigarettes had not been smoked. His performance was slowed up for one hour after smoking and possibly longer.

Kohs Block Design Test

This test, which measures performance ability, was given to a total of 9 subjects, 6 users and 3 non-users. The average score without the drug was 18.5, and after cigarettes had been smoked 14.7. This difference in score of 3.8 points indicates a loss in efficiency of 21 per cent.

Memory Tests

Rote Memory. Thirteen users and 9 non-users took this test. Neither in repeating digets forward nor in giving them in reverse did the subjects show any disadvantageous effects from the use of marihuana cigarettes, the average scores before and after smoking being 6.9 and 7.1 respectively for the digits forward test and 5.2 and 5.1 for the digits reversed test. The only explanation for this deviation from the results obtained when marihuana was taken in pill form is the inability to control the dosage when marihuana is given in cigarette form.

Object Memory. Thirteen subjects took this test. Object memory was not impaired by the smoking of marihuana, the average scores being 6.8 before the cigarettes were smoked and 7.1 when the subjects were "high."

Visual Memory. There was an .8 point loss (from 10.5 to 9.7) in the average score of the 20 subjects, 11 users and 9 non-users, who took this test. This represents an impairment of about 8 per cent.

Effect of Marihuana Cigarettes on Users and Non-Users

The difference in intensity of effect of marihuana cigarettes on the user and on the non-user was not the same as the difference in the effect of the marihuana concentrate on these two groups. The user was usually more affected by smoking marihuana than was the non-user, probably because the non-user did not smoke as much or as intensely as the user and was not as much under the influence of the drug.

EFFECTS ON WOMEN

Five women were used in this experiment, 1 marihuana user and 4 non-users. The group as a whole was of average intelligence, with an I.Q. of 101.3, range 85 to 115, on Bellevue Adult Intelligence Test. Verbal I.Q. was 101.0, range 89 to 116; performance I.Q. 101.5, range 83 to 117. Average age for the group was 30.3 years, range 28 to 34.

The tests used and the procedure employed were the same for the women as for the men with the following exceptions: (1) the Army Alpha test was given every hour instead of every half-hour; (2) no form board tests were given; (3) no group tests with cigarettes were given.

Test results for the female subjects were not entirely like those obtained for the men. In the case of the women, intellectual impairment, as measured by Army Alpha total scores, was more severe and lasting under 2 cc. of marihuana than it was under 3 to 5 cc. This was also true of learning ability as measured by Pyle's Digit Symbol test. The ability to carry out a routine task showed impairment only when tested under the influence of 3 to 5 cc. of the drug. The ingestion of the drug in either dosage brought about an improvement in rote memory (digits forward), while in the digits reversed test there was an impairment under 2 cc. and no change under 5 cc. Object memory remained unchanged when the subject had had 2 cc. of marihuana, and was slightly impaired with 3 to 5 cc. and cigarettes. There was a drop in score for visual memory (Army Designs Test) under both 2 cc. and 5 cc. of the drug. Kohs Block Design Test (a performance test which requires integrative functioning at higher intellectual levels) was given only twice, once without the drug and once with 5 cc. There was a loss in efficiency on this test when taken under marihuana which was comparable to that reported for the men.

It should be noted that the performance of the female subjects showed great variability. The variability may have been due either to the small number of subjects employed, or to their special selection, or both, and the findings can only be considered suggestive of possible trends. The fact that in some tests the subjects were more adversely affected by 2 cc. of marihuana than by larger doses is probably due to the fact that the 2 cc. dose was always administered before the larger dosage, and possibly also to the seemingly greater suggestibility of this particular group of women.

CONCLUSIONS

1. Marihuana taken either in pill or in cigarette form has a transitory adverse effect on mental functioning.

2. The extent of intellectual impairment, the time of its

onset, and its duration are all related to the amount of drug taken. Small doses cause only slight falling off in mental ability while larger doses result in greater impairment. The deleterious effect is measurable earlier with large doses than with small ones, and the impairment continues for a greater length of time with large doses than with small ones.

3. The degree of intellectual impairment resulting from the presence of marihuana in the system varies with the function tested. The more complex functions are more severely affected than the simpler ones.

4. In general, non-users experience greater intellectual impairment for longer periods of time than the users do. This suggests the possibility of an habituation factor.

5. The falling off in ability which occurs when an individual has taken marihuana is due to a loss in both speed and accuracy.

6. Indulgence in marihuana does not appear to result in mental deterioration.

Emotional Reactions and General Personality Structure

Florence Halpern, MA

The purpose of this part of the study was twofold: to discover (1) what effect marihuana has on the emotional reactivity of the person taking it, and (2) what differences in emotional reaction and general personality structure exist between the marihuana user and non-user.

TESTS

Two types of tests are available for studying personality. These are the paper-pencil tests and the projective tests. Projective techniques which reveal the subject's personality through his treatment of the test material are generally more valid and more revealing than the paper-pencil tests which require the underlining of words or the answering of "Yes" or "No" to a list of questions. This is true of all subjects but seemed to apply more particularly to those used in this study. Such tests as the Psychosomatic Inventory and the Bell Adjustment Test were tried out in the initial stages of the investigation but were soon discontinued as the subjects gave continued evidence of a desire to ingratiate themselves with, or to make a showing for, the examiner. Questions whose intent was obvious were almost invariably answered as the subject thought the examiner wanted them to be or as he thought would look best on his record. For this reason most of the tests employed were those whose purposes were less easily interpreted by the subjects.

Rorschach Test

One of the primary tests employed for examining the personality of the subjects was the Rorschach Test. It consists of ten standardized ink blots printed on 7- by 9½-inch white cards. Some of the blots are black, some red and black, and some multicolored. The cards are presented to the subject one at a time and he states what they look like to him, what he sees. The manner in which the subject interprets the plates gives an indication of his formal approach to various types of situations. The extent and directions of the subject's affective reactions, his drive, his ability to make good social adjustment, and his emotional stability are some of the personality traits which can be determined on the basis of this test.

Goodenough Test (Drawing of a Man)

This test was standardized originally as an intelligence test for children, but clinical use has demonstrated its value as an instrument for personality diagnosis. The subject is given a sheet of paper 8½ by 11 inches and asked to draw the figure of a man. In his drawing he unconsciously portrays his own body image so that the picture by its emphasis and omissions betrays which body parts are important or unimportant to him —how he sees himself. Although results from this type of interpretation have not, to our knowledge, been standardized, they may nevertheless be used for comparing the marihuana user and non-user in terms of their attitudes toward their body images and for noting the differences in these concepts before and after the administration of marihuana.

Level of Aspiration Test

The purpose of a Level of Aspiration Test is to ascertain the relationship between the goal a person sets for himself and the level of his performance. Roughly, there are three possible reactions: (1) the individual, in an attempt to protect his ego, sets himself so low a goal that he must inevitably reach or surpass it; (2) he exposes his ego to failure for overevaluating his ability and sets a goal which he cannot possibly reach or surpass; or (3) he sets a goal commensurate with his ability. The test devised for this experiment is a very simple one. The subject is required to place sixteen colored cubes in a box, red side up. Before beginning he is asked to estimate how long it will take to complete the task. He is then given the signal to proceed and at the end of the trial is told how much time was actually consumed. On the basis of this result, the subject is again asked to state how much time he thinks he will need to fulfill the task and again at its completion is told how long it actually took him. The subject's estimate given before he had any actual experience with the test is disregarded. From the nine subsequent trials, averages of the subject's estimate (the goal he set for himself) and of his actual performance times are calculated. The difference between these two averages gives a measure of his level of aspiration.

Frustration Test

When a person is prevented from finishing a task correctly, thus being left with an incomplete gestalt, he has definite feelings of frustration. His reactions to such feelings will vary depending upon his general manner of emotional response. In this investigation, the method used to frustrate the subjects was to present them with a series of relatively simple mazes (Wechsler Self-Administering Mazes), the third or fourth one being so blocked off that no exit is possible. The subject is highly praised for his performance on the first two or three and, when he becomes involved in the closed one, is aggravated by the comments of the examiner concerning the success of some of the other men with this identical maze. After fifteen seconds of futile attempts to get out the subject is told that his time is up. Immediately after this he is given the Level of Aspiration Test, the assumption being that frustration might affect this level in some way.

Binet Lines

Suggestibility is a specific rather than a general trait and can therefore be interpreted only with reference to the situation in which it is tested. For example, a man may be very responsive to the suggestions of his attractive secretary but negativistic to those of his business rival.

Binet's Suggestibility Test, which consists of twelve rectangular pieces of cardboard on which are drawn lines of varying length, was used in this investigation. The length of the first five lines increases by specific amounts; the sixth line does not increase but is identical with the fifth, the seventh line again is longer; the eighth is its equivalent; and so on. The assumption is that the progressive increase of the first five lines will influence the suggestible person and he will continue to increase the lines for some time before he becomes aware of the fact that they are no longer consistently lengthening.

The following directions are given: "I want to see how well you can estimate length. I am going to show you some cards, each with a line drawn on it. Some of the lines are long and some are short. I'll show you each card for just two seconds and when I take it away you must draw the line. Try to make it exactly the length of the line on the card." The subject is given a sheet of paper which has a vertical line drawn about half an inch in from the left-hand edge of the paper. Numbers, placed about half an inch apart, appear inside this margin, beginning at the top with number 1 and going through number 12. The subject is told to begin his line opposite the number and right up against the vertical-line margin. As soon as he has drawn his line it is covered with the card and the next card is presented.

Results are scored in accordance with Binet's method. The average amount of increase (measured in sixteenths of an inch) for the even lines which actually should not increase is divided by the average increase in the odd lines which should increase, and the quotient is multiplied by 100.

Wechsler Vocational Interest Blank

The Wechsler Vocational Interest Blank consists of a list of forty jobs or vocations, each followed by the letter "L" or "D." These vocations may be classed as professional, artistic, industrial, or manual. The subject is told that for the moment he is to assume that each job pays the same amount and that he has the training and ability to do any of them. The only thing to influence his choice of a job is his own inclination, that is, whether or not that type of work appeals to him. If it does he is told to encircle the "L," but if it does not he is to encircle the "D." The choice of certain constellations of jobs, such as painting, teaching, and working in a florist shop, indicates a general feminine trend, while preference for others gives evidence of strongly masculine inclinations. Again, the selection of many positions may be taken to indicate an active, outgoing nature, while a small number of likes reflects a less active, more critical attitude.

Loofbourrow Personal Index: Test 1

This test is given to adolescent boys to measure their proneness to delinquency. In this study it was employed as a measure of self-confidence. It consists of one hundred words of which thirty are nonexistent, that is, words which look like unusual but real words but which are actually not part of the English language. If at any time, drugged or undrugged, a subject indicates familiarity with a significantly larger number of words than on another occasion, the assumption is that the increase in vocabulary corresponds to a rise in the subject's estimate of his own ability and mental capacity.

Wechsler Free Association Test

This test consists of a list of forty-five words chosen for their obvious value in personality study. The examiner reads the words one at a time to the subject and records his responses and his reaction time in fifths of a second. Reaction times and average deviation are computed for each subject, and those words for which the reaction time is delayed, that is, words which fall beyond the limits of the average deviation, are considered disturbing stimuli.

Pressey X-O Test

There are four parts to this test, each one consisting of twenty-five lines of five words each. In Test I the subject is asked to cross out every word whose meaning is unpleasant to him and to encircle the one word in each row whose meaning is the most unpleasant. In Test II each row of words is preceded by a word in large print and the subject is instructed to cross out every word in the row which is connected in his mind with the word in large letters at the beginning of the row. At the end of this test the subject encircles the one word in each row which he most closely associates with the word in large letters. Test III requires the subject to cross out every word he thinks has a bad meaning and then to encircle the one thing in each row he thinks is worst. Test IV follows the same procedure, only here the subject crosses out everything he has ever worried about and encircles the one thing in each row he has worried about most. Norms have been established on college students, giving the average number of words crossed out and the modal word to be encircled.

Downey Will-Temperament Test: Test I

This test consists of a series of paired personality traits such as sociable or unsociable, clumsy or graceful. The subject is asked to underscore the trait of each pair which he thinks describes him more accurately. The test is not intended as a self-rating personality index, and therefore there are no norms for responses of this nature. It was used in this study solely to determine if the ingestion of marihuana produces changes in the individual's self-evaluation as indicated by a comparison of the traits he thinks apply to him when he is in his normal condition and when he is under the influence of the drug.

Thematic Apperception Test

This test employs a series of pictures which are handed to the subject one at a time with the following directions: "This is a test of creative imagination. I am going to show you some pictures. Around each picture I want you to compose a story. Outline the incidents which have led up to the situation shown in the picture; describe what is occurring at the moment—the feelings and thoughts of the characters; and tell what the outcome will be. Speak your thoughts aloud as they come to your mind. I want you to use your imagination to the limit." Productions are recorded verbatim. Scoring takes into account the needs of the subject as revealed in his stories and the environmental forces acting upon him.

PROCEDURE

All the tests dealing with emotional reactions were given as individual tests. Although they are not as subject to practice effect as the Intelligence tests, practice does alter the results somewhat. For this reason every possible effort was made to give examinations during drugged and undrugged periods as far apart in time as possible and to divide the groups so that half the subjects took the initial examination while under the influence of marihuana and the other half before the administration of the drug.

Rorschach Test

This test was given once without marihuana and once under maximum dosage (3 cc. to 6 cc.) or with cigarettes, the number of cigarettes smoked being optional with the subject. Four subjects took the test three times, once without the drug, once with the drug in pill form, and once with cigarettes, but it was found impracticable to give the test more than twice in four weeks both because of the time it consumed and because of the subjects' growing boredom with it. In all, 45 subjects, 27 users and 18 non-users, took this test.

Goodenough, Level of Aspiration, Binet Lines, Vocational Interest Tests and Downey Test I

These tests were given to all subjects at least twice and some subjects took them as often as four times, that is, without the drug, under 2 cc., under 5 cc., and after smoking marihuana cigarettes. The number of times a subject was tested was determined primarily by the amount of time available. Twenty-seven users and 18 non-users took the Goodenough, Level of Aspiration and Vocational Interest Tests; 25 users and 17 non-users the Binet Lines; and 14 users and 8 non-users the Downey Will-Temperament Test.

Frustration, Free Association, and Pressey X-O Tests, and Loofbourrow Test I

These tests were added later in the testing program and were therefore given to a limited number of subjects. They were administered twice, once without marihuana and once either with cigarettes or with large oral doses (3 cc. to 5 cc.).

Thematic Apperception Test

In an effort to conserve time, the administration of this test was not in accordance with the directions. Instead of relating the story to the examiner, the subject sat in a room by himself and recited his tale into the dictaphone. In addition to the time saved, this had the advantage of sparing the subject considerable embarrassment, since most of the men were very self-conscious about telling these stories when anyone was present. The disadvantage of this procedure lay in the examiner's inability to persuade the subject to give a fuller story. The test was given to each subject twice, once with and once without cigarettes. Only the following pictures were used: 3, 4, 5, M-11, M-12, M-13, M-15, M-18, M-19, M-20, F-14, and F-19. Although the results showed promise of interesting findings, the administration of the test was limited to only 9 subjects because so many mechanical difficulties were involved.

FINDINGS

Rorschach Test

Table 14 gives the Rorschach findings for 45 subjects both in the undrugged and drugged states. The measurable changes on the test which occurred during the period of drug intoxication were few and not far-reaching. They may be considered indications of tendencies rather than of significant alterations of the personality.

TABLE 14

Effect of marihuana on personality structure as shown on the Rorschach Test

	45 SUBJECTS		27 USERS		18 NON-USERS	
	Without Marihuana	*With Marihuana*	*Without Marihuana*	*With Marihuana*	*Without Marihuana*	*With Marihuana*
Average number of responses	20.0	23.3	19.4	21.5	20.8	26.2
Type of response (per cent of total)						
Whole	40	36	36	34	46	39
Detail	43	42	47	43	38	40
Rare detail	17	21	17	22	16	21
Form	57	56	62	59	50	52
Form + ...	92	86	92	90	93	82
Ms	11	10	9	9	13	10
C	10	9	9	8	11	10
Chiaroscuro	14	15	11	14	17	16
FM + m	12	12	11	11	14	13
A	36 }54	35 }51	37 }58	36 }55	35 }48	34 }48
Ad	18	16	21	19	13	14
H	13	13	11	11	14	14
Hd	8	9	8	10	7	8
P	27	20	29	20	25	19
M:C	2.3:1.6	2.9:2.1				

When the subjects were under the influence of marihuana (either 3-6 cc. or cigarettes, the number of cigarettes being at the discretion of the smoker) there was a slightly freer flow of associations than there was when they were in the undrugged state, an increased productivity which coincided with the impressions obtained from general observation of the subjects when they were "high." Without drug the average number of interpretations made was 20.0, with drug 23.3. This increased number of responses was due primarily to the subject's greater awareness of small, extraneous details which in his undrugged state he overlooked. Thus, while 17 per cent of the subjects' answers were small or rare detail responses when no marihuana had been administered, with marihuana this increased to 21 per cent. Coincidental with his increased absorption in the irrelevant there was a slight decrease in the subject's drive to organize and synthesize. Whereas without drug 40 per cent of the responses involved the entire blot, with drug this was true of only 36 per cent of the interpretations. Under the influence of marihuana there was a mild tendency for the subject to become preoccupied with minutiae rather than to concern himself with the larger, more important aspects of a situation, and this implies some falling off in meaningful constructive behavior.

When the subject had taken marihuana there was some decrease in the objectivity with which he sized up situations. This was indicated by the fact that without drug 92 per cent of his interpretations were good form, that is, they corresponded to the form of the blot, while with drug this percentage fell to 86 per cent. The drug had an adverse effect on the individual's critical faculty and he was more prone to jump to erroneous conclusions than he was when he was in the undrugged state.

The only other change that occurred on the Rorschach test after the ingestion of marihuana was the decrease in the subject's ability to think in line with the group. This showed itself in the decreased number of popular interpretations made, the drop being from 27 per cent without drug to 20 per cent with drug. In other words, during the period of drug intoxication an individual is somewhat less likely to see the obvious and the commonplace than he is in his normal state.

As important, or possibly even more important, than the changes which occurred on the Rorschach after ingestion or smoking of marihuana, is the fact that some of the most basic personality attributes remained unchanged. Thus it appeared that 33 per cent of the subjects in the undrugged state were what is described as introversive, that is, they were individuals who tend to withdraw somewhat from the world about them and depend primarily on their own inner resources for emotional stimulation; 20 per cent were extraversive, depending mainly on their environment for affective satisfaction; 20 per cent were ambivert, showing equal potentialities in both directions; and 27 per cent were emotionally constricted to the point where they gave little or no evidence of emotional response of any type. With drug 36 per cent were introversive, 22 per cent were extraversive, 20 per cent were ambivert, and 22 per cent were constricted. Marihuana ingestion or smoking served to dilate the emotional life of only 2 of the subjects and shifted the type of 1. In all 3 cases the change was actually a very slight one. The fact that the emotional trends remain essentially unchanged under the influence of marihuana was further revealed by the fact that the ratio for evaluating the individual's emotional type, that is, the ratio of movement to color, remained roughly the same before and after he had taken the drug, being 2.3:1.6 when he was in the undrugged state and 2.9:2.1 when he was in the drugged phase.

Although the quantitative changes occurring with marihuana ingestion or smoking were not large, there was a qualitative difference in the protocols obtained from the subjects in the undrugged and drugged stages. Not only was there a slight increase in the actual number of interpretations made, but the amount of talking and extraneous comment increased. The subject played around with answers and often repeated them. He seemed anxious to get his every thought clearly across to his audience. More than this, he was much freer in the type of interpretation he allowed himself. For example, one interpretation on Card II read: "Two dogs. Now wait a minute. I don't want to jump to conclusions but it looks as if the dogs were having intercourse and there was a rupture." This response was not repeated when the subject was retested in the undrugged state. Nor was this individual unique in showing this qualitative difference. The disinhibition and lessening of restraint which was a definitely observable effect of the drug was also reflected in the assured explanations and lengthy tirades which the subject offered on topics which in his undrugged state he would undoubtedly feel were beyond him. Thus one subject interpreted Card X as "old bark of trees, roots dried up. It's thousands of years old; it takes thousands of years to do that. I got to tell you that. I got to cover for you. You wouldn't know about a thousand years ago. I'm smart now." In some instances the "cockiness" induced by his drugged condition produced an entirely new attitude in the subject. Instead of the customary deferential, almost ingratiating approach there was now a confident "know-it-all" manner.

The effects of marihuana ingestion on user and non-user were essentially the same, as indicated by the findings in Table 14, except that on the whole the alterations which did occur were more marked for the non-user than for the user. Thus, for example, while the average number of responses given by the user increased only 11 per cent, those of the non-user rose 26 per cent. Again, the user when drugged gave only 6 per cent fewer whole answers as against a decrease of 15 per cent in the whole responses of the non-user in the drugged state. The user showed a 29 per cent increase in small detail interpretations, the non-user 31 per cent. There was only a 2 per cent drop in good form interpretation by the user as against a 12 per cent drop for the non-user. Only in the loss of popular interpretations did the user exceed the non-user, his falling off being as great as 31 per cent as compared with 24 per cent for the non-user. While the number of subjects in both groups was too small to allow of definite statements, the trend seemed to indicate that the ingestion or smoking of marihuana has a greater adverse or disorganizing effect on the neophyte than on the experienced smoker, again, as was the case in the study of mental functioning, suggesting the possibility of psychological habituation.

When the protocols obtained from these marihuana users in their undrugged state are compared with those of the non-users or with the norms postulated for average adults of this age level, certain deviating personality traits in these users may be noted. The most striking deviation is the small percentage of users who showed an extraversive personality. Only 15 per cent of the marihuana users used in this study responded primarily to emotional stimuli in the world about them as compared with 28 per cent of the non-users. While no definite figures are given in the literature for the degree of extraversion in the general population, it seems definitely more than 15 per cent. Altogether the personality types among the non-users show a much more even distribution than those among the users as seen in Table 15. Judging by the personality types the majority of marihuana users lack social ease and adroitness and are likely to find it difficult to make good outgoing social contacts.

TABLE 15

Personality types of user and non-user subjects as shown on the Rorschach Test

Personality Types	Users	Non-Users
Extraversive	15%	28%
Introversive	37%	28%
Ambivert	19%	28%
Constricted	30%	17%

Sixty-two per cent of the marihuana users' interpretations were determined by the form or outline of the blot. Such responses require an objective critical attitude unmodified by emotional factors. However, when this attitude is maintained to the point where more than 50 per cent of the answers are of this nature the individual has a constricted affective life, the degree of constriction being in proportion to the increase in form interpretations. Thus, as was previously noted, there was more than average emotional inhibition evident among the marihuana users studied in this experiment. Since emotional inhibition frequently causes intellectual constriction, it is not surprising to find that the stereotypy in these records was slightly above expectancy, as indicated by the fact that 59 per cent of the responses were animal or animal detail interpretations as compared with a norm of from 25 to 50 per cent.

Finally the marihuana users (as well as the non-users in this experiment) showed a depressive outlook in that more of their responses were determined by the gray and black colors than by the vivid colors. In interpreting this fact it must be borne in mind that the subjects were all prisoners and their depressive attitude may have been a reflection of their present situation rather than of a basic trait.

Goodenough Test (Drawing of a Man)

This test is helpful in studying each individual both in the drugged and undrugged state, but group results are not meaningful (except for one finding given below) because of a lack of similarity both in the drawings obtained in the undrugged state and in the direction of change which occurred after drug ingestion or smoking. However, certain qualitative findings proved interesting and are therefore reported here. In a number of cases the identical drawing was produced in the undrugged, 2 cc., 5 cc., and cigarette state, but the size of the figure increased consistently with the amount of marihuana taken. This increase in size may have been a reflection of a physical sensation induced by the drug, may have been due to a tendency to macrographia which was noted in the writing of some subjects, or may have been the psychological representation of increased feelings of confidence and security.

With marihuana there was an increase in the percentage of subjects who remembered to give their man ears. This again may have been due to a heightened awareness of ears because of physical or auditory sensations or might denote a greater receptivity to what others have to say.

In some cases the amount of time consumed in execution of the drawings was considerably greater when the subject was "high." This additional time was rarely used for elaborating the picture but was caused by the subject's altered mood. In many instances the laughter and joking in which he indulged kept him from completing the job with dispatch. In other cases depression or nausea slowed him up. Although aware of the details which should be included, the subject was often satisfied to indicate such items by a single line or dash rather than discipline himself to the point where he could make a careful picture. In some of these cases the drawing had attributes which resemble the findings sometimes seen in productions of individuals in a manic mood.

When a person is given a sheet of paper and is asked to draw a man on it, the paper and the figure he draws become the situation he must manipulate. If the figure is well centered so that the finished product gives a balanced composition, the subject has handled the circumstance in adequate fashion. The one consistent finding for this test was the fact that the subject's ability to handle situations was not improved by drug ingestion or smoking. In the case of both user and non-user the percentage of balanced compositions produced in the various drug states did not change from the results obtained in the undrugged condition. It is, however, interesting to note that 59 per cent of the marihuana users made "unbalanced" drawings in the undrugged state as compared with only 29 per cent of the non-users. It may be inferred from this that fewer users than non-users are inclined to come out into the center of the scene. This carries with it implications of poor adjustment and insecurity.

Level of Aspiration Test

In the undrugged state the majority of the subjects manifested reactions which are usual in the experience of other experiments, namely, the tendency to place their estimate just a little above their actual performance. This was demonstrated by the fact that while the average performance time needed for carrying out a set task (putting sixteen blocks in a box, red side up) was 23.6 seconds, the subjects' average estimate for accomplishing this was 21.9 seconds. As their performance improved with practice, the subjects tended to allow themselves less time for the job. Such statements as, "I should do better this time," or "I'll take a chance," were not infrequent. Some subjects wanted to know the best score ever made, and worked energetically to attain it.

With 2 cc. of marihuana there was a slight increase in the average estimated time for the entire group although there was no concomitant increase in performance time. Under this dosage the estimated time was 23.1 seconds, performance time 23.4 seconds. Although the subject actually took no longer to do the job, he thought he would work more slowly and in predicting his achievement gave himself more time. His attitude during the test was a much easier, more happy-go-lucky one. He occasionally stopped in the middle of the experiment to discuss something with the examiner or call out to someone passing in the hall. There thus appeared to be a small loss in drive which, though not revealed by significant statistical differences, was indicated by the numerical trend and by the subject's attitude toward the test.

After the ingestion of 5 cc. of marihuana the average estimated time was 23.2 seconds and the performance time 24.4 seconds. Here the relationship between estimated and performance time was similar to that found in the undrugged phase, that is, there was a 1.2-second gap between them. During this drug phase the subjects seemed less relaxed than they were under 2 cc., and their main interest seemed to be to get back to bed and be left undisturbed.

Under the influence of marihuana cigarettes the trend was similar to that found with 2 cc., the difference between the estimated time and the performance time being only .3 second. As with 2 cc., subject's behavior was generally happy and relaxed.

When the group was divided into users and non-users the trend was the same for both.

TABLE 16

Average time estimated and taken for Level of Aspiration Test

Dose	AVERAGE TIME (IN SECONDS)								
	Users and non-users			Users			Non-users		
	Est.	Perf.	Diff.	Est.	Perf.	Diff.	Est.	Perf.	Diff.
0 cc.	21.9	23.6	1.7	22.1	23.5	1.4	21.8	23.6	1.8
2 cc.	23.1	23.4	.3	23.7	23.7	0.0	22.6	23.1	.5
5 cc.	23.2	24.4	1.2	23.7	25.0	1.3	22.7	23.8	1.1
Cigs.	24.1	24.4	.3	24.1	24.7	.6	24.1	24.1	0.0

On the whole it appears that small doses of marihuana and of marihuana cigarettes tend to lower the individual level of aspiration, that is, there is a slight lessening in the subject's drive and his will to achieve. Larger doses (5 cc.) do not produce this effect.

Frustration Test

The results of the frustration experiment indicated no statistically significant differences between the subject's reactions before and after he had taken marihuana. Again, after the ingestion of marihuana there was a slight trend toward lowering the level of aspiration (Table 17), but the over-all change was not startling when compared with results on the Level of Aspiration Test when no frustrating experience was introduced.

TABLE 17

Average time estimated and taken for Frustration Test

Dose	AVERAGE TIME (IN SECONDS)								
	Users and non-users			Users			Non-users		
	Est.	Perf.	Diff.	Est.	Perf.	Diff.	Est.	Perf.	Diff.
0 cc.	21.4	22.6	1.2	21.5	22.7	1.2	21.3	22.4	1.1
5 cc.	23.6	23.1	0.5	24.5	23.2	1.3	22.7	23.0	0.3
Cigs.	22.6	22.6	0.0	23.1	23.1	0.0	22.0	22.0	0.0

Binet Lines

Binet's interpretation of this test was based upon the principle that suggestible individuals, once embarked on a particular form of activity (in this instance, drawing lines of increasing length), are more prone to continue this activity when the stimulus is altered than are less suggestible people. Judging by the results as given in Table 18, small doses of marihuana (2 cc. and cigarettes) induced this type of perseverative behavior in the users but not in the non-users. In other words, the marihuana user when under the influence of the drug tended to continue an activity he had started without being too discriminatory or controlled about it. The non-user, on the other hand, showed a curtailment in activity and responsiveness. One possible explanation of this difference in effect on user and non-user appears to lie in the fact that the drug made the user more relaxed and easy-going and less controlled in motor activity than he was in his undrugged

TABLE 18

Average scores on the Binet Lines Test

Dose	Users	Non-Users
0 cc.	90.2	99.2
2 cc.	105.9	60.9
5 cc.	81.1	98.7
Cigs.	106.3	87.3

state, while the non-user was often more tense and disturbed. As was so often the case in the personality tests, the effect on the user of large doses of the drug (5 cc.) was contrary to that of the small ones, probably because in many cases he was made physically uncomfortable and intellectually disorganized.

The lack of consistency in the findings seems to suggest that the individual's psychological and physiological "set" toward the drug affects his reaction and behavior. Thus small doses, which the marihuana user anticipates with pleasure, make him more easy-going and therefore probably more suggestible than he would be in his undrugged state, while large doses have a contrary effect. The non-user, on the other hand, appears to be less suggestible as a result of drug ingestion than he ordinarily is.

Wechsler Vocational Interest Blank

The average number of positions chosen by the subjects when they were in the undrugged state was 13.2. With 2 cc. of marihuana the average was 12.9; with 5 cc., 12.7; and with cigarettes, 11.8. There was a very slight but not statistically significant trend toward a decrease in job interest. However, the absence of any appreciable change in the number of positions liked after the ingestion or smoking of marihuana indicates that no real withdrawal is implied.

Analysis of the type of position chosen shows that under the influence of marihuana there was no swing to the more feminine occupations, but in the case of some subjects, especially marihuana users, there was a falling off in the popularity of some jobs which require considerable activity. For example, under the influence of 2 cc. of marihuana or of marihuana cigarettes the jobs of detective, policeman and taxi driver were found among his least desired occupations though they were not in this place when he was in the undrugged state.

The trend was the same for the user and the non-user in both the drugged and undrugged phase. For the user the jobs of aviator, gymnasium teacher, newspaper reporter, sailor and soldier were most frequently chosen; for the non-user aviator, doctor, explorer, forest ranger, newspaper reporter and prize fighter were most popular.

Loofbourrow Personal Index: Test I

Before taking marihuana, the user and non-user on an average indicated familiarity with an identical number of words, 65.2. After he had smoked marihuana cigarettes, the user's vocabulary showed a gain of 6 words, the non-user's 5 words. In both cases the subject's confidence in his verbal capacity was enhanced by the use of marihuana.

Wechsler Free Association Test

In the undrugged state the user and non-user were disturbed by the same stimulus words, namely "lonely," "passionate," "insult," and "sin." The only differences were the disturbance the user showed in response to the words "wish" and "murder" and the delayed reaction of the non-user to the word "pity."

Under the influence of 5 cc. of marihuana or of marihuana cigarettes the user was less disturbed by all these words with the possible exception of "insult," but there was a sharp increase in the agitation aroused by the words "suicide" and "death." It appears that the feeling of well-being produced by the drug tended to alleviate the loneliness, guilt, and frustration which the subject felt, but it was also accompanied by a fear of death. This may be tied up with the anxiety the marihuana user always experiences in regard to the amount of drug he is taking, the always present fear of his "blowing his top," or it may be a reflection of the problems which were most disturbing to him.

The non-user, after taking marihuana, was also less disturbed by the words "lonely," "passionate," and "sin." His reaction to "pity" was also diminished but he, too, was still upset by the word "insult." The new disturbing stimulus words were not those which upset the user but those which were more closely related to his own immediate problems namely "honest," "money," and "sex." Since the non-user in our group was generally an individual who had been sent to prison because of stealing or a sex offense, it seems it was these problems which the disinhibiting action of the drug brought to the fore.

Pressey X-O Test

This test was taken by only 10 subjects, 5 users and 5 non-users. In general, the smoking of marihuana brought about some increase in the number of words which had an unpleasant meaning to the subject and in the number of things about which he had worried. There was some decrease in the number of things for which the drugged subject thought a person should be blamed. The number of his associations with any one word remained roughly the same in the drugged and undrugged state.

Although less inclined to censure when under the influence of marihuana, the subject was nevertheless more readily disturbed and worried. This undercurrent of irritability and anxiety seemed to be a concomitant of the more obvious feeling of general well-being which is the predominant effect of the drug. Two possible explanations can be given here for this finding: the physiological changes occurring with the smoking of the drug gave the subject a feeling of anxiety, and the disinhibition which occurred at this time released the restraints which had been imposed not only on the happier reactions but on all the repressed unpleasantness as well, and things which the subject had repressed because he wished to forget them now came to the fore. This was noted when at least two of the subjects had "crying jags" when drugged, reproaching themselves for what they had done to their mothers and wives.

Downey Will-Temperament Test: Test I

The changes in the subjects' responses on this test showed a shift in their attitude toward themselves as a result of marihuana ingestion. On the whole, more subjects appeared to think better of themselves when they were "high" than they did in their undrugged state. This is indicated by the fact that there was an increase in the number of individuals who under the influence of 5 cc. of marihuana or of marihuana cigarettes believed themselves to be careful, cautious, ambitious, accurate, industrious, impulsive, enthusiastic, and possessing superior characters. There was also a decrease in the number who considered themselves suggestible or extravagant. The only negative traits which the subject admitted to more frequently when he was "high" than he did in his normal state were suggestibility, poor memory and aggression. The change in attitude in regard to aggression was most striking among the marihuana users, 88 per cent of whom considered themselves aggressive after they had had the drug as compared with only 42 per cent in the undrugged state. This increase in the feeling of aggression was not paralleled by the findings of the other tests nor by the behavior of the subjects when they had taken the drug. Like the increased vocabulary noted on the Loofbourrow it can best be interpreted as an indication of the subject's increased feelings of confidence and self-assurance.

In general the changes which occurred on this test after the subject had had marihuana were not consistent for the user and the non-user or for different amounts of the drug. They

TABLE 19

Average number of words marked in Pressey X-O Test

Tests		Without Marihuana	With Cigarettes
Test I			
(No. of words with unpleasant meaning)			
	Average	48.4	58.2
	Range	26–76	34–106
Test II			
(No. of words associated with the stimulus word)			
	Average	32.5	34.4
	Range	25–48	25–54
Test III			
(No. of things subject thinks are wrong)			
	Average	79.0	64.5
	Range	48–86	27–99
Test IV			
(No. of things subject has worried about)			
	Average	31.3	42.1
	Range	23–41	26–62

merely served to indicate that when the subject was under the influence of marihuana there were shifts in his feelings about himself which reflected a prevailing mood of confidence and self-satisfaction.

Thematic Apperception Test

Without cigarettes the needs most frequently expressed in the subjects' stories were "affiliation," "aggression," "sex," "dominance," "succorance," "self-abasement," and "play." These terms may be defined as follows:[1] Affiliation: to be sociable, to make friends, to love. Aggression: to fight, to criticize, to blame, to accuse or ridicule maliciously, to injure or kill, sadism. Sex: to seek sex objects, to court, to enjoy intercourse. Dominance: to influence or control others, leadership. Succorance: to seek aid, protection or sympathy. Self-abasement: to comply, to surrender, to accept punishment, to apologize, to condone, to atone, to depreciate ego, masochism. Play: to relax tension and alleviate stress by pleasurable and humorously irresponsible activity, motor, verbal or mental.

1 Directions for Thematic Apperception Test prepared by Robert W. White and R. Nevitt-Sanford, Harvard Psychological Clinic, February 1941.

In general the frequency with which all needs were expressed fell off after the subjects had smoked marihuana cigarettes. The most striking drops were in the need for self-abasement and aggression where the frequency of occurrence changed from 2.4 to 1.1 for the former, and from 2.7 to 1.7 for the latter. Contrary to the general trend there was an increase in the need for dominance.

When the subjects were not "high" the environmental influences most frequently mentioned in their stories were illness and death and accepting parents. After smoking marihuana the general trend was similar to that noted for the "needs," that is, there was a falling off in the frequency with which the subjects used most of the concepts. There was, however, no diminution in the number of times that illness and death played a part in their tales, the average number being 2.1 before smoking and 2.2 after smoking. Likewise the awareness of restraint and imprisonment remained constant, occurring 1.1 times before smoking and 1.2 after. Contrary to the general trend there was an increased awareness of an accepting love object. This concept appeared in the stories on an average of .8 time before smoking and 1.2 after.

The decrease in the number of times both needs and environmental pressures were expressed in the stories given after the subjects had had cigarettes was not due to a curtailment in the length of the story. The tales were often more wordy in the drugged than in the undrugged state, but their length was frequently due to embellishment and repetition, and there was likely to be less meaningful material. In general the stories obtained from the subjects after smoking indicated that they had less capacity for expressing themselves directly and clearly, and also less concern with self-abasement and aggression. As defined on this test these needs represent a conflict between aggression against the self and against others and appear to stem from insecurity and feelings of guilt and inadequacy. In the drugged state the subjects appeared less disturbed by this conflict and had less need to harry themselves and others. They had a greater need for dominance, a desire for leadership. This ties in with the greater self-assurance demonstrated by other tests and with the increased awareness of acceptance by a love object found on this test.

It is interesting to note that these subjects showed no falling off in their awareness of illness and death or of restraint and imprisonment after smoking. The frequency of the latter concept was undoubtedly related to their status as prisoners, while the former ties in with the findings on the Free Association

Test where the word "death" remained a disturbing factor even after marihuana had been smoked or ingested.

FINDINGS ON WOMEN SUBJECTS

As in the case with the men, when the female subject was under the influence of marihuana her basic personality structure did not change and only some relatively superficial emotional reactions were different. As a group, the women used in this study showed a somewhat constricted personality, and this constriction was not lessened when the subject was "high." The emotional reactions revealed in the Rorschach Test showed that the subjects in this particular group were primarily extraversive, and this remained unchanged after the administration of marihuana. Again, like the men, when under the influence of the drug the women lowered the achievement levels they set for themselves. However, they did not show any increased self-confidence as did the men, either by an increase in the number of words they claimed to know in the Loofbourrow Test or in their appraisal of themselves as indicated in the Downey Will-Temperament Test. In general, the women exhibited a loss of drive for participation in anything requiring effort. This is inferred from their performance in the Level of Aspiration Test, the Vocational Interest Blank, and the Binet Lines Test, as well as from their behavior.

BEHAVIOR DURING THE TEST PERIOD OF SUBJECTS UNDER THE INFLUENCE OF MARIHUANA

The findings reported here have all been in terms of objective, quantitative measures. Some effects of the drug, observable during examinations, cannot be quantified but are nevertheless important to the understanding of the drug action. These effects were reflected in those reactions of the subjects which were not directly related to the test situation.

Behavior was somewhat different when the subject had ingested marihuana concentrate than it was when he had taken the drug in cigarette form. With pills gastro-intestinal disturbances were more pronounced and drowsiness and fatigue seemed greater and more enduring. Some individuals were so overcome by fatigue that they worked for a few seconds only, and then sat with their heads on the table. If spoken to, they made a great effort to do the work but rarely continued for very long. When summoned to take the test, especially toward the end of the day when they were almost invariably lying on their beds, the subjects were overcome with fatigue and were aroused only with the greatest difficulty. In some instances there was definite resentment of this disturbance and the impression was that only the presence of the police officer and all the implications in the prison set-up prevented a definite refusal to continue cooperatively. With both pills and cigarettes many of the men had difficulty in concentrating and maintaining a fixed goal. Subjects often stared vacantly for long periods and when addressed came back to the test with a start. Many burst into uncontrollable laughter over a test which in their undrugged state had evoked no merriment. The laughter frequently affected the entire group and most markedly those who had been given marihuana.

The behavior of the user and non-user with marihuana cigarettes was somewhat different. The user was pleasantly excited at the thought of smoking, selected his cigarettes with the manner of a connoisseur, and criticized or praised the product offered him. His smoking took on something of a ritualistic ceremony and was done in a careful and prearranged fashion which varied slightly from individual to individual. In general the men first opened the end of the cigarette to examine the marihuana, then wet the "stick" by inserting it in their mouths to prevent the paper from burning too rapidly. When the cigarette was ignited the men took several short puffs, at the same time inhaling as much air as possible. This caused the tip of the "stick" to glow and resulted in a succession of low gasping sounds from the subject. The smoke was retained as long as possible, occasionally causing severe paroxysms of coughing. Although eager to be "high" the user was consistent in his fear of "blowing his top," and there was always a point beyond which no amount of talking or cajoling could make them continue smoking. As a rule, the user liked to smoke in company. He was generally satisfied if one friend, a "kick partner," could be with him. To this friend he would explain his thoughts and feelings which to the objective observer were very superficial. In trying to make a point, and usually a minor one at that, the user, when smoking, would talk on endlessly and soon lose his goal. He cracked many "jokes" which were uproariously funny to him. In some instances "leaping" or involuntary jerking of the arms, head, shoulders or legs occurred. The subject described his sensations as floating, leaping, rocking or most often as being "in the groove." He was obviously enjoying pleasant physical sensations and wanted to be left to himself to lie on his bed, listen to soft music and dream or carry on "deep" conversations. The test questions were frequently called a "bring down" in that they forced the subject to face reality and abandon his pleasurable feelings. Several subjects concurred in describing part of their drug experience as comparable to the twilight state between sleeping and waking in which the individual floats pleasantly and does not allow outside stimuli to impinge. Just as strong extraneous sensations will bring the sleeper face to face with reality, so the insistence of the examiner that the subject perform certain tasks served to destroy his general feeling of well-being. Aside from the test situation any unpleasant circumstances can serve as a "bring down." This "bring down" apparently only results in destroying the subject's pleasure but cannot do away with the disadvantageous effect on intellectual functioning.

When testing was completed the subject generally lay on his bed and dozed or listened to the radio. His drowsiness persisted for many hours.

Most non-users approached the smoking with apprehension. They were instructed by the users in the art of lighting and inhaling, but they rarely cooperated to the fullest extent, though this was undoubtedly unconscious on their part.

The effects of marihuana on the non-users were variable. A few of them enjoyed the results so much that they claimed they would continue to smoke whenever they had a chance. They described such sensations as "lying in fur," and "floating in space." Some became acutely nauseous and could not continue with their work, while others experienced little or no change in feeling, undoubtedly because they never smoked correctly.

When the subjects were "high," particularly in the case of the non-user, there was a general loss of inhibition and lessening of many social restraints which had previously been exercised. Thus, all the men talked much more freely, confronted each other more directly, and manifested a state of well-being at times amounting to euphoria. They were much more confiding, talked spontaneously about love and sexual affairs, and in two instances exposed themselves and masturbated.

Although there was an undeniable increase in overt sex interest following the ingestion of marihuana, it seems probable that this interest was not the result of direct sexual stimulation but rather a manifestation of a falling off in inhibiting factors. This sex interest seems to have been due primarily to the fact that these men had been imprisoned for varying periods and had not had access to women. It is not at all certain that under free conditions or with different subjects this behavior would have been manifested. In any case, the behavior of these prisoners was more like that which any man deprived of sexual activity for a long period of time would display under a releas-

ing stimulus and not at all like the behavior shown at marihuana "tea-pads."

SUMMARY AND DISCUSSION

Under the influence of marihuana changes in personality as
shown by alterations in test performance are slight. They are
not statistically significant and indicate only tendencies or
trends. Moreover, the drug effect is not always in proportion
to the amount taken, nor are the changes consistently in one
direction. In many instances the effect of small doses (2 cc.) or
of marihuana cigarettes is the opposite of the effect of larger
doses (5 cc.).[2]

The personality changes observed when the subject is under
the influence of 2 cc. of marihuana or marihuana cigarettes
demonstrate that the subject experiences some reduction in
drive, less objectivity in evaluating situations, less aggression,
more self-confidence and a generally more favorable attitude
toward himself. These reactions can be ascribed to two main
causes, namely, an increased feeling of relaxation and disinhibition and increased self-confidence. As the drug relaxes the
subject, the restraints which he normally imposes on himself
are loosened and he talks more freely than he does in his undrugged state. Things which under ordinary circumstances he
would not speak about are now given expression. Metaphysical
problems which in the undrugged state he would be unwilling
to discuss, sexual ideas he would ordinarily hesitate to mention,
jokes without point, are all part of the oral stream released
by the marihuana.

At the same time that he verbalizes more freely, there is a
reduction in the individual's critical faculty. This is probably
due both to the intellectual confusion produced by the drug
and to the less exacting attitude his feeling of relaxation induces. He holds himself less rigidly to the standards of his
undrugged phase and does not drive himself to achieve. He is
satisfied with himself and willing to accept himself as he is.
This self-satisfaction undoubtedly helps produce the feeling of
self-confidence which allows the subject to come out more
freely in fields which he formerly avoided. This increased
confidence expresses itself primarily through oral rather than

2 While sufficient experimentation has not been made to validate the
finding, it should be noted that the personality changes produced by 2
cc. or marihuana cigarettes are almost always in agreement in contrast
to the changes resulting from the ingestion of 5 cc. The 2 cc. dosage apparently more nearly approximates the amount a person would take if
left to his own devices.

physical channels. Physically the subject reports pleasant sensations of "drifting" and "floating" and he allows himself to become enveloped in a pleasant lassitude.

After the administration of larger doses of marihuana (5 cc.) the pleasurable sensations appear to be outweighed by concomitant feelings of anxiety and, in some cases, of physical distress, such as nausea. Under these circumstances, for many subjects there is little increase in confidence but rather heightened insecurity which precludes outgoing reactions and tends to evoke generally negativistic attitudes to most stimuli.

It is important to note that neither the ingestion of marihuana nor the smoking of marihuana cigarettes affects the basic outlook of the individual except in a very few instances and to a very slight degree. In general the subjects who are withdrawn and introversive stay that way, those who are outgoing remain so, and so on. Where changes occur the shift is so slight as to be negligible. In other words reactions which are natively alien to the individual cannot be induced by the ingestion or smoking of the drug.

Although in most instances the effects of the drug are the same for the user and the non-user, there are some differences both in kind and extent. Where the effects for the two groups are in the same direction they generally are more marked in the case of the non-user. This is not unexpected in view of the non-user's lack of habituation to the drug action. For the non-user his present experience is a strange, even hazardous one, and the uncertainty and anxiety attendant upon this impairs the sense of well-being which the drug produces in the user. Thus the non-user frequently feels less secure when he is "high" than he does normally and is less well adjusted than he is in ordinary circumstances.

When the productions of the undrugged marihuana user are studied, certain personality traits which serve to differentiate him from the non-user and from the "average" individual can be discerned. As a group the marihuana users studied here were either inhibited emotionally or turned in on themselves, making little response to stimuli in the world about them. People with this type of personality generally have difficulty adjusting to others and are not at ease in social situations. This withdrawal from social contacts apparently finds little compensatory or sublimating activity elsewhere. These subjects did not have a desire or urge to occupy themselves creatively in a manner which might prove socially useful. They showed a tendency to drift along in passive fashion and gave a good portion of their attention to relatively unimportant matters. These men were poorly adjusted, lonely and insecure. As indicated by their history they seldom achieved good heterosexual adjustment.

CONCLUSIONS

1. Under the influence of marihuana the basic personality structure of the individual does not change but some of the more superficial aspects of his behavior show alteration.

2. With the use of marihuana the individual experiences increased feelings of relaxation, disinhibition and self-confidence.

3. The new feeling of self-confidence induced by the drug expresses itself primarily through oral rather than through physical activity. There is some indication of a diminution in physical activity.

4. The disinhibition which results from the use of marihuana releases what is latent in the individual's thoughts and emotions, but does not evoke responses which would be totally alien to him in his undrugged state.

5. Marihuana not only releases pleasant reactions but also feelings of anxiety.

6. Individuals with a limited capacity for effective experience and who have difficulty in making social contacts are more likely to resort to marihuana than those more capable of outgoing responses.

Family and Community Ideologies

Adolph G. Woltmann, MA

At the outset of the study it seemed worth while to supplement the quantitative data by some qualitative procedures of the projective type which might throw light on the social reactions of the individuals who were being studied. One of the methods that has shown its possibilities, particularly in its use with children, is the play technique in which the individual is permitted to give free expression to some of his unconscious motivations in a way that is not immediately apparent to him. The limitation of this technique is the fact that it is highly interpretive, but it has the advantage of permitting observations of the subject's personality reactions in problem situations.

Such a study was accordingly carried out on 18 subjects in the early part of the investigation.

METHOD

Two situations were studied: one, subsequently to be referred to as the family set-up, in which toys were used to build an apartment or home, and another, subsequently to be known as the community set-up, in which a second variety of toys were used to construct a town setting.

The Family Set-up

The equipment used in this part of the study consisted of a box of household toys of the type available in the ten-cent store, including beds, dressers, chairs, tables, sinks, a stove, a bathtub, a wash basin, a piano, lamps, flower boxes, a telephone, doll sets of a man, woman, boy, girl, and maid, and, in addition, several small wooden slats which were intended to be used as room partitions.

The box of toys and materials was presented to the subject with the following directions: "Here are a number of toys which can be placed in such a manner that a house can be built from them. You are supposed to be this doll (man). Go ahead and build yourself a house or apartment. You may use as few or as many toys as you wish. You may also make believe you are a bachelor or a married man with or without a family."

The Community Set-up

In studying the community set-up the following items were employed: eighteen wooden houses, trees, cars, trucks, fire engines, an ambulance, a radio police car, a railroad train, airplanes, and numerous figures representing men, women, and children from different walks of life. All these toys were handed to the subject at the same time with the instruction to build a town or city. As in the family set-up, no further help or suggestions were given.

The actual method of handling these materials allows for two approaches. In the free method the subject is encouraged to play with any toy and to create and act out any situation that the nature of the toy suggests to him. No help, clues, or hints are given. In the controlled methods either the subject is told to create a specific pattern or his responses and reactions to a predetermined particular situation are elicited. Both methods were used in this study.

After the subject had completed either his family or his community set-up and answered questions regarding certain situations about which the examiner had questioned him the following points were investigated: (1) subject's marital status, both real and assumed; (2) type of home he built for himself (number of rooms, type of furnishing); (3) subject's assumed occupation; (4) monthly income and rent which he posited; (5) his reaction to attempted burglary; (6) his reaction to his wife's and his own infidelity; and (7) the attitude he would take toward civic problems if given a position of responsibility such as mayor. In addition, the examiner appraised the subject's neatness and orderliness in his home and community set-up. The experiment was given first when the subject was undrugged and then when he was under the influence of marihuana.

FINDINGS

Results were collated in terms of the type and frequency of responses to different situations both before and after taking marihuana and in terms of number of items (toys) employed in the set-up, as, for example, in the case of the home situation, the number of rooms the subject thought necessary for his apartment and the amount of rent he thought he ought to pay and its relation to the income he posited for himself; in the case of the community set-up, the number of times the subject provided for ambulances, firemen, and policemen; in the case of the subject's reaction to burglary, whether he took a passive or a resistant attitude toward the burglary and whether he assumed the burglar had absconded with most of the property and so on; in the case of his attitude toward his wife's adultery, whether he thought he ought to divorce her or try for reconciliation; and, when the subject was unfaithful, whether he thought his wife ought to forgive his delinquency.

In most cases comparisons between responses or reactions showed little difference in attitude before and after the ingestion of marihuana and therefore it would not be too profitable in this short summary of the work to present all the data obtained. However, by way of illustrating the type of material procured, the following tables are given:

TABLE 20

Marital status of subjects

| Marital status | In reality | DURING PLAY | |
		Without Marihuana	Under Marihuana
Married	4	14	13
Single	14	3	3
	18	17	16*

* The differences between the number of subjects accounted for under different rubrics is due to the fact that occasionally a subject was not available for the test or retest experiment.

TABLE 21

Number of rooms planned for apartment during play

Number of Rooms	NUMBER OF SUBJECTS PLANNING APARTMENTS	
	Without Marihuana	Under Marihuana
1	–	–
2	1	–
3	–	2
4	3	8
5	4	3
6	8	1
7	1	2
	17	16

The majority of the patients, though unmarried in real life, assumed families and responsibilities in the play situation, and in a free situation acted out family activities and ideologies.

These figures reveal that, on the average, the subjects when under the influence of the drug tended to build apartments with somewhat fewer rooms. The impression of the examiner was that this was due primarily to the subject's desire to get through with the task as quickly as possible in order to return to his room to rest and sleep.

TABLE 22

Frequency with which various toys were used during play

Toy	NUMBER OF TIMES SUBJECTS USED TOYS	
	Without Marihuana	Under Marihuana
Ambulance	14	7
Fire engine	6	6
Burglar	5	4
Police	5	2

A "make-believe" sickness or accident necessitating the use of an ambulance was the most frequently observed play pattern. When the subjects were under the influence of the drug the incidence of the ambulance and the police was considerably less than it was when they were in the undrugged state.

TABLE 23

Basic reactions to wife's adultery

Type of reaction	NUMBER OF SUBJECTS REACTING	
	Without Marihuana	Under Marihuana
Passive	8	9
Aggressive	7	6
Not suspicious	2	1
	—	—
	17	16

The most frequent form of passive reaction to his wife's infidelity was that the subject would pack up and leave home. The aggressive reactions consisted of ordering the wife out of the home in three instances, jailing the wife and lover in one instance, throwing the wife out in one instance, killing the lover but leaving the wife unmolested in one instance, and beating up the lover and leaving the wife unharmed in one instance.

The following are examples of subjects' responses to the adultery situation. When he was facing the pretended situation before taking marihuana, one subject immediately left his house, borrowed money from his employer, and traveled to the West Coast. After he arrived there he proceeded to drink and in due time became a derelict on the Barbary Coast. When asked about his children he said, "That's closed with the rest of the chapter. Let her ardent lover support the children. I take on an assumed name. Others might get a divorce and custody of the children but in my case my home life would be a closed chapter." After the administration of marihuana he still showed a passive attitude, but, having assumed the role of a psychologist, he felt obliged to act accordingly. At first he considered divorce action, but since that would deprive the children of a home, he finally forgave his wife. Then he stopped in his contemplations, looked at the examiner and said, "Why do I become altruistic? . . . That's beyond me . . . Maybe I become a martyr . . . I commit an act of martyrdom." Another subject, when in the undrugged condition, ordered his wife out of the house and later divorced her. In the drugged state customary procedures were reversed. The subject went to his parents and remained passively at home while his mother unsuccessfully tried to bring about a reconciliation.

The subject's attitude toward adultery did not change in the drugged state. The data in Table 24 illustrate the fact that

TABLE 24

Final solution to the problem of wife's adultery

	NUMBER OF SUBJECTS	
Solution	*Without Marihuana*	*Under Marihuana*
Reconciliation	2	2
Separation	1	1
Divorce	7	5
Separation without legal advice	7	8
	17	16

ingestion of marihuana generally does not alter the subject's basic attitude.

Practically all the subjects approved of saloons. Gambling was rejected because it deprives wives and children of money and leads to trouble. A heavy loser may try to recoup his losses through holdups, and fights and homicide may develop from quarrels. Prostitution was condoned by about 50 per cent of the subjects both before and after the ingestion of the drug, but the use of marihuana was frowned upon more often when the subject was undrugged than when he was in the drugged state.

TABLE 25

Attitude toward saloons, gambling, prostitution and marihuana

		NUMBER OF SUBJECTS EXPRESSING ATTITUDES	
Attitude toward various civic problems		*Without Marihuana*	*Under Marihuana*
Saloons:	Approval	12	13
	Disapproval	2	1
Gambling:	Approval	4	4
	Disapproval	10	10
Prostitution:	Approval	9	8
	Disapproval	5	6
Marihuana:	Approval	4	8
	Disapproval	10	6

SUMMARY AND CONCLUSIONS

Eighteen subjects who participated in the marihuana study were subjected to the play situation with the idea of seeing whether the pattern of play or the ideas investigated were materially altered in consequence of the ingestion of the marihuana. Among the ideologies which were appraised were: (1) attitude toward family set-up; (2) attitude toward different occupations; (3) attitude toward income; (4) attitude toward situations ordinarily calling for aggression, namely an attempted burglary of his home and sexual infidelity on the part of his wife; (5) attitude toward authority.

In general the subject's attitude toward family and community ideologies as manifested in play did not change markedly as a result of the ingestion of marihuana. The subjects (in play) were not intolerant of infidelity or aggressive toward lawbreakers either before or after the ingestion of marihuana. On the whole the initial passive reactions already observed in other parts of the study were likewise observed in the play situation experiment. The only very definite change as a result of the ingestion of marihuana was in their attitude toward the drug itself. Without marihuana only 4 out of 14 subjects said they would tolerate the sale of marihuana while after ingestion 8 of them were in favor of this.

Another significant manifestation in the play situation pertains to the construction of the community set-up. In general the community was less orderly and well organized when the subjects had had marihuana. It is probable that this poor organization may be ascribed to the generally indifferent attitude and lack of motor coordination already observed in the more controlled studies.

On the whole, the experiment with play technique gave less information as to the effect of marihuana on subjects than had been hoped for. This may have been due to the incompleteness of the method employed or possibly to the fact that this technique is designed to give data about the basic personality of the individual rather than such alterations in it as might be caused by pharmacological agents.

Comparison Between Users and Non-Users from the Standpoint of Mental and Physical Deterioration

A careful testing of the motor and sensory functions of the nervous system was included in the general physical examination of each subject. Of motor functions, reflex activity and muscular response and coordination were determined; of sensory functions, perception of touch, pain and temperature stimuli; of specialized functions, taste, hearing and vision. In the eye, the corneal and light reflexes were tested and a retinal examination was made. In this neurological examination no pathological conditions were found in any of the subjects.

In the psychiatric examination attention was paid to general intelligence and knowledge in relation to the subject's background, to relevancy of talk in conversation, to orientation as to time, place and situation, to memory of past and recent events, to ability in simple arithmetic, to judgment in reaching decisions, and to the presence of abnormal mental content shown by delusions, hallucinations, obsessions, and ideas of persecution. There was no evidence of disordered cerebral functioning in any of the group.

As would be expected, differences in grades of intelligence and in orderliness in thinking and reasoning were noticeable. The Bellevue Adult Intelligence Test was administered to a total of 60 male subjects, 40 marihuana users and 20 non-users. The average I.Q. for the user group was 96.7, range 70 to 124, and for the non-user group the average I.Q. was 104.5, range 93 to 114. Both groups may therefore be classified as of average intelligence.

When analyzed according to racial distribution the two groups were even better equated intellectually than the total results indicate. For the 28 white subjects examined (13 users and 15 non-users) the average I.Q. for the users was 106.1, range 77 to 124, and for the non-users the average I.Q. was 106.3, range 96 to 114. There were 24 Negro subjects, 19 users and 5 non-users. The average I.Q. for the users was 92.6, range 70 to 112, while for the non-users the average I.Q. was 98.8, range 93 to 101. Although the non-users averaged 6.2 points higher than the users, it must be taken into account that the number of Negro non-users tested was small. In any event, the disparity in results would not be considered significant. The average I.Q. of the 2 Puerto Rican users was 91.0, range 72 to 100.

Reports on mental deterioration due to toxic, organic or psychotic factors as given in the literature reveal that in such cases the individual scores on the Bellevue Adult Intelligence Test show marked irregularity, depending upon the functions involved in the deteriorative process. As a group, the marihuana users tested in this study showed very even functioning, and what little irregularity occurred can be explained on the basis of language and racial factors.

The physical and psychiatric examinations were of a qualitative rather than a quantitative nature. In the special examinations and tests of organ and system function, quantitative measurements were obtained for 17 marihuana users. These subjects were selected for the reason that they had smoked marihuana for the longest period of time. The figures for years of usage and number of cigarettes smoked daily were taken from each subject's statement.

Marihuana users accustomed to daily smoking for a period of from two and a half to sixteen years showed no abnormal system functioning which would differentiate them from the non-users.

There is definite evidence in this study that the marihuana users were not inferior in intelligence to the general population and that they had suffered no mental or physical deterioration as a result of their use of the drug.

Addiction and Tolerance

A drug addiction is characterized by a compelling urge to use the drug for the prevention or relief of distressing mental and physical disturbances which occur when the necessary dose is delayed or omitted. A drug habit is also characterized by an urge to use the drug, but this is not compelling. The abstinence symptoms, which are expressions of nervous states, are not particularly distressing and do not occur as long as the person's attention is placed on other matters.

Drug tolerance in the narrower sense used here means that larger doses than those originally used are required to bring about the effects desired by the subject. In the case of morphine, tolerance develops because of addiction, but in other instances tolerance may be present without addiction and addiction without tolerance. When both are present the matter takes on greater importance because of the extremes to which the addict goes to obtain the drug constantly and in increasing quantities.

As our group of subjects included 48 users of marihuana, opportunity was afforded for some conclusions concerning marihuana addiction and tolerance. Practically all of our group of users stated that they could and often did voluntarily stop the smoking for a time without any undue disturbance from the deprivation. In the sociologic study reported by Dr. Schoenfeld it was found that smokers had no compelling urge for marihuana. If "reefers" were not readily available there was no special effort made to obtain them from known sources of supply. Dr. Walter Bromberg, Psychiatrist-in-Charge, Psychiatric Clinic, Court of General Sessions in New York, states: "The fact that offenders brought up on marihuana charges do not request medical treatment on their incarceration (with its cessation of drug supply) argues for the absence of withdrawal symptoms."[1] From interviews with several hundred marihuana users he concludes that true addiction was absent.

The evidence submitted here warrants the conclusion that as far as New York City is concerned true addiction to marihuana does not occur.

The evidence concerning acquired tolerance is less clear-cut. Tolerance develops during the periods when the drug is being taken and accounts for the necessity of increasing the dosage to bring about the desired effects. How long the tolerance persists after the drug administration is stopped has not been definitely established in any instance.

The statements of marihuana usage and time since stoppage given by eight of our subjects are summarized in Table 26.

TABLE 26

History of marihuana use among eight subjects

Subjects	Years of Usage	Number of Cigarettes Smoked Daily	Period of Deprivation
J.B.	5	5	2 weeks
W.C.	5	8	4 weeks
J.P.	14	10	7 weeks
A.B.	5	5	2 months
J.H.	4	7	2 months
F.G.	8	10	2½ months
O.D.	10	2	7 months
C.B.	8	6	2 years

On one or more of the numerous occasions on which marihuana was administered each of these subjects received what was considered a minimal effective dose. One (J.B.) was given 1 cc., another (A.B.) 3 cc., the others 2 cc. In all instances the customary physical effects, conjunctival injection, dilated and sluggishly reacting pupils, tremors and ataxia, were observed. With these doses the subjects also experienced the sensation described as "high." The only conclusion warranted here is that if acquired tolerance does occur it persists for a limited period only.

Further evidence, though indirect, was brought out by Dr. Shoenfeld's investigation and by personal interviews with our 48 users. There is agreement in the statements that among users the smoking of one or two cigarettes is sufficient to bring on

1 Bromberg, W. "Marihuana: a psychiatric study." *J.A.M.A.* 113:4, 1939.

the effect known as "high." When this state is reached the user will not continue smoking for fear of becoming "too high." When the desired effects have passed off and the smoker has "come down," smoking one cigarette brings the "high" effect on again. This could not be the case had a steadily increasing tolerance developed.

The evidence available then—the absence of any compelling urge to use the drug, the absence of any distressing abstinence symptoms, the statements that no increase in dosage is required to repeat the desired effect in users—justifies the conclusion that neither true addiction nor tolerance is found in marihuana users. The continuation and the frequency of usage of marihuana, as in the case of many other habit-forming substances, depend on the easily controlled desires for its pleasurable effects.

Possible Therapeutic Applications

If a drug has well-marked pharmacological actions and low toxicity, as appears to be the case with marihuana, a consideration of special interest is its possible therapeutic application. In the older clinical literature marihuana was recommended for use in a wide variety of disorders, but in recent years it has almost disappeared from the materia medica and it was dropped from the United States Pharmacopeia twenty years ago.

In view of the laboratory and clinical findings obtained in this study the question of the therapeutic possibilities of the drug was considered. Marihuana possesses two qualities which suggest that it might have useful actions in man. The first is the typical euphoria-producing action which might be applicable in the treatment of various types of mental depression; the second is the rather unique property which results in the stimulation of appetite. In the light of this evidence and in view of the fact that there is a lack of any substantial indication of dependence on the drug, it was reasoned that marihuana might be useful in alleviating the withdrawal symptoms in drug addicts.

At the Riker's Island Penitentiary observations were made on 56 inmates who were addicted to morphine or heroin. Two groups were selected, the addicts in each being matched with those in the other group as to age, physical condition, duration and intensity of habit, and number of previous attempts at cure. The subjects in one group received no treatment or were given Magendie's solution according to the usual hospital regimen, while those in the other group were treated with 15 mg. of tetrahydrocannabinol three times daily with or without placebo (subcutaneous water injection). An attempt was made to evaluate the severity of the withdrawal signs and symptoms. The impression was gained that those who received tetrahydrocannabinol had less severe withdrawal symptoms and left the hospital at the end of the treatment period in better condition than those who received no treatment or who were treated with Magendie's solution. The ones in the former group maintained their appetite and in some cases actually gained weight during the withdrawal period.

Since psychological factors play a large part in the withdrawal symptoms of at least a certain proportion of morphine addicts, there are grounds for the assumption that a drug having the properties of marihuana might be of aid in alleviating mental distress during the withdrawal period. However, the studies here described were not sufficiently complete to establish the value of such treatment, and before conclusions can be drawn the problem must be investigated under completely controlled conditions.

PHARMACOLOGICAL STUDY[1]

S. Loewe, MD[2]

SUMMARY

1. This review of the pharmacology of marihuana is centered around the chemical and pharmacological identification of the active principles of hemp. Coordination of chemical and pharmacological investigations as a prerequisite to success in the search for unknown principles and of the analysis of the structure-activity relationship of these compounds is discussed.

2. In a survey of the sources of preparations with marihuana activity, hemp seeds are disclosed as a heretofore unknown source of active substances.

3. Varieties of hemp can be distinguished according to genotypic differences of the content of active principles which persist over generations independently of soil and climate.

4. The pharmacological actions of marihuana are analyzed with regard to their specificity and their usefulness as indicators of specific components.

1 From the Department of Pharmacology, Cornell University Medical College.

2 Part of the experimental work here reported was conducted in collaboration with W. Modell.

5. Sixty-five substances from the new class of cannabinols and related classes are reviewed, among which are the essential components of the marihuana-active hemp oils. The discovery of this class, the synthesis of these representatives, and their structural elucidation led the way to the discovery of the active substances.

6. Quantitative assay procedures are described for the most important marihuana effects that are observed in the animal experiment. The assay of the ataxia effect in the dog and of the synergistic hypnotic effect in the mouse with refined procedures are shown to be reliable expedients for measuring these two marihuana actions, whereas the areflexia effect in rabbits failed to show the reproducibility required for quantitative purposes.

7. With the aid of these methods the natural tetrahydrocannabinols are shown to be active principles responsible for ataxia in dogs and psychic action in man. They are intermediate products between the two ineffective substances which compose the bulk of hemp oil: a labile excretion product of the plant, cannabidiol, and a stable end-product, cannabinol. The conversion of cannabidiol into active tetrahydrocannabinol by a natural environmental influence has been paralleled by ultraviolet irradiation *in vitro*.

8. Numerous isomers, homologs and analogs of tetra- and hexahydrocannabinol are shown to possess the specific marihuana action. The potency varies enormously and is highest in natural, optically active—laevogyrous—tetrahydrocannabinols.

9. The significance of many of the structural details of the tetrahydrocannabinol molecule for marihuana activity is elucidated by quantitative determinations of relative potency. Special attention was devoted to a study of the importance of variations in the length of the 3-alkyl side chain of tetrahydrocannabinols. In studying methyl to nonyl homologs of the original amyl derivative occurring in nature, it was found that the maximum potency is not at the amyl, but at the hexyl homolog, and in two out of four homologous series at the representatives with still longer side chains.

10. In addition to the ataxia and the psychic action, other pharmacological attributes of the tetrahydrocannabinols are a decrease in the respiratory and an increase in the pulse rates in the non-narcotized dog.

11. The synergistic hypnotic action of marihuana in the mouse is to be attributed to the otherwise inert cannabidiol.

12. The corneal areflexia action in the rabbit was much stronger in impure distillate oils than in pure tetrahydrocan-

nabinols, which leads to the conclusion that this action is either poorly reproducible or must be attributed to a different, as yet unknown, principle.

13. Only one among the numerous cannabinol derivatives, 7-methyltetrahydrocannabinol, was found to produce a motor stimulant—convulsant—action concomitant with ataxia action. A cannabidiol derivative, tetrahydrocannabidiol, was found to have specific convulsant action in the dog.

14. A central stimulant (benzedrine) considerably increased the ataxia action of marihuana, whereas a hypnotic (amytal) had no influence.

BIBLIOGRAPHY

1. Adams: Science, *92*, 115, 1940.
2. Adams, Hunt and Clark: Jour. Amer. Chem. Soc., *62*, 196, 1940.
3. Adams, Cain and Wolff: Jour. Amer. Chem. Soc., *62*, 732, 1940.
4. Adams, Hunt and Clark: Jour. Amer. Chem. Soc., *62*, 735, 1940.
5. Adams, Wolff, Cain and Clark: Jour. Amer. Chem. Soc., *62*, 1770, 1940.
6. Adams, Pease and Clark: Jour. Amer. Chem. Soc., *62*, 2194, 1940.
7. Adams, Pease, Clark and Baker: Jour. Amer. Chem. Soc., *62*, 2197, 1940.
8. Adams, Cain and Baker: Jour. Amer. Chem. Soc., *62*, 2201, 1940.
9. Adams, Baker and Wearn: Jour. Amer. Chem. Soc., *62*, 2204, 1940.
10. Adams and Baker: Jour. Amer. Chem. Soc., *62*, 2208, 1940.
11. Adams, Wolff, Cain and Clark: Jour. Amer. Chem. Soc., *62*, 2215, 1940.
12. Adams, Pease, Cain, Baker, Clark, Wolff, Wearn and Loewe: Jour. Amer. Chem. Soc., *62*, 2245, 1940.
13. Adams, Pease, Cain and Clark: Jour. Amer. Chem. Soc., *62*, 2402, 1940.
14. Adams and Baker: Jour. Amer. Chem. Soc., *62*, 2405, 1940.
15. Adams, Loewe, Pease, Cain, Wearn, Baker and Wolff: Jour. Amer. Chem. Soc., *62*, 2566, 1940.
16. Adams, Loewe, Jellinek and Wolff: Jour. Amer. Chem. Soc., *63*, 1971, 1941.
17. Adams, Smith and Loewe: Jour. Amer. Chem. Soc., *63*, 1973, 1941.
18. Adams, Cain and Loewe: Jour. Amer. Chem. Soc., *63*, 1977, 1941.
19. Adams, Cain, McPhee and Wearn: Jour. Amer. Chem. Soc., *63*, 2209, 1941.
20. Adams, Loewe, Smith and McPhee: Jour. Amer. Chem. Soc., *64*, 694, 1942.
21. Balozet: League of Nations, O.C./Cannabis/1542, 1937.
22. Bergel and Wagner: Annalen d. Chem., *482*, 55, 1930.
23. Bergel, Todd and Work: Chem. Industry, *86*, 1938.
24. Bembry and Powell: Jour. Amer. Chem. Soc., *63*, 2766, 1941.
25. Blatt: Jour. Wash. Acad. Sci., *28*, 465, 1938.
26. Bouquet: League of Nations, O.C./Cannabis/14, 1939.
27. Bouquet: League of Nations, O.C., 1545 (c), 1937.
28. Buergi: Deutsch. Med. Wochenschr., 1924, No. 45.

29. Cahn: Jour. Chem. Soc., 1342, 1932.
30. Cahn: Jour. Chem. Soc., 1400, 1933.
31. Casparis and Baur: Pharm. Acta Helv., *2*, 107, 1927.
32. Chopra and Chopra: Indian Jour. Med. Research Mem. (Mem. No. 31), p. 1, 1939.
33. Fraenkel: Arch. exp. Path. u. Pharmakol., *49*, 266, 1903.
34. Ghosh, Todd, Pascell and Wilkinson: Jour. Chem. Soc., 118, 1940.
35. Ghosh, Todd and Wilkinson: Jour. Chem. Soc., 118, 1940.
36. Ghosh, Todd and Wilkinson: Jour. Chem. Soc., 1393, 1940.
37. Ghosh, Todd and Wright: Jour. Chem. Soc., 137, 1941.
38. Gayer: Arch. exp. Path. u. Pharmakol., *129*, 312, 1928.
39. Goodall: Pharm. Jour., *84*, 112, 1910.
40. Haagen-Smit, Wawre, Koepfli, Alles, et al.: Science, *91*, 602, 1940.
41. Hare: Therap. Gazette, *11*, 225, 1887.
42. Houghton and Hamilton: Amer. Jour. Pharm., *80*, 16, 1908.
43. Jacob and Todd: Nature, *145*, 350, 1940; Jour. Chem. Soc., 649, 1940.
44. Joel: Pflügers Arch., *209*, 526, 1925.
45. Loewe: Jour. Pharmacol. and Exper. Therap., *66*, 23, 1939.
46. Loewe: Jour. Amer. Pharm. Assoc., *28*, 427, 1939.
47. Loewe: Jour. Amer. Pharm. Assoc., *29*, 162, 1940.
48. Loewe and Modell: Jour. Pharmacol. and Exper. Therap., *72*, 27, 1941.
49. Liautaud: Ac. Sc., 149, 1844.
50. Macdonald: Nature, *147*, 167, 1941.
51. Marx and Eckhardt: Arch. exp. Path. u. Pharmakol., *170*, 395, 1933.
52. Matchett, Levine, Benjamin, Robinson and Pope: Jour. Amer. Pharm. Assoc., *29*, 399, 1940.
53. Matchett and Loewe: Jour. Amer. Pharm. Assoc., *30*, 130, 1941.
54. Merz and Bergner: Arch. der Pharmaz., *278*, 49, 1940.
55. Powell, Salmon, Bembry and Walton: Science, *93*, 522, 1941.
56. Robinson: Jour. Amer. Pharm. Assoc., *30*, 616, 1941.
57. Robinson and Matchett: Jour. Amer. Pharm. Assoc., *29*, 448, 1940.
58. Russell, Todd, Wilkinson, Macdonald and Woolfe: (a) Jour. Chem. Soc., 169, 1941; (b) ibid. 826, 1941.
59. See: Deutsch, Med. Wochenschr., 679, 1890.
60. Todd: Nature, 829, 1940.
61. U. S. Treasury Dept.: Review of Progress on Marihuana Investigation during 1938.
62. U. S. Treasury Dept.: Marihuana: Its Identification, Washington, 1938.
63. U. S. Treasury Dept., Bureau of Narcotics: Report of the Marihuana Investigation, Summer 1937.
64. Viehoever: Amer. Jour. Pharmacy, *109*, No. 12, 1937.
65. Walton: Marihuana, Philadelphia-London, 1938.
66. Walton, Martin and Keller: Jour. Pharmacol. and Exper. Therap., *62*, 239, 1938.
67. Wiechowski: Arch. exp. Path. u. Pharmakol., *119*, 59, 1927.
68. Wollner, Matchett, Levine and Loewe: Jour. Amer. Chem. Soc., *64*, 26, 1942.
69. Wood, Barlow, Spivey and Easterfield: Jour. Chem. Soc., *69*, 539, 1896.

70. Wood, Barlow, Spivey and Easterfield: Jour. Chem. Soc., *75*, 20, 1899.
71. Work, Bergel and Todd: Biochem. Jour., *33*, 124, 1939.

ADDENDUM TO BIBLIOGRAPHY:

72. Adams: Harvey Lectures, Ser. XXXVII, 1941-1942, p. 168.
73. Adams, Smith and Loewe: Jour. Amer. Chem. Soc., *64*, 2087, 1942.
74. Alles, Haagen-Smit, Feigen and Dendliker: Jour. Pharm. and Exp. Ther., *76*, 21, 1942.
75. Alles, Icke and Feigen: Jour. Amer. Chem. Soc., *64*, 2031, 1942.
76. Bergel, Morrison, Rinderknecht, Todd, Macdonald and Woolfe: Jour. Chem. Soc., 286, 1943.
77. Fulton: Indus. & Engin. Chem., *14*, 407, 1942.
78. Hitzemann: Arch. der Pharmazie, *276*, 353, 1941.
79. Leaf, Todd and Wilkinson: Jour. Chem. Soc., 185, 1942.
80. Madinaveitia, Russell and Todd: Jour. Chem. Soc., 628, 1942.
81. Russell, Todd, Wilkinson, Macdonald and Woolfe: Jour. Chem. Soc., 826, 1941.
82. Simonsen and Todd: Jour. Chem. Soc., 188, 1942.

SUMMARY

George B. Wallace, MD, Chairman

The widespread publicity describing the dangerous effects of marihuana usage in New Orleans and other Southern cities, especially among school children, had its repercussion in the city of New York, and some anxiety was experienced as to the possibility that similar conditions were present or might develop here. Because of this, Mayor LaGuardia asked The New York Academy of Medicine for an opinion as to the advisability of studying the whole marihuana problem. The Academy recommended that such a study be made and outlined its scope in general terms. Following this, the Mayor appointed a committee empowered to make the study. This committee consisted of two internists, three psychiatrists, two pharmacologists, and one public health expert, and the Commissioners of Correction, of Health, and of Hospitals, and the Director of the Division of Psychiatry of the Department of Hospitals, ex officio.

The Committee formulated a plan for the study, and the expenses were arranged for through grants by the New York Foundation, the Friedsam Foundation and the Commonwealth Fund. The study was begun in April 1940.

The first phase of the study concerned the extent of marihuana smoking in New York City, its incidence among school children, its relation to crime, and its effects on individuals using it. For obtaining this information, the Commissioner of Police assigned to the Committee six police officers, four men and two women, who served as "plain clothes" investigators. These investigators circulated in the districts in which marihuana appeared to be most widely used, particularly Harlem, associated with marihuana users, and found out as much as possible about sources of supply, means of distribution, and effects of marihuana on users. Included in this survey were a careful watch on school children in both grade and high schools and interviews with school principals.

As a result of this investigation the Committee came to the conclusion that marihuana distribution and usage is found mainly in Harlem, the population of which is predominantly Negro and Latin-American, and to a less extent in the Broadway area extending from 42nd to 59th Streets. The local supply comes from individual peddlers and from "tea-pads," which are establishments for marihuana smoking. There are no figures available as to the number of marihuana users in New York City, but a conservative estimate is that there are some 500 peddlers and 500 "tea-pads" in Harlem.

The marihuana users with whom contact was made in this study were persons without steady employment. The majority fall in the age group of 20 to 30 years. Idle and lacking initiative, they suffer boredom and seek distraction. Smoking is indulged in for the sake of conviviality and sociability and because it affords a temporary feeling of adequacy in meeting disturbing situations.

The confirmed user smokes from 6 to 10 cigarettes a day. The effects are easily recognized by the smoker, the desirable stage being what is known as "high." When this is reached, the smoking is stopped. If a "too high" state is reached, the taking of beverages such as beer or sweet soda pop, or a cold bath are considered effective countermeasures.

In most instances, the behavior of the smoker is of a friendly, sociable character. Aggressiveness and belligerency are not commonly seen, and those showing such traits are not allowed to remain in "tea-pads."

The marihuana user does not come from the hardened criminal class and there was found no direct relationship between the commission of crimes of violence and marihuana. "Tea-pads" have no direct association with houses of prostitution, and marihuana itself has no specific stimulant effect in regard to sexual desires.

There is no organized traffic in marihuana among New York City school children, and any smoking that occurs in this group is limited to isolated instances.

Smoking marihuana can be stopped abruptly with no resulting mental or physical distress comparable to that of morphine withdrawal in morphine addicts.

The second division of the study was the clinical one, the purpose of which was to ascertain the effects of marihuana on the individual user. There were two phases of this work, the general medical study and the psychological study. Wards in the municipal hospital on Welfare Island (now known as Goldwater Memorial Hospital) were made available by the Commissioner of Hospitals. The subjects for the study were drawn from the prison population at the Penitentiary on Riker's Island, as arranged by the Commissioner of Correction. They were under sentence for terms varying from three months to three years, most of them for what would be called minor criminal offenses. They volunteered for the study, the purpose and procedure of which had been fully explained to them. They were kept in the hospital in groups of 6 to 10, for a period of study of approximately a month. The subjects afforded the sample especially desired, for over half of them were marihuana smokers and the others of the class from which marihuana smokers come. The personnel conducting the study consisted of a physician in charge, with an assistant physician, three psychologists, and a secretary. The subjects were under the constant supervision of the medical staff, nurses and attendants.

In studying the effects of marihuana on the 77 subjects selected for the study, the drug was given either in the form of an extract taken by mouth, or was smoked in cigarettes. The dose given to produce definite systemic reactions ranged from a minimal one to 1 cc. to a maximum of 22 cc. of the extract, and from 1 to 10 cigarettes. The effects of smoking appeared immediately and usually passed off in from one to three or four hours. Those from the extract came on more gradually and persisted for a longer time, in some instances for twenty-four hours or more. As the dose for any individual was increased, the effects usually were more marked and of longer duration, but the effect of any given dose varied with the individual subjects.

Although some of the subjects became restless and talkative under marihuana influence, a mental state characterized by a sense of well-being, relaxation and unawareness of surroundings, followed by drowsiness, was present in most instances when the subject was left undisturbed. Generally, there was observed a difficulty in focusing and sustaining mental attention. In company, the subjects were lively and given to talkativeness, fits of laughter and good-natured joking. The pleasurable effects, classed as euphoric, were frequently interrupted or replaced by a state of apprehension of varying degree.

In a limited number of the subjects there were alterations in behavior giving rise to antisocial expression. This was shown by unconventional acts not permitted in public, anxiety reactions, opposition and antagonism, and eroticism. Effects such as these would be considered conducive to acts of violence. However, any tendency toward violence was expressed verbally and not by physical actions, and in no case was restraint by force needed.

In addition to its effect on mental states, physical symptoms resulting from the administration of marihuana were recorded. Of these, tremor, ataxia, dizziness, a sensation of floating in space, dilation of the pupils, dryness of the throat, nausea and vomiting, an urge to urinate, hunger, and a desire for sweets were the most striking. Tremor and ataxia and dizziness were of the greatest frequency. These symptoms may be disturbing to the subject, and if marked enough, cause anxiety and interrupt the euphoric state.

On some occasions, instead of the marihuana concentrate, preparations supplied by Dr. Roger Adams were given. These were tetrahydrocannabinol, made from cannabidiol, corresponding to a principle found in the plant, a synthetic tetrahydrocannabinol, an isomer of the natural one, and a synthetic hexyl-hydrocannabinol. They all produced effects similar in character to those from the concentrate. Their relative potency could be determined only approximately. The rough estimate was that 1 cc. of the concentrate had as its equivalent 15 mg. of the natural tetrahydrocannabinol, 60 mg. of the hexyl-hydrocannabinol, and 120 mg. of the synthetic tetrahydrocannabinol.

In the total group studied, what are known as psychotic episodes occurred in 9 of the subjects. In 6 instances, they were of short duration, persisting for from three to ten hours, and were characterized by mental confusion and excitement of a delirious nature with periods of laughter and of anxiety. These effects correspond to those often reported in marihuana literature and are examples of acute marihuana intoxication, which in many ways is similar to acute alcoholic intoxication. In the other 3 cases, one subject had a mild psychotic reaction after smoking one cigarette. Later, a typical psychotic state came on four hours after the subject had taken tetrahydrocannabinol and persisted for six days. This subject subsequently was found to have a history of epileptic attacks so that the psychotic episode was probably related to epilepsy. The second subject had previously been a drug addict. She was given

marihuana on several occasions, at times showing only euphoric effects and other times confusion and worriment. She
left the hospital depressed and moody, and a week later was
committed to a state hospital with the diagnosis of psychosis.
After six months, she was discharged as cured. The third
subject showed no unusual effects of marihuana which was
given on several occasions during his stay at the hospital.
Some days after his return to the penitentiary he developed
a psychotic state diagnosed "Psychosis with psychopathic personality." This was considered an example of what is known
as "prison psychosis," a condition which has been noted in
persons emotionally unstable subjected to the depressing atmosphere of prison incarceration. The precise role of marihuana in the psychotic states in the three unstable subjects
is not clear. In the case of the second and third subject, the
fact that they were sent back to prison to complete their sentences must be considered an important if not the main factor
in bringing on the psychosis.

In the clinical study of the effect of marihuana on functions
of various organs of the body, there were found an increase
in pulse rate and blood pressure and an increase in blood
sugar and metabolic rate. No changes were found in the circulation rate and vital capacity. Tests on renal and liver
function were negative. No changes were found in blood
counts and hemoglobin, or blood nitrogen, calcium and phosphorus concentrations. The electrocardiogram showed no abnormalties which could be attributed to direct action on the
heart, and from a few observations made, marihuana appeared
to be without effect on gastric motility and secretion. The
positive results found, as well as the occurrence of nausea
and vomiting, an increase in the frequency of urination, and
the sensation of hunger and an increase in appetite, may be
considered results of central nervous excitation, producing
peripheral effects through the autonomic nervous system.

The psychological study, planned and carried out by experienced psychologists, was concomitant with the general
medical one and was devoted to determining the effects of
marihuana on psychomotor responses and certain special abilities, on intellectual functioning, and on emotional reactions
and personality structure.

For psychomotor effects, procedures were followed which
gave records affording quantitative measurement. Static equilibrium and hand steadiness were the functions most strongly
affected by marihuana. The body swaying was general in
direction and not greater in one axis than in others. These
effects came on during the first hour after the extract was

given, reached a peak in about four hours, and persisted for some eight hours. After smoking, the effects came on much sooner—within a few minutes—and were of shorter duration, about three hours. Complex hand and foot reactions showed impairment, but simple reaction time, the strength of grip, speed of tapping, auditory acuity and musical ability, and estimation of short time intervals and small linear distances were unchanged. The findings in the women correspond to those in the male subjects. In both groups there was marked individual variability, irrespective of dosage.

It was found that marihuana in an effective dose impairs intellectual functioning in general. Included under this heading are adverse effects on speed and accuracy in performance, on the application of acquired knowledge, on carrying out routine tasks, on memory, and on capacity for learning.

Marihuana does not change the basic personality structure of the individual. It lessens inhibition and this brings out what is latent in his thoughts and emotions but it does not evoke responses which would otherwise be totally alien to him. It induces a feeling of self-confidence, but this expressed in thought rather than in performance. There is, in fact, evidence of a diminution in physical activity. While suggestibility may be increased by small doses, larger ones tend to induce a negativistic attitude.

From the study as a whole, it is concluded that marihuana is not a drug of addiction, comparable to morphine, and that if tolerance is acquired, this is of a very limited degree. Furthermore, those who have been smoking marihuana for a period of years showed no mental or physical deterioration which may be attributed to the drug.

The lessening of inhibitions and repression, the euphoric state, the feeling of adequacy, the freer expression of thoughts and ideas, and the increase in appetite for food brought about by marihuana suggest therapeutic possibilities. From limited observations on addicts undergoing morphine withdrawal and on certain types of psychopathic disturbances, the impression was gained that marihuana had beneficial effects, but much more extensive and controlled study is required for definite conclusions to be drawn concerning therapeutic usage. It should be borne in mind that the effects of marihuana, more than in the case of other drugs, are quite variable in different individuals and in the same one at different times.

The chapter on the pharmacology of marihuana, prepared by Dr. Loewe, reviews the results of collaborative work of three laboratories (The Pharmacological Laboratory at the Cornell Medical College, the William Albert Noyes Laboratory at the University of Illinois, and the Laboratory of the Bureau of Narcotics at Washington, D. C.) which led to the discovery of the active principles, the elucidation of their origin, and the assembling of data on the relationship between chemical structure and biological activity. The chapter is introduced by a survey of the geographical distribution and botanical relationships of plants with marihuana activity.

The principles involved in bioassay are discussed and a method for marihuana assay described. The synthetic tetra-hydrocannabinol of Adams was taken as the standard of reference and the characteristic reaction of ataxia in dogs measured quantitatively for the degree of activity. By this method the potency of samples and preparations of marihuana and of natural and synthetic principles has been determined and relationships between chemical structure and pharmaco-logical activity elucidated.

The main components which have been isolated from mari-huana oil containing the active principles are cannabidiol, cannabinol and isomeric tetrahydrocannabinols. The first two, but not the last, have been obtained as crystalline substances. The chemical structure and synthesis of these compounds have been described by Adams.

The typical effects of marihuana on man are ascribed to actions on the central nervous system. In dogs, the character-istic effect is ataxia. A delayed increase in pulse rate, a decrease in respiratory rate and blood pressure, and retching and vomiting were also observed. These effects are produced by tetrahydrocannabinol but not by cannabinol or cannabidiol. A derivative of the latter, tetrahydrocannabidiol, after a latent period of from thirty to seventy minutes following intravenous injection, had a specific convulsant action on the dog.

In rabbits a characteristic effect of marihuana extracts is corneal areflexia. This is also not produced by cannabidiol or cannabinol but does occur after tetrahydrocannabinol. How-ever, impure oil mixtures have this action to a greater extent, from which it is suggested that a third unknown principle is present in the plant.

Cannabidiol has a synergistic hypnotic action with pernoston in mice. Neither cannabinol nor the synthetic tetrahydrocan-nabidiols had this effect.

The ataxia action of marihuana was considerably increased by a central stimulant, benzedrine.

No evidence was found of an acquired tolerance for the drug.

In examination of the data presented in the detailed clinical study it is seen that the effects reported were in the main those produced by the extract of marihuana taken by mouth. With the extract, the absorption is gradual and the action persists as long as the active principles are circulating throughout the body. The doses given were fixed ones and once taken the effects were beyond the subjects' control. Giving the extract thus afforded a longer period for study and insured greater accuracy in dosage. In New York, as far as is known, marihuana is rarely if ever taken in this form but is smoked in cigarettes. However, it is shown in the study that the effects from smoking correspond in kind to those from the extract. The difference is that, in smoking, the effects come on promptly and are of much shorter duration. How marked the reaction becomes depends on the number of cigarettes smoked and this is entirely under the subjects' control. The sensations desired are pleasurable ones—a feeling of contentment, inner satisfaction, free play of imagination. Once this stage is reached, the experienced user realizes that with further smoking the pleasurable sensations will be changed to unpleasant ones and so takes care to avoid this.

CHAPTER TWO

PSYCHIATRIC ASPECTS OF MARIHUANA INTOXICATION

Samuel Allentuck, MD, and
Karl Bowman, MD

Because it flatly contradicted many of the marihuana myths, the following paper caused something of a stir both in the press and in medical circles when it was read at the ninety-eighth annual meeting of the American Psychiatric Association, held in Boston in May 1942. The findings of Dr. Allentuck and Dr. Bowman—both practicing psychiatrists—were based upon exacting studies which they conducted for the Mayor's Committee on Marihuana. Dr. Allentuck, whose medical degree is reinforced by a doctorate in biochemistry, was the clinical director of the Committee.

"The Psychiatric Aspects of Marihuana Intoxication" was originally published by the American Journal of Psychiatry *in September 1942. It has since taken its place as one of the key reference works in the medical literature on marihuana.*

Marihuana has been known as a passport to euphoria since ancient times. It has fascinated men of imagination, and descriptions of its effects upon the mind and body have been given in popular and scientific literature countless times. The literature has been adequately considered by Walton (1) and by Bromberg (2), and will therefore not be reviewed at the present time.

The observations to be presented here are based on research conducted in New York City under the auspices of the Mayor's Committee on Marihuana. Studies were made of the effect of marihuana on a series of 77 subjects, including some who had previously used marihuana for varying periods of time. The work was done at Welfare Hospital with the assistance of Drs. Frank Anker and Louis Gitzelter. A monograph based on this and collaborative work is now in the course of preparation, and deals with the pharmacological, clinical, therapeutic, social, psychological, and psychiatric aspects of marihuana. This paper consists mainly of a description of the psychiatric manifestations caused by the drug.

The active principle in the plant is an oil, occurring in maximum concentration in the flowering tops. The drug is ingested or inhaled after being prepared for use in various ways in different parts of the world. In this hemisphere it is usually smoked, but may be eaten in the form of candy, or drunk in various liquid preparations. The strength and quality of the effect of marihuana vary with the geographical source of the plant. It is strongest in the African derivative, less strong in its Central American form, and weakest as found in the temperate zones of this country.

Marihuana is unique in the reactions it produces in the users, although its physiological effects have been likened to those of the atropine group of drugs, and its psychic effects to those of alcohol. The following is a clinical picture of the sequence of events resulting from the ingestion of marihuana. The sequence of events is the same whether the drug is ingested or inhaled, but the latter produces its effects more rapidly.

Within one-half to one hour after the ingestion of marihuana the conjunctiva reddens, the pupils dilate and react sluggishly to light; photophobia, lacrimation, tremulousness of the eyelids, and nystagmus upon lateral gaze become evident. Ophthalmoscopic examination reveals nothing unusual in the nerve head, vessels or retinal background. The vision for distance, proximity, and color changes but slightly. The tongue becomes tremulous and dry, and the mouth and throat patched, suggesting a diminution in salivary secretion. Cardiovascular changes consist of an increase in the radial pulse rate and a rise in the blood pressure which closely follows the pulse increase. The extremities become tremulous, and there are involuntary twitching, hyperreflexia, increased sensitivity to touch, pressure, and pain stimuli. Pyramidal tract signs are not elicited. There is equilibratory and nonequilibratory ataxia, as revealed by marked swaying and abnormal finger-to-finger test performance. Not all of these phenomena occur in every subject, but when any of them does, it lasts for about twelve hours. Elaborate laboratory studies of the effects of marihuana intoxication for shorter and longer periods, on users and non-users, reveal no significant systematic alterations.

Mental phenomena arise two to three hours after ingestion, or almost immediately after inhalation of the drug. The subject admits being "high." This state is characterized by a sensation of "floating in air," "falling on waves," lightness or dizziness in the head, ringing in the ears, and heaviness in the limbs. Euphoria is first manifested objectively in volubility and increased psychomotor activity, and later subjectively in a delicious and confused lassitude. Distance and time intervals subpectively appear elastic. In three to six hours after ingestion of marihuana, hunger, manifested mainly in a craving for sweets, and a feeling of fatigue and sleepiness become prominent. The individual may sleep from one to six hours and on awakening is "down"; that is, he no longer feels "high." The clinical phenomena may linger for another few hours.

The mental status usually reveals a hyperactive, apprehensive, loquacious, somewhat suspicious individual. His stream of talk may be circumstantial; his mood may be elevated, but he does not harbor frank abnormal mental content such as delusions, hallucinations, phobias, or autistic thinking. Attention, concentration and comprehension are only slightly disturbed, as is evidenced by the fact that the results in his educational achievement tests are only slightly lowered.

Marihuana may precipitate a psychosis in an unstable, disorganized personality, when it is taken in amounts greater than he can tolerate. Under such circumstances, the previously mentioned physical and psychic manifestations become quantitatively greater and new events arise. The respiration becomes labored; pallor and perspiration become evident; tachycardia and irregularity of pulse occur. The subject complains of urinary urgency, diarrhea and nausea; and may retch or actually vomit. His apprehension may be interrupted by laughing and weeping, by volubility or mutism. Marked irritability, negativism, and cerea flexibilitas-like phenomena may be elicited. The subject may assume grotesque, statuesque positions. He may experience visual pseudohallucinations in the form of flashes of light and apparitions. Micropsia and macropsia may occur. More intense intoxication may elicit auditory hallucinations similar to those met with in the alcoholic psychoses, such as alcoholic hallucinosis or delirium tremens.

Limitations of time will not permit detailed description of the nine psychoses precipitated in our series of 77 subjects. However, it should be noted that a characteristic marihuana psychosis does not exist. Marihuana will not produce a psychosis *de novo* in a well-integrated, stable person. In unstable users the personality factor and the mood preceding the ingestion of marihuana will color any psychosis that may result. In no two of the cases developing psychoses in our series were the patterns similar. Marihuana psychosis is protean in its manifestations and may be mistaken for schizophrenic, affective, paranoic, organic, psychoneurotic or psychopathic reaction types. Should a psychosis be precipitated in an unstable personality it may last only a few hours or it may continue for a few weeks. It may be controlled by withdrawal of the drug and the administration of barbiturates. After a few hours of sleep following the psychotic episode treated with barbiturates, the patient may awaken with complete memory for his experience and with his insight unimpaired.

The prolonged effects of the drug are strongly subjective, and consist of an increase in fatigability and vague generalized aches and pains. The aftermath of marihuana intoxication resembles an alcoholic "hangover." However, in contrast to alcoholics, marihuana users do not continue their indulgence beyond the point of euphoria, and soon learn to avoid becoming ill by remaining at a pleasurable distance from their maximum capacity for the drug. It may be mentioned that marihuana is no more aphrodisiac than is alcohol. Unlike damiana, yohimbin, testosterone propionate, etc., which produce genital engorgement directly, marihuana, like alcohol, acts only indirectly through the cerebral cortex in this respect.

Marihuana differs from the opium derivatives in that it does not give rise to a biological or physiological dependence. Discontinuance of the drug after its prolonged use does not result in withdrawal symptoms. The psychic habituation to marihuana is not as strong as to tobacco or alcohol. Use of marihuana over a long period of time may conduce to ingestion of progressively larger amounts merely through accessibility and familiarity. This increment however does not give rise to a more intense pleasurable experience. Thus a person experiencing pleasure with two marihuana cigarettes does not achieve any greater pleasure with six cigarettes, though he may indulge in them.

A physiologically active constituent has been isolated from the crude marihuana by Dr. Roger Adams and his associates, working in the Noyes Chemical Laboratory of the University of Illinois, in Urbana, as was reported by Dr. Adams in his Harvey Lecture in February 1942. This substance or its synthetic equivalent elicits somatic and psychic phenomena identical to those obtained with the crude drug. Only brief mention need be made of these substances since they are explained in detail in Dr. Adams' report. Thus, natural tetrahy-drocannabinol is obtained by the isomerization of cannabidiol, through the action of p-toluene sulphonic acid. Synthetic tetra-hydrocannabinol is 1-hydroxy-3-n-amyl-6,6,9-trimethyl-7,8,9, 10-tetrahydro-6-dibenzopyran. Another synthetic equivalent called synhexyl is 1-hydroxy-3-n-hexyl-6,6,9-trimethyl-7,8,9,10-tetrahydra-6-dibenzopyran. The natural product is most potent, the synthetic equivalent least potent, and the synhexyl ranks between them.

In the course of our investigation we studied the therapeutic application of marihuana derivatives and allied synthetics to opiate drug addiction, functional and organic depressions, and psychoneurotic disorders in which dysphoria and anorexia existed. The rationale for such therapeutic use was that, while exerting no permanent deleterious effects, marihuana or its derivatives or synthetics give rise to pleasurable sensations, calmness and relaxation, and increase the appetite.

A series of cases were selected from among drug addicts undergoing treatment. Subjective and objective criteria were employed. Comparative results were charted for the gradual withdrawal, total withdrawal, and marihuana derivative sub-stitution, as methods of treatment. A modification of the technic of Kolb and Himmelsbach was employed in studying the abstinence syndrome. Forty-nine subjects were studied. The results in general, although still inconclusive, suggest that the marihuana substitution method of treatment is superior. Thus, the withdrawal symptoms were ameliorated or eliminated sooner, the patient was in a better frame of mind, his spirits were elevated, his physical condition was more rapidly rehabili-tated, and he expressed a wish to resume his occupation sooner.

In conclusion it is worthy of note that marihuana is probably taken by its users for the purpose of producing sensations com-parable to those produced by alcohol. It causes a lowering of inhibitions comparable to that elicited by alcohol in a blood concentration of 2-3 mg. per cent. The user may speak and act more freely, is inclined to daydreaming, and experiences a feeling of calm and pleasurable relaxation.

Marihuana, by virtue of its property of lowering inhibitions, accentuates all traits of personality, both those harmful and those beneficial. It does not impel its user to take spontaneous action, but may make his response to stimuli more emphatic than it normally would be. Increasingly larger doses of mari-huana are not necessary in order that the long-term user may capture the original degree of pleasure.

Marihuana, like alcohol, does not alter the basic personality, but by relaxing inhibitions may permit antisocial tendencies formerly suppressed to come to the fore. Marihuana does not of itself give rise to antisocial behavior.

There is no evidence to suggest that the continued use of marihuana is a stepping-stone to the use of opiates. Prolonged use of the drug does not lead to physical, mental, or moral degeneration, nor have we observed any permanent deleterious effects from its continued use. Quite the contrary, marihuana and its derivatives and allied synthetics have potentially valuable therapeutic applications which merit future investigation.

BIBLIOGRAPHY

1. Walton, R. P. *Marihuana.* J. B. Lippincott Company.
2. Bromberg, Walter. "Marihuana: A psychiatric study." *J.A.M.A.,* 113:4, July 1, 1939.
3. Kolb, Lawrence and Himmelsbach, C. K. "Clinical studies of drug addiction, III." *Am. J. Psychiat.,* 94:759, Jan. 1938.

CHAPTER THREE

A NEW EUPHORIANT FOR DEPRESSIVE MENTAL STATES

George Tayleur Stockings, MB, BS, DPM

In 1943, a short time after Dr. Roger Adams' brilliant work in the isolation and synthesis of a number of the active principles of marihuana, one of his synthetic discoveries, synhexyl, was tested at the federal hospital in Lexington, Kentucky. Preliminary findings by Dr. Samuel Allentuck and other investigators had indicated that the new drug might prove successful in the treatment of patients withdrawing from opiate addiction. Subsequent results, however, were not consistent, for in many instances the striking euphoria-producing qualities of synhexyl could not allay the far more intense physical pain and psychic anxiety of the morphine abstinence syndrome. Some patients did derive some measure of relief, but it was felt that results were too variable to merit further experimentation in that area.

It was not until 1947, then, that an important therapeutic use for synhexyl was dramatically demonstrated in an article entitled "A New Euphoriant For Depressive Mental States," which appeared in the British Medical Journal of June 28, 1947. The author, George Tayleur Stockings (MB, BS, DPM; late major, specialist in Psychological Medicine, RAMC; Ernest Hart Memorial Scholar, British Medical Association), is one of England's most noted experimental psychiatrists, the author of several books and numerous scientific articles on mental illness. His interest in what are termed "consciousness-expanding drugs" began early in his career: in 1940 he published a monograph in the Journal of Mental Science *on mescaline, a psychedelic substance, as is marihuana, but far more powerful. Tayleur Stockings had little reason to experiment with synhexyl as an analgesic or palliative in the treatment of opiate withdrawal largely because England had never had a heroin problem. The much-discussed British System of treating opiate addiction as a disease rather than as a crime possibly accounts for the fact that there are only several hundred opiate addicts in the British Isles; they are legally registered and are encouraged to receive medical care for their illness at a cost of a few pennies a week. England* did *have other problems in 1946, however, and they were particularly evident in the high rate of depressive neurosis brought about, one may surmise, by the pressures of a long and bitter war.*

It is clear, then, why Tayleur Stockings was anxious to explore the possibilities of synhexyl as a euphoriant in the treatment of depressive mental conditions. As an experimental psychiatrist, he stated that

> The most important advances in psychiatry, as in general medicine, have been the discovery of specific pharmacological and physical agents for the various disease conditions. Similarly, a logical answer to the thalamic dysfunction (*depressive mental states,* Ed.) would be a drug possessing a specific reversing effect . . . that is, a powerful euphorigenic drug which would be therapeutically effective and at the same time free from the objectionable properties usually associated with narcotic compounds.

Stockings pointed out that

> The ideal euphoriant for clinical use should . . . induce a high degree of euphoria, must be stable and fully active by the oral route, be reasonably rapid-acting, and have a prolonged action. It must be of low toxicity, non-cumulative, and free from after-effects and undesirable effects on the higher cortical functions, such as impairment of concentration, judgment and memory. Most important of all, it must not have the property of inducing the condition of addiction or physical dependence when administered for long periods.

Stockings tested synhexyl on himself, a group of normal subjects, and a group of fifty depressive patients. He drew the following conclusions:

The discovery of the synthetic cannabis-like derivatives . . . within the last few years . . . has placed in our hands an entirely new type of euphoriant drug with properties which render it an extremely promising therapeutic agent in psychiatry. . . . My findings confirm that the drug is a powerful euphoriant with a specific action on the higher centres . . . The general effects in normal man are . . . a pleasant feeling of happiness and exhilaration with a marked sense of physical well-being and self-confidence; there is a sense of relief from tension and anxiety, and the threshold for unpleasant affect is markedly raised, while that for pleasant feeling-tone is correspondingly lowered. There is increased enjoyment of normally pleasant impressions, and the zest for life and working capacity may be actually increased in the early stages of the intoxication. . . . A generalized sensation of pleasant warmth diffused throughout the body is characteristic.

One of the ironic mysteries of present-day medicine is the failure of subsequent investigators to follow up and exploit, with further and broader studies, the exciting psycho-pharmacological promise demonstrated in this pioneering study by George Tayleur Stockings on the treatment of repressive neuroses with synhexyl.

The Syndrome of Thalamic Dysfunction

The syndrome of thalamic dysfunction, or neurotic depression, is the commonest of psychiatric conditions encountered in general practice, and often one of the most intractable and difficult to treat effectively. The commonest forms of the condition are the chronic neurotic depressions, anxiety states, reactive and hysterical depressions, and obsessional disorders. The milder forms of depressions of later life, in which the dysphoria is unaccompanied by hallucinosis, delusions, and other gross psychotic symptoms, may also be included in this group of conditions.

The essential feature common to all of these disorders is a condition of the nervous system in which the perception-threshold for unpleasant affects and sensory impressions is markedly lowered, while that for pleasant affect and sensation is correspondingly raised—the anhedonic or dysphoric syndrome. The resulting dysphoria or mental pain may present itself in one or two forms, or a combination of both. In the manifest type it takes the form of conscious depression or unpleasant mental tension; in the sensorial or conversion type it presents itself as a persistent and disagreeable bodily sensation, either localized or diffuse, common examples of which are pressure-headache, generalized pains, hyperalgesia, gastric pains without organic basis, vertigo, and feelings of abnormal tiredness and weakness.

Although it is generally taught at the present day that these conditions are entirely psychogenic in origin, there would appear to be strong evidence that the basis of the condition is primarily a disturbance of the thalamic-hypothalamic mechanisms, possibly a metabolic disorder. Suggestive facts are the absence in a large proportion of such cases of any evidence of mental conflict, and the concomitant symptoms of disturbed body-metabolism and autonomic imbalance, such as vasomotor disturbances, central nervous instability as shown by muscular tremors, hyperalgesia, and other sensory disorders, vegetative disturbances, and metabolic anomalies as demonstrated by biochemical tests.

The commonest symptoms of thalamic dysfunction in order of frequency are: depression, irritability, and emotional instability, with anxiety and sense of unpleasant mental tension, in the affective sphere; in the sensory sphere, pains and paraesthesias of various kinds, such as pressure-headache, various vague pains and aches of infinite variety, which may be referred to any part of the body, gastralgia, low backache, and dysuria or other symptoms referred to the urogenital tract; in the sphere of thought, inability to concentrate, obsessional thoughts, phobias, and transient periods of confusion ("blackouts"); in the motor system, tremors, sensations of weakness and loss of energy, with abnormal tiredness; and in the vegetative systems, insomnia, anorexia, gastrointestinal disturbances, vertigo, sexual dysfunctions, and vasomotor symptoms such as flushing, palpitations, effort syndrome, and syncopal attacks without apparent organic basis.

The thalamic dysfunction state may be regarded as a response of the organism to stresses of various kinds. It is one of the commonest causes of chronic ill-health and loss of efficiency, and one of the most unsatisfactory of conditions to treat. Its victims form a large proportion of the "chronics" who regularly attend hospital outpatient clinics, and there is probably no patient who is more dreaded by the overworked practitioner than the chronic neurotic-depressive.

Treatment of the thalamic dysfunction syndrome is often unsatisfactory because there is no specific drug therapy known at present for the condition. Psychotherapeutic methods are lengthy, tedious, and often unsatisfactory, since in a large proportion of such cases the causal factors (unsatisfactory home life, faulty conditioning in childhood, etc.) cannot be removed, while not uncommonly it is found that the neurotic behaviour-patterns persist even when the precipitating stresses have been removed. Psychotherapeutic methods usually require specialized training in the physician, and an effective symptomatic therapy aimed at keeping the patient fit and in full working efficiency during the period of analytic or other treatment is at present lacking, since the commonly employed remedies, such as cortical sedatives and stimulants, offer at best only partial relief on account of their lack of specific effect on the thalamic centres, while endocrine preparations, vitamins, and measures to improve the general health have, generally speaking, proved largely unsuccessful.

Principles of Treatment by Euphorigenic Drugs

The most important therapeutic advances in psychiatry, as in general medicine, have been the discovery of specific pharmacological or physical agents for the various disease conditions. Similarly, the logical answer to the thalamic dysfunction states would be a drug possessing a specific reversing effect on the thalamic disturbance—in other words, a powerful euphorigenic drug which would be therapeutically effective and at the same time free from the objectionable properties usually associated with narcotic compounds.

The ideal euphoriant for clinical use should possess the following properties. It must induce a high degree of euphoria, must be stable and fully active by the oral route, be reasonably rapid-acting, and have a prolonged action. It must be of low toxicity, non-cumulative, and free from after-effects and undesirable effects on the higher cortical functions, such as impairment of concentration, judgment, and memory. Most important of all, it must not have the property of inducing the condition of addiction or physical dependence when administered for long periods.

The last-mentioned point is of especial importance, since there is a common and widespread belief that all euphoriant drugs are necessarily habit-forming, whereas this is in fact not the case. The true addiction syndrome (physical craving, tolerance, abstention syndrome, and personality deterioration) is peculiar to the drugs of the ecgonine (or cocaine) and phenanthrene (or morphine) groups; whereas mescaline and *cannabis indica,* the two most powerful euphoriants known, do not induce a comparable addiction. The addiction-forming property would therefore appear to depend on chemical constitution rather than degree of euphorigenicity, since the two compounds just mentioned are chemically unrelated to the cocaine and morphine drugs. Theoretically, therefore, the addiction problem should not offer an insuperable obstacle to such a form of therapy, provided the compound employed is not one of the ecgonine or phenanthrene class.

Up to the present time no drug which fulfills these requirements has been known to medicine. During the last century attempts were made to utilize the euphorigenic properties of cannabis in the treatment of depressive states, but these were found to be unsatisfactory for various reasons: chief of these were the difficulty of obtaining reliable and stable preparations of this drug, its uncertain action, and its peculiar and undesirable side effects, of which actual intensification of the dysphoria is one of the commonest. The discovery of the new synthetic cannabis-like derivatives of the dibenzopyran class within the last few years, however, has placed in our hands an entirely new type of euphoriant drug with properties which render it an extremely promising therapeutic agent in psychiatry.

The Synthetic Tetrahydrocannabinols

These compounds have been produced as the result of the work carried out by Adams and his colleagues in America and of Todd and his colleagues and the Roche Research Department in this country.

Several compounds of this type are known, and one of the most active pharmacologically is the synthetic hexyl analogue called in America synhexyl, pyrahexyl, or parahxl. . . .

Pharmacology of Synhexyl in Man

The pharmacological properties of synhexyl are in many respects similar to those of cannabis, but there are several important qualitative differences in the human subject. The following data were obtained as the result of a series of experiments which I carried out on myself, a group of normal subjects, and a group of 50 depressive patients. My findings confirm that the drug is a powerful euphoriant with a specific action on the higher centres, particularly the thalamic system and its cortical connexions. Synhexyl is rather more potent weight for weight than natural cannabis, the effective dosage being from 5-15 mg. in normal subjects to 60-90 mg. in depressive patients. In narcotic drug addicts doses of 60-240 mg. three times daily may be given without ill effects (Himmelsbach). On account of its resinous nature the drug is most active when administered by the oral route, and the preparation I used was in the form of a powder made by absorbing the drug on silicic acid and contained in gelatin capsules, or as compressed tablets after absorption on kieselguhr.

The general effects in normal man are as follows: There is first a latent period of 1½ to 3 hours before any effect is felt, this being about twice the latent period for the same dose of cannabis. The onset of the synhexyl effect is characteristically abrupt, with a sudden and peculiar sensation of lightness and mild intoxication accompanied by acceleration of the pulse and feelings of anxiety, and vertigo may occur at the onset, but these usually pass off in the course of a few minutes to half an hour. The euphoric effect quickly follows, and consists of a pleasant feeling of happiness and exhilaration with a marked sense of physical well-being and self-confidence; there is a sense of relief from tension and anxiety, and the threshold for unpleasant effect is markedly raised, while that for pleasant feeling-tone is correspondingly lowered. There is increased enjoyment of normally pleasant impressions, and zest for life and working capacity may be actually increased in the early stages of the intoxication. Later this effect gives way to a sense of dreamy apathy and contentment, which with the larger dosages may reach the stage of ecstasy. There is often increased speed of the stream of thought, with a marked increase in the power of fantasy and vividness of visual imagery. With the larger dosages there may in the early stages be a tendency to flight of ideas and pressure of activity. In the sensory sphere there is little or no true analgesic effect of the opiate type. With the higher doses there may be some degree of blunting of sensation, but the senses of taste and hearing may actually become more acute. A generalized sensation of pleasant warmth diffused throughout the body is characteristic.

Hallucinatory phenomena and distortion of the tempero-spatial perception sense of cannabis-mescal type are not found, although elementary visual sensations in the form of photopsias and simple coloured patterns may occur when the eyes are closed or the subject is in darkness. A peculiar visual illusion is sometimes seen in which the colours and outlines of objects appear abnormally vivid and a soft golden radiance seems to be diffused over the whole room. With larger doses visual illusions of cannabis type may be experienced in which simple patterns appear to acquire complex and fantastic forms, the whole effect being extremely pleasing to the subject. On the motor side there may be slight restlessness in the early stages, similar to what is found with moderate doses of benzedrine. Hyperreflexia is common, but ataxia and motor incoordination are seen only with the largest doses. Catatonia and rigidity as seen with mescaline are never found.

The vegetative effects are very slight, consisting of moderate tachycardia in the early stages, slight mydriasis, and dryness of the mouth. Appetite is usually increased, there is no respiratory or peristaltic depression, and sleep following the intoxication is normal and dreamless. Slight drowsiness may occur in the later stages, but "hangover" effects are seen only after very large doses.

Characteristic of the synhexyl effect is intermittency; the symptoms, as with cannabis and mescaline intoxication, occur in rhythmic waves with intervening periods of apparent normality. The average duration of the effects is from 8 to 10 hours from the time of onset of the symptoms.

With excessively large doses, the toxic effects are frightening rather than actually dangerous, resembling those of acute cannabis poisoning. The onset occurs with a sudden feeling of acute apprehension and collapse, with rapid bounding pulse, mydriasis and dryness of the mouth and throat, hyperreflexia, clonic twitchings, mental confusion, headache, and vertigo. Euphoria is absent, the emotional reaction being one of acute anxiety and apprehension. These symptoms usually pass off completely in 12 to 24 hours. The biochemical changes produced by the drug are slight, consisting of increased blood concentration and haemoglobin value, and mild hypoglycaemia. There may be slight diuresis and rise of temperature; other changes include a slight rise in blood pressure, cerebral hyperaemia, and increase in the venous pressures.

Absorption of the drug apparently takes place through the lacteal vessels of the small intestine, since it is a resinous substance and cannot therefore be absorbed direct through the stomach wall, as is the case with alkaloids and other water-soluble substances. This would account for the long latent period between ingestion and onset of symptoms of intoxication, which is normally of the order of two or three hours. The drug is partly destroyed by oxidation in the liver, but a certain proportion is excreted unchanged in the urine, in which respect it resembles natural cannabis and mescaline.

Effects on the Intellectual Functions

Studies which I made on myself and a group of normal subjects show that with ordinary therapeutic doses there is little or no deleterious effect on the intellectual performance. Seven of my depressive patients were studied by means of psychometric tests selected from the revised Terman-Merrill scale. The results suggest that memory work calling for the use of reasoning powers and logical integration of facts suffers slightly after taking the drug, but that the more mechanical memory is unimpaired and may actually show a slight improvement. In normal subjects engaged in work of an intellectual nature there appears to be little or no falling-off of intellectual capacity, the only inconvenience experienced from the drug being the slight distractibility and pressure of ideas, and the tendency to daydreaming and wandering of the stream of thought in the later stages.

Therapeutic Trials in Depressive Patients

Therapeutic trials were made with the drug in a series of 50 patients showing the thalamic dysfunction syndrome, including cases of both the dysoxic (depressive-psychotic) and the neurotic-depressive types. The dosages employed varied from 15 to 90 mg., the drug being administered in all cases immediately on rising in the morning before a meal was taken. Suggestion and other psychological factors which might have vitiated the results were eliminated by substituting, without the patient's knowledge on certain days, inert control tablets of exactly similar appearance to those containing the synhexyl.

The general effects were found to be qualitatively similar to those in the normal subject, except that a considerably higher average dose was required to produce improvement of the depressive symptoms. It was found that the dysphoria itself was ameliorated to a much greater degree than the other symptoms (obsessional thoughts, pains, paraesthesias, etc.); these features, although themselves little affected, were rendered less distressing and obtrusive to the patient by the action of the drug.

Of the 50 cases tested 36 showed a definite improvement in affective reaction, while 14 were unaffected or made worse. Twenty-seven of the series were neurotic-depressives, 20 of whom showed improvement; of these 27, 12 were typical chronic mental hospital cases, of whom 9 benefited from the drug. Of the 12, 9 had previously been treated with electro-anoxia with no improvement, and 3 had been subjected to prefrontal leucotomy with no response. The remaining 23 patients were cases of dysoxic depression, of whom all but 4 were chronic institutionalized patients with mild symptoms of dysphoric type. Four of the 23 had previously received electro-anoxia with temporary improvement only; of these 4, 2 responded favourably to the drug.

Of the whole series 16 patients showed associated organic diseases, as follows: gross bony deformity, 2; pulmonary tuberculosis, 2; cardiovascular disease, 5; senile changes, 4; malignant disease, 1; organic nervous disease, 1; thyrotoxicosis, 1. No untoward side effects from the synhexyl were noted in any of these cases. Untoward effects were noted in 5 of the neurotic-depressive cases; these included tachycardia, slight dizziness, loss of concentration, drowsiness, and mild degrees of impairment of the intellectual performance.

The criteria for a positive response were taken as the following: amelioration of mood, as shown subjectively by the patients' own statements and objectively by clinical evidence of diminution of retardation, anxiety, and inward preoccupation; increased zest for and interest in work and occupation; and increased psychotherapeutic rapport. The effect of the drug on obsessional and depressive ideas and pains and paraesthesias of central origin was also noted. The nursing staff were carefully instructed to note during the tests any changes in the general behaviour and demeanour of the patients while receiving the drug. The results with synhexyl were then compared with response to inert control tablets.

Of the dysoxic patients those in the chronic stationary phase of their disease made the best response. Three dysoxics in the acute depressive phase either showed no response or were actually made worse when synhexyl was given in doses of 60-90 mg.

Of the neurotic group, the quiet apathetic type with depression and general asthenia appeared to do best; this type required the smallest dosage to effect improvement—15 mg. The tense and overanxious type also showed a good response but tended to require a rather higher dosage—30-60 mg. The anxiety cases with multiple pains and paraesthesias were found to improve considerably as regards the dysphoria, but the drug seemed to have little effect on the actual sensory features. Six of the neurotic cases were severe examples of the obsessive-ruminative type, only one of whom failed to improve with the drug.

Neurotic-depressive cases showing a negative response included psychopathic personality with dysphoric features (two cases) and acute hysterical grief reaction with pseudo-hallucinosis (one case).

Illustrative Cases

Case 1.—A woman aged 60, with a history of recurrent attacks of depression over the last three years. On examination she was tense, agitated, acutely apprehensive, restless and excitable at times, and expressed self-depreciatory ideas of being wicked and worthless. Orientation and memory were unaffected and insight and judgment were moderately good, but she co-operated poorly in examination owing to her constant preoccupation with delusions of unworthiness. Physical findings were negative. She received electric convulsion treatment with no real improvement, remaining in the agitated state described above. After receiving 30 to 45 mg. of synhexyl daily she showed marked improvement; she said she felt brighter, and the agitation and tension were definitely diminished. Although the ideas of unworthiness persisted in mild degree, these were much less obtrusive and distressing. No untoward symptoms were noted, and response to control tablets was negative.

Case 2.—A man aged 65. The history was very incomplete, but it appeared that he was originally admitted in 1938, following the sudden onset of an acute depressive-confusional state with paranoid and possibly hallucinatory features. On examination he was depressed, apathetic, hypochondriacal and full of ideas of visceral dysfunction, totally lacking in initiative, but well behaved and clean in habits. There were no signs of hallucinosis or paranoid features, but he showed a mild degree of personality deterioration, being at times facile, rambling, and irrelevant in conversation. Physical investigations were negative. He responded fairly well to 30 mg. of synhexyl daily, becoming brighter, less querulous and preoccupied with his aches and pains, and stated that he felt more cheerful and energetic. The symptoms of cortical deterioration and institutionalization were, however, unchanged. No side effects were apparent during the period of medication.

Case 3.—A woman aged 67 with a history of recurrent depressive attacks since 1936, and two previous admissions to hospital for acute depression. Examination showed her to be depressed, solitary, and lacking in interest and initiative. She complained of obstinate insomnia, and required constant nocturnal sedation. She displayed no evidence of delusions and hallucinations, but tended to be mildly retarded and sat about aimlessly all day in the ward. Physical examination revealed a slow-growing breast carcinoma, for which operation had been considered inadvisable. She had previously received E.C.T. with little or no improvement. She received synhexyl in a dosage of 15 mg. daily with considerable subjective and objective improvement. She felt brighter, more alert and cheerful, and showed increased initiative and spontaneous activity. Side effects were absent, and administration of control tablets failed to reproduce the synhexyl effect.

Case 4.—A woman aged 45. She had a history of the onset, three months previously, of acute depression with agitation, ideas of bodily disease, and delusions of sin and unworthiness, apparently precipitated by an unhappy home environment.

When she was first seen the acute phase of the illness had subsided and she talked rationally, showing considerable insight. She complained of mild depression, fatigability, and insomnia, with a variety of vague stomach pains and soreness and pains in her throat. She insisted that she had "swollen and painful glands" in her neck; but examination showed only a small palpable cervical gland on the right side, the throat and tonsils being normal. She also complained of feelings of "being all trembly inside." Delusions of unworthiness were not in evidence. She was a small, pale, anxious-looking women, but no signs of organic disease were present. She was described by the nursing staff as depressed, solitary, and apathetic in habits. The administration of 45 mg. of synhexyl produced an immediate effect; she stated that she felt subjectively brighter and more cheerful, showed increased interest, and her hypochondriacal ideas receded into the background. Vasomotor side effects were absent, control tests giving a negative result.

Case 5.—A woman aged 52, with thalamic dysfunction of conversion hysteria type. She had a history of depression for 18 months following evacuation during the flying-bomb raids and an accident to her son. She had also had a previous depressive attack 28 years ago. On examination she was depressed, tense, emotional, and anxious. Her main complaints were of insomnia, inability to face up to her household duties, and a persistent neuralgic pain located under the left breast. Physical findings were completely negative. A few weeks previously she received seven applications of E.C.T. with slight improvement but speedy relapse. The response to 30 mg. of synhexyl was immediate, she lost her anxiety and depression, said she felt much brighter, and the thoracic pain became much less insistent and distressing, although not completely abolished. Control tablets and bromide in full dosage failed to reproduce these effects. No side effects from the synhexyl were complained of during the period of administration.

Case 6.—A woman aged 32 with thalamic dysfunction of anxiety type. She had a history of anxiety symptoms 18 months previously, and partial remission but recurrence four months before admission, at which time she had gone to live with and look after her invalid mother. On examination she was a superior and intelligent type of woman, outwardly cheerful in manner, but actually tense, anxious, and mildly depressed. She complained of insomnia, intermittent panic sensations with palpitation, and acute feelings of inner tension and "shivering sensations," and loss of concentration. Physical findings were negative, and no signs suggestive of thyroid hyperfunction were evident. The symptoms failed to respond to bromide therapy and psychotherapy. She responded well to synhexyl in doses of 30 mg. daily, the anxiety attacks and dysphoria being completely abolished. She stated that she felt much brighter, more confident, and was no longer apprehensive of the anxiety attacks. Her symptoms recurred on changing over to control tablets or discontinuing the synhexyl.

Of these six cases, selected at random from my series, the first four were dysoxic (psychotic-depressive) cases and the last two examples of simple thalamic dysfunction (neurotic depression). The four dysoxic cases were all patients who had passed through the acute phase of their illness and who presented as the principle symptom a residual dysphoria of chronic and intractable type. Of these four, one (Case 2) showed some degree of personality deterioration. The two neurotic cases were of recent onset and in the early stages of their illness. Of the six cases, three (Cases 1, 3, 5) had previously failed to respond satisfactorily to E.C.T. It will be evident from this series that synhexyl is as effective in the milder forms of dysoxia as in the purely neurotic-depressive states.

As regards the mechanism of improvement, it should be pointed out that synhexyl does not effect a permanent "cure" in the same way as electro-anoxia does in typical dysoxic depressions. The effect lasts only during the period of administration of the drug, it is therefore a substitution therapy, like insulin treatment in diabetes or liver extract in pernicious anemia. The action would seem to be a combination of stimulation and depression, resulting in a general raising of the anhedonic threshold. The principal site of action of the drug is almost certainly the thalamic centres and their cortical connexions, as is the case with morphine and other powerful central analgesic drugs.

The beneficial effects of synhexyl do not appear to be adversely affected by chronicity, concomitant organic disease, or the presence of an organic brain lesion, whether pathologically or surgically induced. There is evidence, however, that drugs of this class are ineffective in the acute dysoxic depressions, and cannot be regarded as substitutes for anoxic therapy in this form of metabolic brain disease.

General Conclusions

The results of these preliminary trials would suggest that we have in this class of compounds a promising therapeutic agent for the treatment of the chronic and intractable depressive states. Synhexyl, the most active of this class, has the advantages of low toxicity, minimum of side effects, ease of administration, and chemical stability. Its use is not contra-indicated by the presence of coexisting organic disease, and it is suitable for out-patient practice. Its use does not interfere with other therapeutic measures, such as occupational therapy and psychotherapy. It is free from the risks and disadvantages of the more drastic forms of treatment, and might replace those methods for the milder depressions of later life where for any reason the more drastic procedures are contraindicated.

Its main drawbacks at present are its insoluble nature, slow and uncertain action, and comparatively weak analgesic effect, so that it is relatively ineffective in severer forms of sensory thalamic dysfunction syndrome. Experiments are at present in progress with the object of producing a water-soluble form with a higher degree of analgesic activity.

Summary

The syndrome of thalamic dysfunction and the principles of its treatment with euphorigenic drugs are described.

The properties and pharmacology of synhexyl, a new drug of the synthetic tetrahydrocannabinol class, are examined.

The results of therapeutic trials with the drug in a series of 50 depressive patients are given.

My acknowledgments are due to the following: The Research Department of Roche Products Ltd. and Dr. W. S. Maclay, of the Board of Control, for kindly providing supplies of synhexyl; Dr. W. A. Bain, of Leeds University, for kindly making up the material for administration; Prof. A. R. Todd, of Cambridge University, for kindly supplying purified cannabis extracts for clinical trial; and Mrs. E. Bathurst, psychologist, Warlingham Park Hospital, for kindly undertaking psychometric tests on the patients tested with the drug.

BIBLIOGRAPHY

1. Adams, R. (1941-2). *Harvey Lectures*, 37, 168.
2. —— and others (1941). *J. Amer. chem. Soc.*, 63, 1971.
3. —— Baker, B. R., and Wearn, R. B. (1940). Ibid., 62, 2204.
4. Allentuck, S., and Bowman, K. M. (1942). *Amer. J. Psychiat.*, 99, 248.
5. Ghosh, R., Todd, A. R., and Wilkinson, S. (1940). *J. chem. Soc.*, pp. 1121, 1893.
6. Himmelsbach, C. K. (1944), *Sth. med. J.*, Nashville, 37, 26.
7. —— and Andrews, H. L. (1943). *J. Pharmacol.*, 77, 17.
8. Russell, P. B., and others (1941). *J. chem. Soc.*, p. 826.
9. Stockings, G. T. (1944). *J. ment. Sci.*, 90, 772.

CHAPTER FOUR

PYRAHEXYL IN THE TREATMENT OF ALCOHOLIC AND DRUG WITHDRAWAL CONDITIONS

Lloyd J. Thompson, MD and
Richard C. Proctor, MD

The results of this study, which appeared in the North Carolina Medical Journal *in 1953, corroborate and supplement the earlier findings of George Tayleur Stockings, which are found in the preceding chapter. In this instance, the use of pyrahexyl, another of the synthetic active principles of marihuana, produced astonishingly favorable results in the symptomatic treatment of one of our major social diseases, alcoholism.*

At the time of writing, Dr. Thompson was Professor of Psychiatry, Bowman Gray School of Medicine of Wake Forest College, and Director of Graylyn Hospital; Dr. Proctor was Assistant Professor of Psychiatry at the Bowman Gray School and Assistant Director of Graylyn Hospital, in Winston-Salem, North Carolina.

The use of cannabis, or marihuana as we best know it, and related compounds antedates recorded history. Its earliest use was in Oriental countries, and it was introduced into Western countries about the middle of the nineteenth century. In reading through the literature one would gain the impression that marihuana-like compounds have been used mainly as intoxicants. Actually this group of drugs has been used legitimately for years in the treatment of various bodily complaints and conditions. For example, Dr. Oscar W. Bethea, in his book, *Practical Materia Medica and Prescription Writing,*[1] published in 1917, listed several prescriptions using cannabis in some form. He mentioned the use of the drug as a sedative, an anodyne, and a narcotic, and suggested its use in the treatment of headache, neuralgia, and kindred conditions. It is unfortunate that through the recent exposés in the popular press marihuana has gained such a bad name.

A few years ago Professor Roger Adams, at the University of Illinois, developed synthetic substances resembling marihuana to be used in the study of the marihuana problem. One of these has been called pyrahexyl in this country and synhexyl in England. We shall not attempt in this clinical paper to go into the various chemical and pharmacologic aspects of marihuana in any detail. Those who are interested may refer to Professor Adams' report, appearing in the 1941–1942 edition of the Harvey Lectures.[2] The first comprehensive study done on pyrahexyl compound was done by Edwin G. Williams and others at the U. S. Public Service Hospital, Lexington, Kentucky.[3]

Effects

Briefly, marihuana produces in the majority of individuals general impairment of cerebral function, with mild clouding of consciousness. The higher physiologic functions—those mediated by the thalamus and the cortex in their normal interrelationship—are the most easily disturbed by the drug. Most observers agree that its central action far outweighs any peripheral effects. It acts predominantly on the higher functions. It appears to impair the activity in most areas of the cortex, although those functions which are commonly localized in the frontal lobe appear to be the most acutely affected.

The observed physical effects are (1) elevation of the pulse rate in direct proportion to the degree of intoxication by the drug; (2) elevation of the blood pressure, varying with the individual but usually rising in direct proportion to the pulse; (3) injection of the conjunctival blood vessels, varying with the dose; (4) dilatation of the pupils and sluggish reaction to light and accommodation; (5) slight change in the vision for proximity, distance, and color; (6) circumoral tremors, with tremulousness of the protruded tongue and the extremities; (7) dryness of the oral and pharyngeal mucous membranes; (8) increased frequency and decreased amplitude of thoracic respiratory movements; and (9) ataxia with hyperreflexia. Not all of these effects occur in all individuals, but one or more will be present.

The observed psychologic effects are (1) apprehension and anxiety; (2) euphoria; (3) loquaciousness; (4) lowering of inhibitions; (5) hunger and thirst; (6) feeling of being "high"; (7) uncontrollable bursts of laughter or giggles; and (8) drowsiness, languor, lassitude, and a pleasant feeling of fatigue. Clinical tests reveal that marihuana produces no significant changes in basal metabolic rates, blood chemistry, hematologic picture, liver function, kidney function, or electrocardiographic studies. Marihuana delays gastric and intestinal motility somewhat, and produces a definite increase in the frequency of the alpha wave in electroencephalographic recordings, thus indicating increased relaxation.

In recent years conflicting reports have appeared in the literature concerning the use of marihuana-like drugs in treating the opiate withdrawal syndrome. Allentuck and Bowman found that with the marihuana substitution method of treatment the withdrawal symptoms were ameliorated sooner.[4] Yet Himmelsbach states that a synthetic marihuana-like drug had no appreciable ameliorative effect on the opiate abstinence syndrome.[5] The dosage used in both case studies was approximately the same.

More recently, work has been done in England by various investigators. Parker and Wrigley reported a total of 62 patients, indicating psychotics of various types as well as depressive states, in which they recorded subjective improvement in cases of melancholia and neurotic depression. However, when an inert drug was given to a control group, similar results were obtained.[6]

Material, Method, and Response

Late in 1949 we were able to secure a supply of pyrahexyl for clinical investigation. In the intervening years we have used the drug in 101 cases. Originally, because of the pharmacologic properties of the drug, which usually produce exaltation and feelings of happiness, and because of the reports in the British literature, we used the drug in treating patients with symptoms of depression. Then, because of results reported by Terry from the Livermore Sanitarium in California,[7] we began to use pyrahexyl in the treatment and management of acute alcoholic withdrawal symptoms and those associated with the withdrawal of various addicting and habituating drugs.

Depressive States

Our method of treatment for the cases of depression was, briefly, as follows: Three 15 mg. doses of pyrahexyl were administered to the patient the first day of admission. If there was no alleviation of symptoms, the dosage was raised by 15 mg. daily, either until improvement resulted or toxic symptoms appeared. The latter included nausea, "giddiness," disturbance in space and time relationships, and other signs which will be mentioned later. The results obtained showed that the drug, in our opinion, was not of sufficient benefit to warrant continuation of this phase of the study. In 20 cases of neurotic depression, only 4 showed evidence of improvement. In the 6 cases of psychotic depression treated we found no improvement. Because of these disappointing results, the use of pyrahexyl in the treatment of depressive states was abandoned.

Alcoholic and Drug Addiction States

The major part of this report is based on the results obtained in the 70 post-alcoholic states and the following drug withdrawal cases: barbitutes 6; morphine 6; Dilaudid 4; Demerol 12; Pantopon 2; and paregoric 1. The most gratifying results were obtained in the 70 post-alcoholic cases. The method of treatment was, in the main, similar to that previously outlined for use in the depressive states.

Most of the patients were admitted to Graylyn in the typical post-alcoholic state. The symptoms presented were tremulousness, restlessness, apprehension, sleeplessness, and anorexia. Their mood was irritable and depressed, and they were unable to sit still. In many instances the patient had eaten little for days prior to admission. Immediately on admission and after a physical examination was done, the patient was given 15 mg. (1 capsule) of pyrahexyl. This dose was repeated twice on the day of admission. Fifteen milligrams 3 times daily was continued for from 3 to 5 days.

In a large percentage of cases the patients showed a favorable response to the medication. From 30 minutes to 2 hours after ingestion of the first capsule the patient became calm, lost his irritability and restlessness, began to feel better, and developed a good appetite. Following the eating of a meal he generally went to sleep for several hours. With the dosage employed, we encountered only a few side reactions. These were usually very mild and confined to generalized dull, aching headaches, minimal ataxia, and dryness of the mucous membranes. During the three to five days of treatment the patients remained mildly euphoric and happy, their appetite remained good, and they slept well. When the medication was stopped, we noted no withdrawal symptoms. Our experience in this respect paralleled that of Allentuck and Bowman,[4] who felt that the use of marihuana does not give rise to a biologic or physiologic dependence, and that discontinuance of the drug does not result in withdrawal symptoms.

Results

In the treatment with pyrahexyl of 70 cases of the post-alcoholic syndrome we can report clinical alleviation of the symptoms in 59, or 84.28 per cent. The 11 cases that did not show improvement (or 15.72 per cent) did not differ a great deal clinically from the other 59. By that we mean that the duration of the last alcoholic bout was about the same, and the amount of alcohol consumed was no different from that in some patients who did show improvement. The same applied to age and sex incidence. We have no explanation as to why 59 out of 70 patients showed improvement while 11 did not. Perhaps an individual idiosyncrasy to the drug is the explanation, for it is known that individual reactions to other drugs do occur.

In the treatment of drug addictions our experience is less extensive but none the less significant. Out of 6 cases of barbiturate addiction, amelioration of symptoms was noted in 4; in 4 cases of Dilaudid addiction we noted alleviation in 3; in 2 cases of Pantopon and one of paregoric addiction all patients reported a smooth withdrawal course, without the usual symptoms noted in such conditions. We were especially pleased with the results obtained in 12 cases of Demerol addiction. With 10 of these patients, or 83 per cent, we were able to withdraw the drug completely in one week's time without having to resort to any other type of medication. Occasionally a patient would report mild apprehension or transient cramplike pains of the lower extremities, but these were infrequent and when they did occur, were mild and transient. The 2 patients who showed no response were long-term users of Demerol who had received treatment on two other occasions by the gradual withdrawal method.

With 6 cases of morphine addiction the results were less satisfying. Only 2 patients reported a course of withdrawal without any markedly unpleasant symptoms with the use of parahexyl. It was necessary in the other 4 patients to use other methods of treatment.

In those cases where results were obtained by the use of pyrahexyl in the treatment of drug withdrawal symptoms, the side symptoms produced were of a mild character. The patients felt physically stronger and showed increased psychomotor activity. They had an increased appetite and such withdrawal symptoms as nausea, diarrhea, and perspiration were diminished or eliminated. The feeling of euphoria produced helped in rehabilitating the physical condition and in facilitating social reorientation. An outstanding result was a subjective feeling of relaxation. The sleep induced by the drug likewise contributed to the general improvement in the patient's health.

Comment

At the time of the first examination the patients with post-alcoholic syndromes were beginning to feel a severe "hang-over" and subjectively complained of remorse, agitation, depression, tremulousness, and tension. They all complained of anorexia and some of nausea. The administration of pyrahexyl produced within 30 minutes to 2 hours a marked change in the psychologic and physiologic status of 84 per cent of the patients in our series. With continued administration of adequate doses over a 3 to 5 day period, the patients passed smoothly through their period of alcoholic withdrawal, without marked subjective complaints. From a psychological standpoint, it is our feeling that this result is beneficial in the overall handling of a patient and in establishing rapport. We do not hold with the opinion that alcoholics must be treated harshly and made to "sweat it out" in order to repent of their actions. Our experience with pyrahexyl indicates that alcoholic patients appreciate consideration for their feelings and respond to it by being more cooperative in therapeutic relationships.

In those patients who presented complaints resulting from the withdrawal of various drugs (or medicaments)—namely, barbiturates and opiate derivatives—the picture was similar. We attribute the difference in the results obtained in Demerol addicts from others to the individual addictive properties of the drug itself and the development of less physiologic dependence on the drug as compared to other opiate derivatives.

Illustrative Cases

The results of treatment with pyrahexyl in one patient with drug addiction and in one with alcoholism will be described briefly:

Drug Addiction (Case 1)

A 32-year-old man entered Graylyn Hospital with the chief complaint of morphine addiction for the past one and one-half to two years, and of pain in both ankles of about two years' duration. He was admitted to the hospital for insulin subshock therapy and for the treatment of morphine addiction. He had been taking from ¼ to ½ grain intramuscularly every 4 hours for a long time prior to entry here. On admission he was extremely lethargic, garrulous, and uncooperative, and complained bitterly of pain in his lower extremities, although there were no positive physical findings referable to this area. He did express a strong desire to be free of drug addiction and to return to normal health again. The physical examination was not remarkable in the main. Laboratory findings were within normal limits.

Following admission to the hospital he was given pyrahexyl tablets—3 the day of admission, 3 then for the next five days, and 1 on the sixth day. During this period mild euphoria was noted and the patient gradually began to complain less of pain in his legs, was much easier to manage, and cooperated to a much greater extent. He did notice a sensation of elation and at times felt rather dizzy, but experienced no nausea or vomiting or any other side effects of note. He was not given morphine from the time of entrance. With the administration of pyrahexyl, paraldehyde, and Sodium Amytal, none was deemed necessary. Throughout his 20-day hospitalization period, during which he received insulin subshock therapy, he did very well and was discharged much improved. He volunteered the information that some type of medicine that we were giving him had made him feel better than anything he had ever used and, as mentioned, he did notice euphoria, elation, and some dizziness.

Alcoholism (Case 2)

A 37-year-old married businessman was brought to the hospital by his brother for consultation about over-indulgence in alcohol. When he first entered the office, it was obvious that the patient had had a drink or two on the way down to fortify himself for the ordeal. He was tremulous, somewhat thick in speech, perspiring freely, and quite restless.

The brother revealed a history of excellent business ability on the part of the patient but told also about numerous periods of excessive drinking. The patient readily admitted the former but minimized the latter. During his denial of any problems he grew more restless and pale, and frankly asked for a drink. He was told that patients were not treated with bourbon or Scotch, but that we had other methods of treatment. He was given a capsule of pyrahexyl, and the interview continued. In about 20 minutes the patient spontaneously remarked that he felt better. He was asked whether he still felt the need for a drink and his answer was in the negative. Admission to the hospital was arranged without further argument or persuasion.

On the day of admission he received 2 more pyrahexyl. capsules. On the following day 2 more were given and then this medication was discontinued. The restlessness and tension had subsided and the patient had joined the group activities.

With the aid of psychologic studies and the efforts of the psychiatric social worker in adjusting family problems, the patient returned to his place in business and in the community, where he has remained sober and efficient for almost a year. In the meantime he has referred another member of his family for treatment of alcoholism.

Conclusions

It is our conclusion that pyrahexyl and related compounds are beneficial in the treatment of withdrawal symptoms from the use of alcohol to a marked degree, and in the treatment of withdrawal symptoms from the use of opiates to a less marked, but still significant degree. We offer for consideration an over-all series of 101 patients in whom pyrahexyl has been used. We have not been able to differentiate, prior to therapy, those patients who would fall into the group successfully treated from those who would not respond. Perhaps this paper will stimulate some to continue this study with such a view in mind. We offer it as a preliminary report and study.

References

1.	Materia Medica and Prescription Writing. Oscar W. Bethea. 2nd Revised Edition. F. A. Davis Company, Publishers, Philadelphia, 1917, p. 114.
2.	The Harvey Lectures—1941-1942. Professor Roger Adams. "Marihuana." pp. 168-197.
3.	Public Health Service Reports, vol. 61, pp. 1050-1083, No. 29, July, 1946. Williams, E. G., Himmelsbach, C. K., Wikler, A., Ruble, D. C., and Lloyd, B. J., Jr.: Studies on Marihuana and Pyrahexyl Compound.
4.	Allentuck, S., and Bowman, K. M.: The Psychiatric Aspects of Marihuana Addiction, Am. J. Psychiat. 99:248-251 (Sept.) 1952.

5. Himmelsbach, C. K., and Andrews, H. L.: Studies on Modification of the Morphine Abstinence Syndrome by Drugs. J. Pharmacol. & Exper. Therap. 77:17-23 (Jan.) 1943.

6. Parker, C. S., and Wrigley, F.: Synthetic Cannabis Preparations in Psychiatry: Synhexyl. J. Men. Sc. 99:276-279 (Jan.) 1950.

7. Letter from Dr. Terry.

   Adams, R., Loewe S., Jelineh, C., Wolff, H.: Tetrahydrocannabinol Homologs with Marihuana Activity, J. Am. Chem. Soc. 63:1971-1976, 1941.

   Pond, D. A.: Psychological Effects in Depressive Patients of the Marihuana Homologue Synhexyl, J. Neurol. Neurosurg. 11:271-279 (Nov.) 1948.

   Stockings, G. T.: A New Euphoriant for Depressive Mental States, Brit. M. J. 1:918-922 (June 18) 1947.

CHAPTER FIVE

POINTS OF DISTINCTION BETWEEN SEDATIVE AND CONSCIOUSNESS-EXPANDING DRUGS

William S. Burroughs

William S. Burroughs' controversial novels—Naked Lunch *and* The Soft Machine, *first published by Olympia Press—were originally banned in the United States. Before his recent overdue literary beatification—he has been ranked with Céline, Beckett and Joyce by serious critics—his work had been noticed and printed in America by several small avant-garde reviews and the jazz magazine* Metronome *(which this anthologist then edited).*
Burroughs is as exceptional a man as he is an artist. More than half of his adult years were spent in the psychological ice-box of heroin addiction. He has written:

. . . I was an addict for fifteen years. When I say addict I mean an addict to *junk* (generic term for opium and/or derivatives including all synthetics from demerol to palfium). I have used junk in many forms: morphine, heroin, dilaudid, eukodal, pantapon, diocodid, diosane, opium, demerol, dolophine, palfium. I have smoked junk, eaten it, sniffed it, injected it in vein-skin-muscle, inserted it in rectal suppositories. The needle is not important. Whether you sniff it smoke it eat it or shove it up your ass the result is the same: addiction. When I speak of drug addiction I do not refer to keif, marijuana, or any preparation of hashish, mescaline, Bannisteria Caapi, LSD, Sacred Mushrooms, or any other drug of the hallucinogen group. . . . There is no evidence that the use of any hallucinogen results in physical dependence. The action of these drugs is physiologically opposite to the action of junk. A lamentable confusion between the two classes of drugs has arisen owing to the zeal of the U.S. and other narcotic departments.

By the time Burroughs was approaching his middle forties he was injecting forty or more grains of heroin daily: an amount that would be lethally toxic for a nonaddict, and increasingly dangerous even for a confirmed user. Of this period of his life he has commented:

. . . at the end of the junk line . . . I lived in one room in the Native Quarter of Tangier. I had not taken a bath in a year nor changed my clothes or removed them except to stick a needle every hour in the fibrous grey wooden flesh of terminal addiction. I never cleaned or dusted the room. Empty ampoule boxes and garbage piled to the ceiling. Light and water long since turned off for nonpayment. I did absolutely nothing. I could look at the end of my shoe for eight hours. I was only roused to action when the hourglass of junk ran out . . . suddenly my habit began to jump and jump. Forty, sixty grains a day. And still it was not enough. And I could not pay.

Burroughs finally understood that he was facing death from the illness known as terminal heroin addiction: "I stood there with my last check in my hand and realized that it was my last check." Summoning up all his courage and what remained of his money, he flew from Tangier to England where, securing legal and humane treatment for his disease, he was finally cured.
William S. Burroughs' experiences as an addict have been projected with passion and brilliant imagery in his novels. Few people, however, know that he has written as a lay expert on drugs for the British Journal of Addiction *and has lectured in the same capacity before the* American Psychological Symposium. *(Burroughs, who was born in 1914, graduated from Harvard, and did post graduate work there in anthropology.) The following essay is the address Burroughs delivered to the* American Psychological Symposium *on September 6, 1961. His remarks are particularly noteworthy here because they ac-*

curately identify marihuana not as an addicting sedative or depressant, but as an agent that expands the consciousness of the user. He reveals that after he broke his dependence upon heroin, he smoked marihuana as a therapeutic device and as an esthetic mechanism in his writing.

When his friend novelist Jack Kerouac read the first drafts of Naked Lunch, *he suggested that title because it meant, in Burroughs' words, "exactly what the words say: NAKED Lunch . . . a frozen moment when everyone sees what is on the end of every fork." That state of vision, Burroughs points out below, was substantially due to the consciousness-expanding properties of the marihuana he smoked at the time, which facilitated insights and images that proved of literary value.*

Unfortunately the word "drug" activates a reflex of fear, disapproval and prurience in Western nervous systems. "Drug" of course is simply a generic term for any chemical agent. Alcohol is a sedative drug similar in action to the barbiturates. Yet because of purely verbal associations we do not think of alcohol as being a drug because it *is* our national drug. The American narcotics department has bracketed substances with opposite physiological effect as narcotic drugs. Morphine is actually an antidote for cocaine poisoning, Cannabis is a hallucinogen drug with no chemical or physiological affinity to either cocaine or morphine. Yet cocaine, morphine, and cannabis are all classified as "narcotic drugs." Unquestionably the term has emotional impact. But used in such a loose fashion it has no useful precision of meaning. I would like to draw at the outset a clear distinction between sedative and hallucinogen agents, between addicting and nonaddicting drugs.

What is addiction? The use of opium or derivatives leads to a state that defines, limits, and describes addiction. So the morphine or heroin addict provides the model and mirror of addiction. The addict functions on heroin. Without it he is helpless as a beached fish out of his medium. As a diver depends on his air line, the addict depends on his heroin connection. This situation of total dependence did not exist prior to his contact with heroin and his subsequent addiction. A month more or less of daily exposure through injection or sniffing the drug and the addict is hooked, that is, addicted for life. Even if the addict is cured and off the drug for years he can be readdicted by one or two shots. Like the alcoholic, he has acquired a lifelong sensitivity to the drug. Investigators still do not know how heroin addiction is contracted. Doctor Isbell of Lexington, Ky., where most U.S. addicts are treated, has suggested that morphine acts on the cell receptors, perhaps altering the molecular structure of certain cell groups in the body.

While the action of morphine is not fully understood, alcohol and barbiturates are definite front-brain sedatives, and increased doses are generally required to achieve sedation. In fact, all sedative drugs may be said to act by sedating, that is, putting out of action some function of the nervous system, by decreasing awareness of surroundings and bodily processes. Addiction would seem to be a prerogative of sedatives and perhaps the opiates are the only class of truly addicting drugs. The symptoms that follow barbiturate withdrawal may be regarded as a mechanical reaction from massive front-brain sedation rather than a biological need for the drug.

What is a hallucinogen? A drug that expands consciousness and increases awareness of surroundings and bodily processes. (I would suggest that the term consciousness-expanding drugs be substituted for hallucinogen drug since actual hallucinations are rare and no precise definition of hallucination has been formulated.) Under the influence of mescaline, LSD, cannabis, the subject is acutely aware of colors, sounds, odors, and the effects of the drug may be said to consist of this phenomenon of increased awareness, which may be pleasant or unpleasant depending on the content of awareness. Colors and sounds gain an intense meaning and many insights carry over after the drug effects have worn off. Under the influence of mescaline I have had the experience of seeing a painting for the first time and I found later that I could see the painting without using the drug. The same insights into music or the beauty of an object ordinarily ignored carry over so that one exposure to a powerful consciousness-expanding drug often conveys a permanent increase in the range of experience. Mescaline transports the user to unexplored psychic areas, and he can often find the way back without a chemical guide.

I will describe a simple experiment that will make the distinction between sedative and consciousness-expanding drugs more precise. So far as I know this experiment has not been carried out in detail. Here is the proposed experiment: Administer a consciousness-expanding drug together with a precise array of stimuli—music, pictures, odors, tastes—timed and recorded so that the entire battery of stimuli can be exactly repeated. Some days later when the effects of the drug are completely dissipated expose the subject to the same stimuli in the same order. To what extent is the hallucinogen experience reactivated? Everyone who has used the conscious-expanding drugs knows that any *one* stimulus experienced under the influence of the drug can reactivate the drug experience. There is every reason to believe that the drug experience could be recaptured in detail with a precise repetition of associated stimuli.

Now try the same experiment with a morphine addict. Administer a dose of morphine together with a battery of stimuli. Wait until withdrawal symptoms occur. Now repeat the stimuli. Is any relief from withdrawal symptoms experienced? On the contrary, the associated stimuli reactivate and intensify need for the drug. The same of course is true of alcohol. Stimuli associated with the consumption of alcohol activate the need for alcohol and conduce to relapse in the cured alcoholic.

The use of sedative drugs leads to increased dependence on the drug used. The use of consciousness-expanding drugs could show the way to obtain the useful aspects of hallucinogen experience without any chemical agent. Anything that can be done chemically can be done in other ways, given sufficient knowledge of the mechanisms involved. Recently a Cambridge dentist has extracted teeth with no other anesthetic than music through head phones. The patient was instructed to turn up the volume if he experienced any pain. The consciousness-expanding experience has been produced by flicker, that is, rhythmic light flashes in the retinae at the rate of from ten to twenty-five flashes per second. I quote from Grey Walters, *The Living Brain:* "The rhythmic series of flashes appeared to be breaking down of some of the physiological barriers between different regions of the brain. This meant that the stimulus of flicker received in the visual projection area of the cortex was breaking bounds, its ripples were overflowing into other areas."

Now it is precisely this overflow of the brain areas, hearing colors, seeing sounds and even odors that is a categorical characteristic of the consciousness-expanding drugs. Along with flicker Grey Walters has produced many of the phenomena associated with consciousness-expanding drugs. Subjects reported: "Lights like comets . . . Ultra unearthly colors, mental colors not deep visual ones. . . ."

The literature of mescaline and LSD abounds in such regrettably vague descriptions of visionary experiences. Further experiments with subliminal doses of mescaline accompanied by flicker, flicker administered under large dosage and repeated later, could well lead to a *nonchemical* method of expanding consciousness and increasing awareness.

There are many consciousness-expanding drugs each with distinct porperties, and scientists are just beginning to explore the chemistry of these drugs. I have had personal experience with mescaline, LSD, *Bannisteria caapi*, kava kava, dimethyltryptamine, and several others in the form of herbal preparations, the content of which was unknown to me. All these drugs open different psychic areas. Some of these areas are pleasant, some are not. Dimethyltryptamine and bufotenine seem to produce in many subjects alarming and disagreeable symptoms, and both drugs in my opinion should be used with great caution or not at all. Overdose of consciousness-expanding drugs can be a nightmare experience owing to the increased awareness of unpleasant or dangerous symptoms. I would like to mention a drug which is neither a front-brain stimulant like cocaine, nor a sedative like morphine and barbiturates, nor a tranquilizer, nor an energizer, nor a hallucinogen, a drug that could act as a useful stabilizing agent when using the consciousness-expanding drugs. This drug is apomorphine. I quote from *Anxiety and Its Treatment* by Doctor John Dent of London: "Apomorphine is made from morphine by boiling with hydrochloric acid, but its physiological effect is quite different—apomorphine acts on the hypothalamus in such a way as to normalize metabolism and regulate the blood serum."

Administered with a consciousness-expanding drug apomorphine stabilizes the experience and reduces anxiety. I have observed and personally experienced dramatic relief from anxiety resulting from consciousness-expanding drugs after a dose of apomorphine. The drug has no sedative or addicting properties. No case of addiction to apomorphine has ever been recorded. Yet because of purely verbal associations the drug has been placed under the Harrison Narcotic Act and is seldom prescribed in this country. Apomorphine is a unique drug in that it acts as a metabolic regulator which stabilizes but does not cancel the consciousness-expanding experience.

In conclusion: The sedative drugs act to decrease awareness, and increased dosage is generally required to achieve or maintain this state of decreased awareness. The consciousness-expanding drugs act to increase awareness, and this state of increased awareness can be a permanent acquisition.

It is unfortunate that cannabis (the Latin term for preparations made from the hemp plant, such as marihuana and hashish), which is certainly the safest of the hallucinogen drugs, should be subject to the heaviest legal sanctions. Unquestionably this drug is very useful to the artist, activating trains of association that would otherwise be inaccessible, and I owe many of the scenes in *Naked Lunch* directly to the use of cannabis. Opiates, on the other hand, since they act to diminish awareness of surroundings and bodily processes, can only be a hindrance to the artist. Cannabis serves as a guide to psychic areas which can then be re-entered without it. I have now discontinued the use of cannabis for some years and find that I am able to achieve the same results by non-chemical means: flicker, music through head phones, cutups and foldins of my texts, and especially by training myself to think in association blocks instead of words, that is, cannabis, like all the hallucinogens, can be discontinued once the artist has familiarized himself with the areas opened up by the drug. Cannabis sometimes causes anxiety in large doses, and this anxiety is promptly relieved by apomorphine.

It would seem to me that cannabis and the other hallucinogens provide a key to the creative process, and that a systematic study of these drugs would open the way to non-chemical methods of expanding consciousness.

CHAPTER SIX

THERAPEUTIC APPLICATION
OF MARIHUANA

Dr. Robert Walton

In 1937 Dr. Walton, Professor of Pharmacology at the University of Mississippi, prepared the following scholarly and comprehensive essay on the medicinal uses of hemp preparations for his book Marihuana. *Sensing that the irrational attitudes engendered by the marihuana panic—then in high gear—might inhibit legitimate scientific inquiry, he wrote:*

The 1937 Federal legislative acts should be wholly effective in making these preparations completely unavailable for any further abuse. More stringent regulations making the drug unavailable for medical and scientific purposes would be unwise, since other uses may be developed for the drug which will completely overshadow its disadvantages. The drug has certain remarkable properties and if its chemical structure were determined and synthetic variations developed, some of these might prove to be particularly valuable, both as therapeutic agents and as experimental tools.

Dr. Walton's fears were well grounded: immediately after the Marihuana Tax Act of 1937[1] was passed, the Federal Bureau of Narcotics issued and proceeded to implement 60-odd pages of "more stringent regulations." These harsh, com-

1 See Appendix 2.

*plex administrative edicts rendered it virtually impossible—
except in limited instances, characterized by red tape and
harassment—to grow, import, buy, sell, use, prescribe, or
experiment with hemp products.*

The therapeutic application of cannabis is more a matter of
history than of present-day practice. Synthetic analgesics and
hypnotics have almost entirely displaced these preparations
from their original field of application. The newer synthetics
are more effective and reliable and, in addition, have been
more intensely exploited by commercial interests. Cannabis
preparations have come to occupy so minor a place among
modern medicinals that it has been suggested that they be
abandoned altogether, this latter point of view being based
on the assumption that they represent a menace from the
standpoint of the hashish habit. Such an action would certainly be too drastic in view of the circumstances. For one
thing, the therapeutic use of cannabis and the hashish habit
are almost entirely unrelated. The drug has been readily available in this country for almost a century without developing
more than a very occasional, isolated instance of hashish
abuse. The marihuana habit came into this country by other
channels, although it is true that once established as a practice, some few individuals have made use of the "drug store"
preparations. The 1937 Federal legislative acts should be
wholly effective in making these preparations completely unavailable for any further abuse of this sort. More stringent
regulations making the drug unavailable for medical and
scientific purposes would be unwise, since other uses may be
developed for the drug which will completely overshadow its
disadvantages. The drug has certain remarkable properties
and if its chemical structure were determined and synthetic
variations developed, some of these might prove to be particularly valuable, both as therapeutic agents and as experimental tools.

Essentially the same general opinion has been expressed
recently by the committee on legislative activities of the American Medical Association. They concluded that

there is positively no evidence to indicate the abuse of cannabis
as a medicinal agent or to show that its medicinal use is leading to the development of cannabis addiction. Cannabis at the
present time is slightly used for medicinal purposes, but it
would seem worthwhile to maintain its status as a medicinal
agent for such purposes as it now has. There is a possibility
that a re-study of the drug by modern means may show other
advantages to be derived from its medicinal use.

Although hemp preparations may have been used by the ancients to produce anesthesia, these drugs were not introduced generally into medicine until about 1840. At this time O'Shaughnessy, Aubert-Roche, and Moreau de Tours observed its use in India and Egypt and proceeded to experiment with its therapeutic possibilities. After using it in different sorts of conditions, they were each enthusiastic in representing it as a valuable therapeutic agent. Their activities resulted in a very widespread and general use of the drug in both Europe and America. During the period 1840-1900 there were something over 100 articles published which recommended cannabis for one disorder or another.

This popularity of the hemp drugs can be attributed partly to the fact that they were introduced before the synthetic hypnotics and analgesics. Chloral hydrate was not introduced until 1869 and was followed in the next 30 years by paraldehyde, sulfonal, and the barbitals. Antipyrine and acetanilide, the first of their particular group of analgesics, were introduced about 1884. For general sedative and analgesic purposes, the only drugs commonly used at this time were the morphine derivatives and their disadvantages were very well known. In fact, the most attractive feature of the hemp narcotics was probably the fact that they did not exhibit certain of the notorious disadvantages of the opiates. The hemp narcotics do not constipate at all, they more often increase rather than decrease appetite, they do not particularly depress the respiratory center even in large doses, they rarely or never cause pruritis or cutaneous eruptions and, most important, the liability of developing addiction is very much less than with the opiates.

These features were responsible for the rapid rise in popularity of the drug. Several features can be recognized as contributing to the gradual decline of popularity. Cannabis does not usually produce analgesic or relax spastic conditions without producing cortical effects and, in fact, these cortical effects usually predominate. The actual degree of analgesia produced is much less than with the opiates. Most important, the effects are irregular due to marked variations in individual susceptibility and probably also to variable absorption of the gummy resin.

The reported therapeutic successes and failures of these drugs are briefly summarized below.

Among the miscellaneous conditions for which it has been used and recommended may be mentioned cough, fatigue, rheumatism, rheumatic neuralgia, asthma, and delirium tremens.

Spastic Conditions

Part of the early enthusiasm for cannabis was based on its presumed value as an antagonist of spastic conditions. It was used and highly recommended in the treatment of tetanus, hydrophobia, puerperal convulsions, chorea, and strychnine poisoning.

In the case of strychnine poisoning, at least, its value is slight. The author, with the help of Horace Dozier, tested the influence of cannabis insofar as it affected the minimal convulsive dose of strychnine in dogs. Even large doses of cannabis did not alter the strychnine effect enough to indicate any significant antagonism. In tetanus and hydrophobia, spasticity is more cerebral in origin and the cannabis antagonism may have been more effective in such cases.

Analgesic Uses

In combatting pain of various causes, cannabis preparations might be expected to be reasonably effective. See declared that it "gives relief from pain and increases the appetite in all cases, no matter on what causes the pain and loss of appetite may depend."

Hare says, ". . . during the time that this remarkable drug is relieving pain, a very curious physical condition sometimes manifests itself; namely, that the diminution of pain seems to be due to its fading away in the distance, so that the pain becomes less and less."

Mercer says that it does not arrest pain but has a "special power over spasmodic pain." Wood says that "as an analgesic, it is very much inferior to opium but may be tried when the latter is for any reason contra-indicated. In full doses, in neuralgic pains, it certainly often gives relief."

Aulde says that "as a remedy for the relief of supraorbital neuralgia no article perhaps affords better prospects than cannabis."

Headache and Migraine

Farlow considered cannabis useful in "nervous headache." MacKenzie says that if continued for some time it is the most valuable remedy he has met with in the treatment of persistent headache. Marshall does not consider that cannabis is generally useful but says however that it appears to be useful in headache of a dull and continuous character.

Regarding migraine, Stevens say that *Cannabis indica* is "sometimes very useful. . . . Two drops of the fluid extract may be given every half hour until the pain abates or until slight dizziness or mental confusion appears. Even larger doses may be used if necessary."

Osler and McCrea have said that for migraine, *Cannabis indica* is probably the most satisfactory remedy. However, in the latest edition of this text it is only suggested that "a prolonged course of *Cannabis indica* may be tried." Solis-Cohen and Githens consider that cannabis is of great service in certain cases of migraine not dependent upon or aggravated by eyestrain. Fantus recently recommended its use in migraine, prescribing doses of 1 cc. of the fluid extract in iso-alcoholic elixir; N. F. McConnell, Bastedo, Hare, Lewis, and Bragman have also favorably mentioned its use in migraine.

Beckmann on the other hand says that whereas the drug was once considered a specific for migraine it has more recently fallen into "a probably deserved disrepute."

Sedative and Hypnotic Action

One of the earlier experimenters with hashish declared that "in its hypnotic and soothing effects on the nervous system, its resemblance to morphia is very great."

Fronmüller made about 1,000 observations on patients in which the soporific effects were compared with other drugs, particularly opium. He considered that the effect on the nervous system was much less dangerous than with opium. In most instances his patients are stated to have fallen asleep in about an hour without any particular side effects.

Bastedo remarks that it may promote sleep in the presence of pain. Poulsson and Dixon say that "sleep has often been seen to ensue without any, or with only slight excitement."

Miller, Berthier, McConnell, Shoemaker, Clendinning, Hiller, and Florshinger have also described its usefulness in procuring sleep. Fantus and Cornbleet use it as a general sedative along with sodium bromide in the treatment of pruritis. Lees was very enthusiastic about the anodyne and soporific action of an aqueous extract, which he considered did not produce any of the excitement effects.

In current practice, the sedative effects are probably most used in veterinary work. Milks and Eichhorn say that

cannabis is a distinct depressant to the brain and cord. In man, this may be preceded by a brief period of stimulation but this action is rarely seen in the horse. It is a distinct depressant and hypnotic and probably ranks ahead of opium for this purpose in equine practice. After full doses the animals feel drowsy, sleepy, have a disinclination to move and may finally pass into a stage of narcosis, which may last from 12 to 24 hours, and then recover.

One half ounce of the solid extract is cited as being sufficient to anesthetize a horse. This drug is relatively safe if considered simply on the basis of its effects on the circulation and respiratory center. It would seem however that a very real source of danger exists in the possible development of bronchopneumonia during the long period of semi-anesthesia.

Mental Conditions

Moreau de Tours was the first to advocate using the hashish euphoria as a means of combatting mental conditions of a depressive character. He reported a number of case histories of manics and melancholics which were improved after such therapy. His conclusions were immediately criticized by Rech. There have been a few other observations agreeing in general with Moreau de Tours and there have been some who reported adversely on such treatment. Straub recently suggested that small doses of a properly standardized preparation may possibly prove useful in depressive melancholias.

Edes found it benefited patients who complained of unpleasant, tiring dreams, and Birch used it in the treatment of chronic chloral and chronic opium poisoning.

Uterine Dysfunction

Some have been particularly enthusiastic regarding the value of cannabis in dysmenorrhea and menorrhagia. Batho says, ". . . considerable experience of its employment in menorrhagia, more especially in India, has convinced me that it is, in that country at all events, one of the most reliable means at our disposal." Referring to the use of Indian hemp in menorrhagia, Brown says, ". . . there is no medicine which has given such good results; for this reason it ought to take the first place as a remedy in menorrhagia."

Effects During Labor

Willis recommended its use in "tedious labour where the patient is restless." Christison used the drug during childbirth and advocated its use as an oxytocic. He believed it stimulated uterine movements more quickly than ergot. Kobylanshi, Grigor and Savignac also reported on its effects during child-birth. These observations may be taken generally as evidence that cannabis does not depress uterine movements. The drug is so lacking in peripheral actions that any special stimulation or depression would hardly be expected.

The question as to the effects of cannabis during labor was recently discussed in the *Journal of the American Medical Association.*

> The sensation of pain is distinctly lessened or entirely absent and the sense of touch is less acute than normally. Hence a woman in labor may have a more or less painless labor. If a sufficient amount of the drug is taken, the patient may fall into a tranquil sleep from which she will awaken refreshed. . . . As far as is known, a baby born of a mother intoxicated with cannabis will not be abnormal in any way.

In South Africa the native women smoke cannabis to stupefy themselves during childbirth. A requisite for the successful use of this technic would seem to be a previous familiarity with the effects of the drug. The African natives no doubt use the drug at other times and accordingly are not as likely to be distressed by the occasionally terrifying phases of the epi-sode. Also some experience is needed in order to regulate the dose when used in this way. In such obstetric use, the drug has one important advantage as contrasted with morphine, that is, the almost complete absence of any depressing effect on the respiratory mechanism.

Diagnostic Usefulness

There have been numerous suggestions that the hashish delirium may be used in psychiatric analysis as a means of removing the barriers to the subconscious. This was one of the purportedly useful features of the drug as declared in the recent legislative deliberations. Although such an application is not unreasonable, the few trials which have been made were not particularly successful. In contrast with cocaine and amytal, the patient usually becomes more absorbed and less communicative. Lindemann and Malamud observed this while studying effects in schizophrenics and psychoneurotics. They reported that "new experiences are created which allow new presentations or new fantasies and an increasing neglect of the outside world in favor of experiences which are in keeping with the patient's desires." They did note that with schizophrenics there was much less change in space and time perception than in psychoneurotic and normal persons.

There is a fictional account of the use of the drug to obtain confessions from suspected criminals. In general, however, the usual effect of the drug is not such as to make it very useful for such purposes. Von Schrenck described some rather inconclusive experimentation involving the use of hashish in hypnotism.

CHAPTER SEVEN

CANNABIS:

A Reference

Dr. William H. McGlothlin

William McGlothlin, PhD, is a Harvard-trained psychologist, associated with the Rand Corporation, who is presently engaged in a research program to assess the effects of LSD on attitudes in normal subjects. This paper, a comprehensive work of genuine scholarship, is a segment of a larger study entitled Hallucinogenic Drugs: A Perspective with Special Reference to Peyote and Cannabis, *which was presented in a modified version at* The Second Conference on the Use of LSD in Psychotherapy, *held in Amityville, New York, in May 1965.*

HISTORY AND DESCRIPTION

The cannabis or hemp plant is probably indigenous to Central Asia and has a very long history. According to Taylor, it was described in Chinese literature in 2737 B.C. and introduced into India prior to 800 B.C. The drug cannabis is obtained from the flowering tops of the female plant, and it was used very early in China as an analgesic in surgery. It has had wide use in indigenous medicine, especially in India, and to some extent in modern medicine beginning about 1860; however, it is now considered obsolete.

The use of cannabis as an intoxicant was well known in India by the ninth or tenth century, and some authors place the date considerably earlier. From India, it spread to North Africa and then to Europe around 1800. It has a fairly long history in Mexico and Latin America, but was not introduced into the United States to any appreciable extent until about 1920. Cannabis currently grows wild in almost all countries and is cultivated for the drug in many. It is used throughout the world as an intoxicant in various degrees—a survey sponsored by the United Nations in 1950 estimated worldwide usage by 200 million persons, the large majority of them in Asia and Africa.

The potency of cannabis as an intoxicant varies widely depending on climate, cultivation, and preparation for use. There are three grades prepared in India. Bhang is cheap, low in potency, and usually ingested as a drink; ganja is two to three times as strong; the most potent is charas, the unadulterated resin obtained from the plant or dried flower. Smoking is the most common mode of consumption for ganja and charas. Cannabis preparations have many other names in various parts of the world—in Morocco it is called kif; in South America, dagga; and in the United States and Latin America, marihuana. These correspond roughly in potency to the bhang of India, though they are mostly smoked rather than ingested. The term *hashish,* when used correctly, is a powdered and sifted form of charas, or a preparation made from it; however, hashish is widely used in the literature to refer to any form of the cannabis drug. The marked differences in potency among the various preparations are probably responsible for some of the discrepancies between Eastern and Western findings that will be discussed later. From a consensus of several reports, the marihuana available in the United States is estimated to be one-fifth to one-eighth as potent as the charas resin in India.

The active ingredient of cannabis has been identified as tetrahydrocannabinol, but the chemistry is extremely complex and not completely understood. Some 80 derivatives of tetrahydrocannabinol have now been synthesized and studied pharmacologically, and most are active in various degrees.

Cannabis Intoxication and Its Similarity to That of Peyote and LSD

Pharmacology texts invariably classify cannabis as a hallucinogen, along with LSD, mescaline, and psilocybin. Recent interest, however, has concentrated on the last three, probably because the "model psychosis" hypothesis grew out of work with these more potent hallucinogens. Also, those interested in examining the therapeutic effects of these agents have preferred to avoid the stigma attached to marihuana. On examining descriptions of cannabis intoxication, however, it is clear that virtually all of the phenomena associated with LSD are, or can, also be produced with cannabis. The wavelike aspect of the experience is almost invariably reported for cannabis as well as for all the other hallucinogens. Reports of perceiving various parts of the body as distorted, and depersonalization, or "double consciousness," are very frequent, as well as spatial and temporal distortion. Visual hallucinations, seeing faces as grotesque, increased sensitivity to sound and merging of senses (synesthesia) are also common. Heightened suggestibility, perception of thinking more clearly, and deeper awareness of the meaning of things are characteristic. Anxiety and paranoid reactions may also accur. Walton writes:

> The acute intoxication with hashish probably more nearly resembles that with mescaline than any of the other well-known drugs. Comparison with cocaine and the opiates does not bring out a very striking parallelism. With mescaline and hashish there are numerous common features which seem to differ only in degree.

The difference between cannabis and the other hallucinogens must be understood in terms of the motivation of the user as well as the strength of the reaction. This is not to say that the set of the user is not very important for the others as well, but cannabis is especially amenable to control and direction so that the desired effects can usually be obtained at will. Michaux, a French writer, has repeatedly explored his own reactions to the various hallucinogens and writes, "Compared to other hallucinogenic drugs, hashish is feeble, without great range, but easy to handle, convenient, repeatable without immediate danger." (83) It is these features, plus the fact that consumption by smoking enables the experienced user to accurately control the amount absorbed, that makes cannabis a dependable producer of the desired euphoria and sense of well-being. This aspect is pointed up in the study by the New York Mayor's Committee which examined the reaction of experienced users to smoking and ingesting marihuana extract. When smoking, the effect was almost immediate, and the subjects carefully limited the intake to produce the desired "high" feeling. They had no difficulty maintaining a "euphoric state with its feeling of well-being, contentment, sociability, mental and physical relaxation, which usually ended in a feeling of drowsiness." When ingested, the effect could not be accurately controlled, and although the most common experience was still euphoria, users also frequently showed anxiety, irritability, and antagonism. It is common knowledge among marihuana users that one must *learn* to use the drug effectively, and that beginners are often disappointed in the effect.

With the much stronger and longer-lasting hallucinogens, LSD and mescaline, there is much less control and direction possible, and even the experienced user may find himself plunged into an agonizing hell. In summary, it appears that the reaction to cannabis is on a continuum with the other hallucinogens and, given the same motivation on the part of the user, will produce some of the same effects. On the other hand, cannabis permits a dependable controlled usage that is very difficult if not impossible with LSD and mescaline.

One distinct difference that does exist between cannabis and the other hallucinogens is its tendency to act as a true narcotic and produce sleep, whereas LSD and mescaline cause a long period of wakefulness. One other very important difference from the sociological standpoint is the lack of rapid onset of tolerance that occurs with the other hallucinogens. The cannabis intoxication may be maintained continuously through repeated doses, whereas the intake of LSD and mescaline must usually be spaced over several days to be effective. In addition, the evidence on the use of these drugs indicates that, although the mild euphoria obtained from cannabis may be desirable daily, or even more frequently, the overwhelming impact of the peyote and LSD experience generally results in a psychological satiation that lasts much longer than the tolerance effect.

Motivation

In this country marihuana users almost invariably report the motivation is to attain a "high" feeling which is generally described as "a feeling of adequacy and efficiency" in which mental conflicts are allayed. (79) The experienced user is able to achieve consistently a state of self-confidence, satisfaction, and relaxation, and he much prefers a congenial group setting to experiencing the effects alone. Unlike the reasons the Indian gives for taking peyote, the marihuana user typically does not claim any lasting benefits beyond the immediate pleasure obtained.

In India and the Middle East, cannabis is apparently taken under a much wider range of circumstances and motivations. The long history, wide range of amount used, and the fact that legal restrictions do not require its concealment permit investigation under a variety of conditions. Most Eastern investigators draw a clear distinction between the occasional or moderate regular user and those who indulge to excess. Chopra states that cannabis is still used fairly extensively in Indian indigenous medicine, and that it is also frequently taken in small quantities by laborers to alleviate fatigue. (29) In certain parts of India this results in a 50 percent increase in consumption during the harvest season. Chopra writes:

> A common practice amongst laborers engaged on building or excavation work is to have a few pulls at a ganja pipe or to drink a glass of bhang towards the evening. This produces a sense of well-being, relieves fatigue, stimulates the appetite, and induces a feeling of mild stimulation, which enables the worker to bear more cheerfully the strain and perhaps the monotony of the daily routine of life.

Similarly, Benabud found moderate use of kif by the country people in Morocco to "keep spirits up." The need for moderation is expressed in the folk saying, "Kif is like fire; a little warms, a lot burns." (13) Bhang is also frequently used as a cooling drink or food supplement.

The habitual use of cannabis as an intoxicant is also considerable, although Chopra states that it has gradually declined over the past thirty years and "at the present time it is almost entirely confined to the lower strata of society. Amongst the upper and middle classes, the use of cannabis is nowadays considered to be derogatory, in spite of the fact that the practice was held in great esteem in ancient India, and early literature is full of references to the virtues of this drug." Chopra found that the current usage is only one-fourth that consumed around 1900, and that the decline is largely due to government reduction of the area under cannabis cultivation and higher excise duty. He estimates the current number of regular users to be between 0.5 and 1.0 percent of the population.

Cannabis also has a long history of religious use in India, being taken at various ceremonies and for "clearing the head and stimulating the brain to think" in meditation. It also plays a central role in the religions of certain primitive African and South American tribes. In India, the religious use of cannabis is by no means always moderate. Chopra writes, "The deliberate abuse of bhang is met with almost entirely among certain classes of religious mendicants."

Cannabis is widely believed to have aphrodisiac properties. Bouquet states that in North Africa the belief that cannabis will preserve, maintain, or improve sexual powers is an important initiating cause of the habit. In a sample of some 1,200, Chopra found 10 percent listed sexual factors as the exciting cause leading to the cannabis habit. While cannabis intoxication may be sexually stimulating for some, several authors have claimed that prolonged and excessive use will eventually cause impotence. (13, 17, 29)

In the United States, two studies of marihuana use in the Army concluded that it frequently produced various homosexual and heterosexual perversions. (28, 76) On the other hand, the Mayor's Committee study in New York concluded "that in the main, marihuana was not used for direct sexual stimulation." Their conclusions were based on the findings of six police men and women who, for a period of one year, posed as marihuana habitués and visited numerous intimate marihuana gatherings and "tea pads," some of which were also brothels. The experimental portion of the study found that in about 10 percent of the 150 marihuana administrations there was some evidence of eroticism. Whatever aphrodisiac qualities cannabis may possess, virtually all investigators agree these are cerebral in nature and due to the reduction in inhibition and increased suggestibility. It is probable that it is little, if any, more effective than alcohol in this respect. In fact, Chopra writes, "Amongst profligate women and prostitutes bhang-sherbet used to be a popular drink in the course of the evening when their paramours visited them. This practice has, however, been largely replaced by the drinking of alcohol which is much more harmful." (30) Chopra also mentions that certain "saintly people who wish to renounce world pleasure use cannabis drugs for suppressing sexual desires." (29)

One final motivation should be mentioned—that of musicians who feel marihuana improves their ability. Walton writes, "The habit is so common among this professional group that it may properly be considered a special occupational hazard." (119) Aldrich and Williams both found that experienced marihuana users perform worse on musical tests under the effects of the drug, whereas the self-evaluation of the subjects indicated the majority felt they had performed better. (3, 122) Williams did report, however, that three out of twelve subjects tested showed "marked improvement" in auditory acuity. Morrow found no change in either musical ability or auditory acuity. (79)

In addition to the stated motivations for using cannabis, evaluations of the underlying sociological and psychological basis are of interest, particularly in instances of excessive indulgence. In this country there is very little evidence of excessive use approaching that of some groups in the East; there is general agreement, however, that the majority of regular marihuana users suffer from basic personality defects. The Mayor's Committee study in New York found that most marihuana users "were unemployed and of the others most had part-time employment." This study also administered extensive personality tests to 48 users and 24 nonusers. The subjects were prisoners, and therefore the sample is somewhat biased; they found, however, that the user group when undrugged was differentiated from the nonuser group by greater emotional inhibition and introversion. Maurer and Vogel characterize the marihuana user as follows:

> Most of them appear to be rather indolent, ineffectual young men and women who are, on the whole, not very productive. . . . Most habitual users suffer from basic personality defects similar to those which characterize the alcoholic.(77)

According to the literature, most marihuana users come from the lower socio-economic classes and there is a preponderance of Negroes and Latin Americans. Four studies of marihuana use in the Army found 90 percent or more of the samples were Negro. (28, 50, 51, 76) In recent years there appears to be an increasing use of marihuana by college students, and by middle- and upper-class groups in certain urban centers.

In the Eastern countries, most investigators dismiss the occasional or moderate regular use of cannabis in about the same way as moderate use of alcohol is considered in this country. Excessive indulgence, however, particularly with the more potent preparations, is invariably considered indicative of serious personality defects. As in the United States, the majority of users are in the lower socio-economic classes.

Benabud stresses that the major problems with cannabis in Morocco exist among the urban slum dwellers, especially among those who have newly come from the country and are "no longer buttressed by traditional customs." By contrast, he points out that although kif is widely used among the country people, there is no sign of compulsive need, such as exists "among the uprooted and poverty-stricken proletariat of the large town." Benabud also cites individual psycho-pathological factors as prominent causes of excessive indulgence:

> The mental attitudes and behavior usual in the emotionally immature are extremely common—prevalence of the imaginary over the real, of the present over the future, with the impulsive need of the habitually frustrated for immediate satisfaction of desire. . . . Thus, the importance and the frequency of constitutional predispositions are clear, a fact which justifies the adaptation of the well-known saying "You are a kif addict long before you smoke your first pipe."

Frequency of Use and the Question of Addiction

The confirmed user takes cannabis at least once per day; however, many others indulge only occasionally. There are no statistics on the ratio of regular to occasional users, but Bromberg found that only a small proportion of those who smoked marihuana in New York used it regularly. (24) Of those who use it regularly in the United States, most report they have voluntarily or involuntarily discontinued the habit from time to time without difficulty.

Several studies have reported that the average number of marihuana cigarettes smoked by regular users in the United States is around 6 to 10 per day. Two experiments in which regular marihuana users were encouraged to consume as much as desired found no evidence of tolerance or withdrawal symptoms. (101, 122)

Chopra collected detailed statistics on the sample of 1,200 regular users in India. Seventy percent had practiced the habit for more than ten years. Seventy-two percent used only cannabis, while the others also took alcohol, opium, or other drugs. Most of those using the bhang drink did not take excessive amounts, but 46 percent of the ganja and charas smokers consumed in excess of 90 grains per day (18 percent used in excess of 180 grains). More than half of both groups used the drug two or more times per day.

Benabud states that confirmed kif smokers in Morocco consumed from 20 to 30 pipes a day and 40 to 50 is not infrequent. As mentioned at the beginning of this section, marihuana available in the United States is, at most, only one-fifth as potent as charas and probably about one-third as potent as ganja. An average consumption of eight marihuana cigarettes (0.5 gram each) per day would thus be roughly equivalent to 12 grains of charas or 21 grains of ganja. When we consider that almost one-half of the ganja and charas smokers in Chopra's sample used from 90 to 360 grains per day, it is clear that the average consumption of marihuana by regular users in the United States is very mild in comparison.

Regarding the question of addiction to cannabis, most investigators agree there is generally no physiological dependence developed and only slight tolerance. This applies particularly to the moderate use observed in the United States. In the Mayor's Committee study, the officers who posed as marihuana habitués found no evidence of compulsion on the part of the user—there was no particular sign of frustration or compulsive seeking of a source of marihuana when it was not immediately available.

Concerning the use of cannabis in India, Chopra writes:

> The tolerance developed in both animals and man was generally slight, if any, and was in no way comparable to that tolerance developed to opiates. Its occurrence was observed only in those individuals who took excessive doses, after its prolonged use. . . . Habitual use of bhang can be discontinued without much trouble, but withdrawal from ganja and charas habits, in our experience, is more difficult to achieve, and is sometimes accompanied by unpleasant symptoms, though they are negligible compared with those associated with withdrawal from opiates and even cocaine.(29)

Chopra writes that many persons indulge in the milder bhang drinks in summer and discontinue it during the winter. (31) In Morocco Benabud found that kif smokers did not show progressively increased consumption, that habituation was not appreciable—only about one-third using it regularly—and that withdrawal was not usually followed by psychic or somatic effects. The only report differing from these findings is one by Fraser who indicated rather severe withdrawal symptoms in nine Indian soldiers addicted to ganja. (49)

Physical and Mental Effects

Some features of the cannabis intoxication have already been discussed. When taken orally, the effects begin in one-half to one hour and usually last from two to four hours. The effects of smoking are almost immediate and typically last from one to three hours. The safety factor is enormous—Walton lists only two deaths due to overdoses which have been reported in the literature.

The Mayor's Committee administered a wide range of physical, mental and personality tests to 72 prisoners under the effects of various dose levels, both ingested and smoked. The physiological effects were minimal—increased pulse rate, hunger and frequency of urination. The major psychomotor effect was decreased body and hand steadiness. Intellectual functions are impaired, and the effect is greater for complex tasks, large doses, and nonusers. Emotional and personality measures showed feelings of relaxation, disinhibition, and self-confidence, but basic personality structures did not change.

Although the dominant emotional reaction is euphoria, acute intoxication can cause severe anxiety, panic, and paranoid reactions. Six of the subjects in the Mayor's Committee study experienced such episodes lasting from three to six hours, all occurring after the drug was ingested rather than smoked.

The Mayor's Committee compared the 48 users and 24 nonusers from the standpoint of mental and physical deterioration resulting from long-term use of marihuana. They also conducted detailed quantitative measures on 17 of those who had used it the longest (mean 8 years, range 2 to 16; mean dose per day 7 cigarettes, range 2 to 18). They conclude that the subjects "had suffered no mental or physical deterioration as a result of their use of the drug." Freedman and Rockmore also report that their sample of 310, who had used marihuana an average of seven years, showed no mental or physical deterioration.

In India, the study of the mental, moral and physical effects of cannabis has had a long history, beginning with a seven-volume report issued by the Indian Hemp-Drug Commission in 1894. Their conclusions, as quoted by Walton, are as follows:

> The evidence shows the moderate use of ganja or charas not to be appreciably harmful, while in the case of bhang drinking, the evidence shows the habit to be quite harmless. . . . The excessive use does cause injury . . . tends to weaken the constitution and to render the consumer more susceptible to disease. . . . Moderate use of hemp drugs produces no injurious effects on the mind . . . excessive use indicates and intensifies mental instability.(119)

The commission continued, as quoted by Chopra: (30) "It [bhang] is the refreshing beverage of the people corresponding to beer in England and moderate indulgence in it is attended with less injurious consequences than similar consumption of alcohol in Europe." Chopra writes, "This view has been corroborated by our own experience in the field."

Chopra provides numerous statistics on the effect of cannabis on health by dose size and mode of consumption. In the previously mentioned sample of 1,200 regular users, there was a distinct difference in the effects on health, as reported by the user, depending on the amount consumed. For those using less than ten grains, none claimed impairment of health, whereas 75 percent of those using in excess of 90 grains per day indicated some impairment.

The most common physical symptom found by Chopra was conjunctivitis (72 percent); this effect is frequently reported by other investigators and is a well-known means of detecting cannabis users. Chopra also found chronic bronchitis was frequent among ganja and charas smokers, as well as a higher than average incidence of tuberculosis. Various digestive ailments were reported, and habitual use of large doses resulted in defective nutrition and a deterioration of general health. The fact that excessive use and the resulting impairment of health are much more common among users of the more potent preparations (ganja and charas) has been recognized by the various governments, and the use of charas is now illegal in all countries. Bhang and comparable preparations in other Eastern countries are often legal, but the cultivation and sale are generally controlled by the government.

Turning now to the relation between cannabis and psychosis, it is well established that transient psychotic reactions can be precipitated by using the drug, and, in susceptible individuals, this may occur even with moderate or occasional use. Out of a total of 72 persons used as experimental subjects the Mayor's Committee reports three cases of psychosis: one lasted four days, another six months, and one became psychotic two weeks after being returned to prison (duration not noted). The Committee concludes, "that given the potential personality make-up and the right time and environment, marihuana may bring on a true psychotic state." On the other hand, Freedman and Rockmore report no history of mental hospitalization in their sample of 310 who had an average of seven years' usage. Similarly, the United States Army investigation in Panama found no report of psychosis due to marihuana smoking in a sample of several hundred users over a period of one year. (101)

Bromberg reported on thirty-one cases admitted to the hospital as a result of using marihuana. (23, 24) Fourteen were described as "acute intoxication" that lasted from several hours to several days and was often accompanied by severe anxiety or hysterical reaction and transient panic states or depressions.

In India and other Eastern countries, cannabis has long been considered an important cause of psychosis, and many of the early authors classified 30 to 50 percent of hospitalized mental cases as cannabis psychosis. It is now considered that the causal effects of cannabis were somewhat exaggerated, but there is general agreement among Eastern writers that the drug plays a significant role in the precipitation of transient psychoses. Benabud cites the following data on psychiatric admissions to one hospital in Morocco. In the two-year period (1955–1956), 25 percent of the some 2,300 male admissions were diagnosed as "genuine" cannabis psychoses, and 70 percent of the total admitted to smoking kif (one-third were regular users). Since the incidence of cannabis use in Morocco is estimated to be considerably less than 10 percent of the population, it is clear that there is a definite associative, if not causative, relationship between cannabis and psychosis. Benabud estimates that of the total population of kif smokers, the number "suffering from recurrent mental derangement" is not more than five per thousand. Of Chopra's sample of 1,200 regular users, 13 were classified as psychotic. Benabud especially stresses excessive use and environmental factors, pointing out that the rate of psychosis among the moderate-smoking country people is only one-tenth that in the large cities.

Benabud classifies the cannabis psychosis as acute or subacute (74 percent), residual (17 percent) and psychical deterioration (9 percent). He describes the first category as usually resulting from a sharp toxic overdose and lasting for several days. The main features are excitation and impulsivity which may produce acts of violence. Sometimes there are continuing disassociations or "spectator ego" and delusions of grandeur, especially identification or kinship with God. Patients in the residual classification have longer lasting syndromes, including schizophrenic-like withdrawal, mental confusion, and mild residual hallucinations. There is little tendency for symptoms to become organized and proliferate, but rather to disappear gradually after a few months. The third class (cannabis deterioration) is described as the result of prolonged, excessive use of cannabis, resulting in precocious senility and over-all physical and mental deterioration. "These are the old addicts, exuberant, friendly, kif-happy vagabonds, often oddly dressed and living by begging."

Bouquet feels the fact that male hospitalized psychotics outnumber females three to one in North Africa is a consequence of cannabis use being almost entirely restricted to males. He considers charas to be much more dangerous in this regard than the milder forms of cannabis, and states that the incidence of cannabis psychosis has appreciably declined because charas is now prohibited and only the "raw cannabis ends" are used.

The chronic cannabis psychosis reported by Eastern writers has not been observed in this country. Most Western authors, while recognizing the role of cannabis in precipitating acute transient psychoses, have questioned the casual role in chronic cases. Mayer-Gross writes: "The chronic hashish psychoses described by earlier observers have proved to be cases of schizophrenia complicated by symptoms of cannabis intoxication." (78) Allentuck states that "a characteristic cannabis psychosis does not exist. Marihuana will not produce a psy-

chosis *de novo* in a well-integrated, stable person." (4) And
Murphy writes: "The prevalence of *major* mental disorder
among cannabis users appears to be little, if any, higher than
that in the general population." (86) Since it is well established that cannabis use attracts the mentally unstable, Murphy raises the interesting question of "whether the use of
cannabis may not be protecting some individuals from a psychosis." Regardless of the issue of chronic psychosis, it is clear
from Eastern descriptions that gross personality changes do result from very prolonged and excessive use of cannabis. The
complete loss of ambition and the neglect of personal habits,
dress, and hygiene resemble characteristics of the skid-row
alcoholic in this country.

Cannabis and Crime

The association of crime with the use of cannabis goes back
at least to around 1300 when Marco Polo described Hasan
and his band of assassins. The drug was reportedly used to
fortify courage for committing assassinations and other violent
crimes, and the words *hashish* and *assassin* are supposed to be
derived from this source. In certain parts of this country, a
near hysteria developed about 1930 when the use of marihuana was claimed to be related to a violent crime wave and
the widespread corruption of school children. Dr. Gomila, who
was Commissioner of Public Safety in New Orleans, wrote that
some homes for boys were "full of children who had become
habituated to the use of cannabis," and that "Youngsters
known as 'muggle-heads' fortified themselves with the narcotic
and proceeded to shoot down police, bank clerks, and casual
by-standers." (53) Sixty percent of the crimes committed in
New Orleans in 1936 were attributed to marihuana users.

Despite these lurid claims, subsequent studies have, for the
most part, failed to substantiate a causal relationship between
major crime and cannabis. Bromberg conducted two large statistical studies and found very little relation between crime and
the use of marihuana. The Mayor's Committee found that
many marihuana smokers were guilty of petty crimes, but there
was no evidence that the practice was associated with major
crimes.

More recent assessments tend to agree with these findings.
The Ad Hoc panel on Drug Abuse at the 1962 White House
Conference states, "Although marihuana has long held the
reputation of inciting individuals to commit sexual offenses
and other anti-social acts, evidence is inadequate to substantiate this." (121) Maurer and Vogel write:

It would seem that, from the point of view of public health and safety, the effects of marihuana present a very minor problem compared with the abusive use of alcohol, and that the drug has received a disproportionate share of publicity as an inciter of violent crime.

Chopra found that the crime rate for the sample of 1,200 regular cannabis users in India was higher than that for the general population. For bhang users, 6 percent had one conviction and 3 percent had more than one; for ganja and charas users, the comparable percentages were 12 and 17. In a further study of serious, violent crimes, however, especially murder cases, Chopra found that cannabis intoxication was responsible for only 1 to 2 percent of the cases. In addition to impulsive acts performed under acute cannabis intoxication, there are frequent references in the literature to criminals using the drug to provide courage to commit violent acts. There has been no evidence offered to substantiate this claim; rather, Chopra writes as follows regarding premeditated crime:

> In some cases these drugs not only do not lead to it, but actually act as deterrents. We have already observed that one of the important actions of these drugs is to quieten and stupefy the individual so that there is no tendency to violence, as is not infrequently found in cases of alcoholic intoxication.(29)

Similarly, Murphy writes:

> Most serious observers agree that cannabis does not, *per se,* induce aggressive or criminal activities, and that the reduction of the work drive leads to a negative correlation with criminality rather than a positive one.

It is interesting that a number of observers, particularly in countries other than the United States, consider alcohol to be a worse offender than cannabis in causing crime. For instance, an editorial in the *South African Medical Journal* states:

> Dagga produces in the smoker drowsiness, euphoria and occasional psychotic episodes, but alcohol is guilty of even graver action. It is not certain to what extent dagga contributes to the commission of crime in this country. Alcohol does so in undeniable measure.(42)

In the United States, probably the most serious accusation made regarding marihuana smoking is that it often leads to the use of heroin. The Mayor's Committee found no evidence of this, stating, "The instances are extremely rare where the habit of marihuana smoking is associated with addiction to these other narcotics." Nevertheless, it is difficult to see how the association with criminal peddlers, who often also sell heroin, can fail to influence some marihuana users to become addicted to heroin.

Summary and Appraisal

Cannabis is an hallucinogen whose effects are somewhat similar to, though much milder than, peyote and LSD. The confirmed user takes it daily or more frequently, and through experience and careful regulation of the dose is able to consistently limit the effects to euphoria and other desired qualities. Unlike peyote, there are typically no claims of benefit other than the immediate effects. Mild tolerance and physical dependence may develop when the more potent preparations are used to excess; however, they are virtually nonexistent for occasional or moderate regular users. There are apparently no deleterious physical effects resulting from moderate use, though excessive indulgence noted in some Eastern countries contributes to a variety of ailments. The most serious hazard is the precipitation of transient psychoses. Unstable individuals may experience a psychotic episode from even a small amount, and although they typically recover within a few days, some psychoses triggered by cannabis reactions may last for several months. In Eastern countries, where cannabis is taken in large amounts, some authors feel that it is directly or indirectly responsible for a sizable portion of the intakes in psychiatric hospitals.

In this country cannabis is not used to excess by Eastern standards; however, it does attract a disproportionate number of poorly adjusted and non-productive young persons in the lower socio-economic strata. There is some evidence that its use among other groups is increasing, but is not readily observable because of the lack of police harassment and publicity. In Eastern countries cannabis use is currently also more prevalent in the lower classes; however, moderate use is not illegal, socially condemned, or necessarily considered indicative of personality defects. The reputation of cannabis for inciting major crimes is unwarranted and it probably has no more effect than alcohol in this respect.

Of those familiar with the use of marihuana in this country, there is general agreement that the legal penalties imposed for its use are much too severe. Laws controlling marihuana are similar or identical to those pertaining to the opiates, including the mandatory imposition of long prison sentences for certain offenses. Many judges have complained that these laws have resulted in excessive sentences (five to ten years) for relatively minor offenses with marihuana. The 1962 White House Conference made the following recommendation: "It is the opinion of the Panel that the hazards of marihuana *per se* have been exaggerated and that long criminal sentences imposed on an occasional user or possessor are in poor social perspective."

The cultural attitude toward narcotics is, of course, a very important determiner of legal and social measures adopted for their control. An interesting commentary on the extent to which these attitudes resist change and influence factual interpretation is afforded by the lively debate that followed the publishing of the Mayor's Committee Report on Marihuana in 1944. (7, 18, 19, 20, 43, 75, 120) This was an extensive study conducted under the auspices of the New York Academy of Medicine at the request of Mayor LaGuardia. Its findings tended to minimize the seriousness of the marihuana problem in New York and set off a series of attacks from those with opposing viewpoints. An American Medical Association editorial commented: "Public officials will do well to disregard this unscientific, uncritical study, and continue to regard marihuana as a menace wherever it is purveyed." (43) And, as Taylor points out, "We have done so ever since." (115) Anslinger, the Commissioner of Narcotics, wrote, "The Bureau immediately detected the superficiality and hollowness of its findings and denounced it." (8) The authors expressed dismay that the report was attacked on the grounds that the findings represented a public danger, rather than on its scientific aspects. (20) Walton, a leading authority on cannabis, wrote:

> The report in question came generally to the same conclusion that any other group of competent investigators might reach if they repeated the inquiry under the same conditions. . . . A scientific study should be expected to report merely what it finds, avoid propaganda, and let the public do what it will with the results.(120)

Murphy raises the question of why cannabis is so regularly banned in countries where alcohol is permitted. He feels that one of the reasons is the positive value placed on action, and the hostility toward passivity:

> In Anglo-Saxon cultures inaction is looked down on and often feared, whereas overactivity, aided by alcohol or independent of alcohol, is considerably tolerated despite the social distur-

bance produced. It may be that we can ban cannabis simply because the people who use it, or would do so, carry little weight in social matters and are relatively easy to control; whereas the alcohol user often carries plenty of weight in social matters and is difficult to control, as the United States prohibition era showed. It has yet to be shown, however, that the one is more socially or personally disruptive than the other.

References

The reference numbers below correspond to those in the original, un-shortened work on hallucinogenic drugs in general.

3. Aldrich, C. K., "The Effect of a Synthetic Marihuana-like Compound on Musical Talent as Measured by the Seashore Test," *Public Health Report, 59,* 1944, pp. 431-433.

4. Allentuck, S. and K. M. Bowman, "The Psychiatric Aspects of Marihuana Intoxication," *Amer. J. of Psychiat., 99,* 1942, pp. 248-251.

7. Anslinger, H. J., "More on Marihuana and Mayor LaGuardia's Committee Report," *J. A. M. A., 128,* 1945, p. 1187.

8. Anslinger, H. J. and W. G. Tompkins, *The Traffic in Narcotics,* Funk & Wagnalls, New York, 1953.

13. Benabud, A., "Psycho-pathological Aspects of the Cannabis Situation in Morocco: Statistical Data for 1956," *Bulletin on Narcotics, 9,* No. 4, 1957, pp. 1-16.

17. Bouquet, R. J., "Cannabis, Parts III-V," *Bull. on Narcotics, 3,* No. 1, 1951, pp. 22-43.

18. ———, "Marihuana Intoxication," *J. A. M. A., 124,* 1944, pp. 1010-1011.

19. Bowman, K. M., "Marihuana Problems," *J. A. M. A., 128,* 1945, pp. 899-900.

20. ———, "Psychiatric Aspects of Marihuana Intoxication," *J. A. M. A., 125,* 1944, p. 376.

23. Bromberg, W., "Marihuana: A Psychiatric Study," *J. A. M. A., 113,* 1939, pp. 4-12.

24. ———, "Marihuana Intoxication," *Amer. J. of Psychiat., 91,* 1934, pp. 303-330.

28. Charen, S. and L. Perelman, "Personality Studies of Marihuana Addicts," *Amer. J. of Psychiat., 102,* 1946, pp. 674-682.

29. Chopra, I. C. and R. N. Chopra, "The Use of Cannabis Drugs in India," *Bull. on Narcotics, 9,* No. 1, 1957, pp. 4-29.

30. Chopra, R. N. and G. S. Chopra, "The Present Position of Hemp-Drug Addiction in India," *Indian J. Med. Res. Memoirs,* No. 31, 1939, pp. 1-119.

31. Chopra, R. N. and I. C. Chopra, "Treatment of Drug Addiction: Experience in India," *Bull. on Narcotics, 9,* No. 4, 1957, pp. 21-33.

42. Editorial, "Dagga," *So. African Med. J., 25:17,* 1951, pp. 284-286.

43. Editorial, "Marihuana Problems," *J. A. M. A.,* 1945, p. 1129.

49. Fraser, J. D., "Withdrawal Symptoms in Cannabis-Indica Addicts," *Lancet,* Pt. 2, 1949, p. 747.

50. Freedman, H. L. and M. J. Rockmore, "Marihuana, Factor in Personality Evaluation and Army Maladjustment," *J. Clin. Psychopathology*, 7 and 8, 1946, pp. 765-782 and 221-236.
51. Gaskill, H. S., "Marihuana, an Intoxicant," *Amer. J. of Psychiat.*, 102, 1945, pp. 202-204.
53. Gomila, F. R., "Present Status of the Marihuana Vice in the United States," in *Marihuana, America's New Drug Problem*, Lippincott, New York, 1938.
75. Marcovitz, E., "Marihuana Problems," *J. A. M. A., 129,* 1945, p. 378.
76. Marcovitz, E., and H. J. Myers, "The Marihuana Addict in the Army," *War Medicine*, 6, 1945, pp. 382-391.
77. Maurer, D. W., and V. H. Vogel, *Narcotics and Narcotics Addiction*, Charles C. Thomas, Springfield, Ill., 1962.
78. Mayer-Gross, W., E. Slater, and M. Roth, *Clinical Psychiatry*, Cassell and Co., London, 1954.
79. *The Marihuana Problem in the City of New York*, Jaques Cattell Press, Lancaster, Pa., 1944.
83. Michaux, H. *Light Through Darkness,* trans. by H. Chevalier, The Orion Press, New York, 1963.
86. Murphy, H. B. M., "The Cannabis Habit: A Review of Recent Psychiatric Literature," *Bull. on Narcotics, 15,* No. 1, 1963, pp. 15-23.
101. Siler, J. F., *et al.*, "Marihuana Smoking in Panama," *The Military Surgeon*, 73, 1933, pp. 269-280.
115. Taylor, N., *Flight from Reality,* Duell, Sloan and Pearce, New York, 1949.
119. Walton, R. P., *Marihuana, America's New Drug Problem*, Lippincott, New York, 1938.
120. ———, "Marihuana Problems," *J. A. M. A., 128,* 1945, p. 383.
121. *White House Conference on Narcotic and Drug Abuse,* U. S. Government Printing Office, Washington, 1963.
122. Williams, E. G., *et al.*, "Studies on Marihuana and Pyrahexyl Compound," *Public Health Reports, 61,* 1946, pp. 1059-1083.

SELECTIONS ON MARIHUANA FROM UN WORLD HEALTH ORGANIZATION REPORTS

The following selections have been taken verbatim from the 1961 Report of the sixteenth session of the Commission on Narcotic Drugs of the United Nations Economic and Social Council. At that time, Harry Anslinger, Commissioner of the Treasury Department's Bureau of Narcotics, did everything in his power, by exerting pressure on the American delegation of the UN Commission on Narcotics, to make member nations accept an international Single Convention on Narcotic Drugs. As may be seen from the ensuing documents, his efforts proved largely successful. Not only did most member nations (with the notable exception of India) adopt restrictive laws concerning marihuana, but numerous scientific reports concerning the antibiotic properties of the plant were given the most cavalier consideration and were rejected.

THE QUESTION OF CANNABIS

Note by the Secretary-General

The Economic and Social Council in resolution 730 E (XXVIII) invited the World Health Organization to prepare, in the light of recent research on the subject, a report on the use of cannabis for the extraction of useful drugs, particularly of the antibotic type, and if possible to make the report available in time for the fifteenth session (April/May 1960) of the Commission on Narcotic Drugs.

The report of the World Health Organization was received on 21 November 1960. In accordance with the above resolution of the Council, the Secretary-General distributed the report as document E/CONF.34/5 to the countries and organizations participating in the United Nations Conference for the Adoption of a Single Convention on Narcotic Drugs, with a view to a possible modification of the provisions of the Single Convention in order to permit the use of cannabis for the extraction of useful drugs.

The report entitled "The merits of Antibiotic Substances obtainable from . . . *Cannabis Sativa*" is attached hereto.

The Merits of Antibiotic Substances Obtainable from Cannabis Sativa

The following facts emerge from the available literature. (1–7)

Substances with antibacterial activity, the structure of which has been determined, can be extracted from this plant. They have a very low solubility (not actually specified) in water, but can be more readily dissolved in alkali or alcohol. They have no action on any Gram-negative species tested, but inhibit the growth of staphylococci, streptococci and other Gram-positive organisims in a concentration of the order of 1 in 100,000. There is a similar action on the tubercle bacillus. It has also been shown that the action is bactericidal and not merely bacteriostatic. This action is much diminished by organic matter, even broth reduces it as compared with peptone water, and blood reduces it by 99 per cent. The effect of pH has also been studied.

Application of extracts has an analgesic effect accompanied by local anaesthesia and sometimes irritation. Therapeutic effects are claimed for many kinds of use. These include treatment of ulcerative conditions of the mouth, dental caries, herpes and thrush, of otitis media, sinusitis, and furunculosis of the nose and ear, of infected wounds, burns and bedsores, and of cracked nipples for the prevention of staphylococcal mastitis. Good effects have been seen in tuberculosis fistulas, and the longest account of clinical uses (3) refers to a paper in which a systemic action from oral administration of cannabis seeds has been claimed in tuberculosis. This could not be verified in guinea pigs.

Information of several kinds which would help in assessing the value of this antibiotic is lacking. No experiments are reported on its effects on isolated mammalian cells. A substance with the beneficial local actions claimed should be innocuous to leucocytes and to tissue cultures of other types of cell. The fact that it has an analgesic effect suggests that it may not be altogether innocuous, and in any case the mechanism of this effect needs to be ascertained.

Secondly, none of the available reports on clinical use appears to refer to a properly conducted trial with adequate controls. Information about the nature of the infection is lacking in most of them; these reports would be more convincing if the antibiotic had been found effective in infections due to sensitive bacteria and ineffective when they are resistant.

Thirdly, it would appear that these studies, which have been going on for several years, have not carried enough conviction to induce a material production of this substance on a commercial scale.

Even if the clinical reports in the publications under survey are to be fully credited, it still remains to be decided whether they illustrate a curative action not obtainable by other and more orthodox means. The fact of success in an infection resistant to penicillin is not sufficient evidence of this since there are many other antibiotics active against Gram-positive bacteria which are effective alternatives. For example, neomycin and bacitracin are much more active in this respect than the antibacterial substances isolated from the cannabis plant; they have a negligible local toxicity, and have been used with great success as local applications to surfaces infected with staphylococci and streptococci. It would be very surprising if a direct comparison between them and the cannabis substances in question did not show that their action, especially if they were used together, was superior.

It is, therefore, concluded that at present the case has not been proved in favor of making cannabis available for the extraction of therapeutic substances, particularly with antibiotic properties equal or superior to those obtainable otherwise.

As regards the question of therapeutic usefulness of *Cannabis sativa* and substances extracted therefrom, the opinion expressed in the third report of the WHO Expert Committee on Addiction-Producing Drugs (8) remains unchanged. Cannabis preparations are practically obsolete and there is no justification for their medical use.

This conclusion does not affect the opinion of the Expert Committee on Addiction-Producing Drugs as expressed in its 10th report.(9) The prohibition or restriction of the medical use of a drug representing a particularly high danger to the community should continue to be recommended by the international organs concerned, but should not be mandatory.

Geneva, 18 November 1960

References

1. Ferenczy, L., Graoza, L. & Jakobey, I. (1958) *Naturwissenschaften*, 45, 188.
2. Kabelik, J. (1957) *Pharmazie, 12*, 439.
3. Krejci, Z. (1958) *Pharmazie, 13*, 155.
4. Krejci, Z., Horak, M. & Santavy, F. (1959) *Pharmazie, 14*, 349.
5. Martinec, T., & Felklova, M. (1959) *Pharmazie, 14*, 276, 279.
6. Schultz, O. & Haffner, G. (1958) *Arch. Pharm. (Weinheim)* 291, 391.
7. Schultz, O. & Haffner, G. (1959) *Z. Naturforsch. B.* 14, 98.
8. Wld Hlth Org. techn. Rep. Ser., 1952, 57, 11.
9. Wld Hlth Org. techn. Rep. Ser., 1960, *188*, 14.

THE QUESTION OF CANNABIS (INCLUDING SCIENTIFIC RESEARCH ON CANNABIS)[1]

Medical Use of Cannabis

175. The Economic and Social Council on the basis of the opinion of the WHO Expert Committee on Addiction-producing drugs that medical use of cannabis was practically obsolete and that such use was no longer justified,[2] and as proposed by the Commission, recommended in resolution 548 F I (XVIII) that governments explore the possibility of discontinuing the medical use of cannabis drugs. The Third Draft of the Single Convention on Narcotic Drugs prepared by the Commission[3] consequently prohibited the medical use of cannabis except in certain systems of indigenous medicine. At its fourteenth session, however, the Commission heard that recent research tended to show that cannabis might contain medically useful substances. At the suggestion of the Commission, therefore, the Economic and Social Council in resolution 730 E (XXVIII) asked WHO to prepare, in the light of recent research in several countries, a report on the use of cannabis for the extraction of useful drugs, particularly of the antibiotic type. The report, entitled "The merits of Antibiotic Substances obtainable from *Cannabis Sativa*,"[4] was presented by the WHO to the Conference for the Adoption of a Single Convention on

1 Agenda items 9 and 10 (E/CN.7/SR.461, 470 and 476).
2 Wld. Hth. Org., *Techn. Rep. Ser.*, 1952, 57, p. 11.
3 E/CN.7/AC.3/9, article 39.
4 E/CN.7/409; E/CONF.34/5.

Narcotic Drugs, which met in New York January–March 1961 and where it served its primary purpose in helping the Conference to draft provisions concerning cannabis drugs in the 1961 Convention.[5] It was noted that the 1961 Convention as adopted by the Conference permitted the medical use of cannabis drugs subject to the same controls as other drugs in schedule I of the Convention. Cannabis and cannabis resin, however, were included in schedule IV of the Convention, which meant that the prohibition of their medical use was recommended. Extracts and tinctures of cannabis were not included in schedule IV but only in schedule I, and therefore their prohibition was not recommended.

176. As regards extracts and tinctures of cannabis, the question was raised whether, in view of article 2 of the 1961 Convention providing that preparations containing drugs were subject to the same control as the drug which they contain,[6] such extracts and tinctures should not be considered to be cannabis preparations and thus subject to the recommendation of prohibition, which would apply to such preparations by virtue of the inclusion of cannabis in schedule IV. It was explained that in the 1961 Convention cannabis extract and tincture were considered as separate drugs and not as cannabis preparations.

177. The Commission learned that in India experts who had been consulted by the Government were of the opinion that the medical use of cannabis should continue in certain cases of indigenous systems of medicine. The Indian Pharmacopoeia Committee also desired to retain cannabis drugs. Cannabis was also used as a sedative in India.

178. The representative of the United Arab Republic informed the Commission that as a result of the recommendation of the Economic and Social Council (Resolution 548 F I (XVIII)) the importation and medical use of cannabis drugs and preparations containing cannabis had been stopped in the Egyptian Province, and stocks had been confiscated and destroyed.

The Cannabis Situation in General and in Individual Countries and Territories

179. At its fifteenth session the Commission had received the last four of twenty-four studies of the cannabis situation in individual countries and territories.[7] It had been suggested

5 E/CONF.34/22.

6 E/CONF.34/22, Article 2, para. 3.

7 Report, fifteenth session, para. 212; E/CN.7/286 and Adds. 1-29.

that with the completion of these country surveys it would be advisable to summarize the results.[8] The Commission had before it a document[9] bringing up to date the developments of various aspects of the cannabis problem and setting out some important conclusions which had emerged from the country surveys and from other official information available to the Secretariat. An annex to the document contained a summary of the twenty-four country surveys.

180. The Commission noted that the summary corroborated some of the conclusions drawn by the Commission on earlier occasions. For instance, there was very little evidence that crops grown for industrial purposes were a source of illicit use of or traffic in cannabis. Wild growth appeared to be a source of illicit traffic in and consumption of cannabis in several countries. Though still used extensively in the Ayurvedic, Unani, and Tibbi systems of medicine of the Indian-Pakistani subcontinent, cannabis drugs were seldom used in "western" medicine today. Legal non-medical use was now confined to the Indian-Pakistani sub-continent, where consumption was subject to strict control and the policy was to prohibit such use as soon as possible. The volume of the illicit traffic had remained high, over 670 tons of cannabis having been reported seized during 1959. While seizures were reported from every continent, a large part of the illicit traffic was domestic or between countries with common frontiers.

181. The Commission was informed that in Greece cannabis was grown illicitly on a small scale and also grew wild, particularly in the northern provinces. However, a large part of the cannabis illegally used in Greece came from Lebanon.

182. The observer for Ghana informed the Commission that in his country cannabis was the most widely misused drug, there was no known case of addiction to manufactured drugs, and that whereas cannabis had formerly mostly been smuggled into the country by sailors, it was now also illicitly cultivated.

183. The Commission noticed in particular that the consumption of cannabis is widespread in Africa. It recalled the social danger of acute cannabis intoxication and referred, among other sources, to the declaration made by the Portuguese permanent representative before the United Nations Security Council[10] during its consideration of the recent troubles that had occurred in Angola. He had expressed his

---

8 Report, fourteenth session, para. 314.

9 E/CN.7/399.

10 S/PV.944, page 38.

opinion that the assailants had taken stimulants, in particular strong doses of cannabis "which created in them a state of aggressiveness and irresponsibility that led to their acts of savagery."

184. The French representative reported the existence of a natural drug, "somorona," on which a communication had been sent to the Academy of Madagascar.[11] The drug is a vascular cryptogam of the Lycopodium genus, used alone or in conjunction with cannabis (Rongony) in order to make the person taking it "brave, unaffected by danger, able to overcome fatigue, and conquer fear." "Somorona" is also administered to fighting cocks and bulls, and to dogs used for boar-hunting. It was considered that the governments of African countries, and that of Madagascar, should be asked to co-operate by reporting any such natural substances having mental effects, so that studies could be undertaken which might possibly lead to the discovery of medicaments of value in psychiatric treatment in particular.

185. In answer to a question regarding the various uses of bhang[12] in India, the Commission was referred to the Survey of the Cannabis Situation in India which contained a detailed account of such uses.[13] While the leaves of the cannabis plant when not accompanied by the tops had been excluded from the rigid regime applicable to cannabis under the 1961 Convention, and would be subject to only a general obligation of parties to prevent the abuse of and illicit traffic in such leaves, they were in fact subject to certain controls in India as regards limits of possession and purchase; they were prohibited in some states, and in other states the legal amount which an individual was allowed to have in his possession was strictly limited. Consumption of cannabis was greatly decreasing in India.

Scientific Research on Methods of Identification of Cannabis

186. The Commission reviewed the progress made during the previous year in the United Nations programme on cannabis research[14] which had been carried out in accordance with resolution 8 (XIV).

187. Since the beginning of the programme, the authorities of Brazil, Canada, Cyprus, the Federal Republic of Germany,

11 Communication of 17 November 1960, by Edmond Heiby.

12 Bhang is the dried mature leaves of the cannabis plant.

13 E/CN.7/286/Add.12, part F.

14 E/CN.7/397 and Add.1.

Greece, Morocco, Sweden, and the United Kingdom had sent samples of cannabis to the United Nations Laboratory. Assistance had also been given by the Geneva Botanical Gardens and the University of Geneva who had provided samples. Although the Laboratory had given priority in accordance with the Commission's directives to the scientific research on opium, a study had been made of the absorption characteristics of cannabis in the ultra-violet region.[15]

188. Regarding the international collaboration in the research programme reference was made to an important contribution by Canada which had furnished a detailed study on the chemical analysis of cannabis and which was in course of publication. The Institute for the Control of Drugs, Zagreb, Yugoslavia, was also carrying out research on cannabis; and Dr. Fritz, Professor of the Faculty of Medicine, Budapest, Hungary, had recently been nominated by the Government of the Hungarian People's Republic to participate in the United Nations research programme. In addition a document on the methods used for the identification of cannabis in the United States of America had been published in the ST/SOA/SER.S/ . . . series.[16]

15 ST/SOA/SER.S/2.
16 ST/SOA/SER.S/3.

CHAPTER EIGHT

THE MARIHUANA
TAX ACT OF 1937

The popular and therapeutic uses of hemp preparations are not categorically prohibited by the provisions of the Marihuana Tax Act of 1937. The apparent purpose of the Act is to levy a token tax of approximately one dollar on all buyers, sellers, importers, growers, physicians, veterinarians, and any other persons who deal in marihuana commercially, prescribe it professionally, or possess it.

The deceptive nature of that apparent purpose begins to come into focus when the reader reaches the penalty provisions of the Act: five years' imprisonment, a $2,000 fine, or both seem rather excessive for evading a sum (provided for by the purchase of a Treasury Department tax stamp) that, even if collected, would produce only a minute amount of government revenue. (Fines and jail sentences were further increased to the point of the cruel and unusual in subsequent federal drug legislation that incorporated the Marihuana Tax Act. It is now possible under the later version of the Act to draw a life sentence for selling just one marihuana cigarette to a minor.)

One might wonder, too, why a small clause, amounting to an open-ended catchall provision, was inserted into the Act, authorizing the Secretary of the Treasury to grant the Commissioner (then Harry Anslinger) and agents of the Treasury Department's Bureau of Narcotics absolute administrative, regulatory, and police powers in the enforcement of the law.

The message becomes entirely clear when, having finished the short text of the Act itself, one proceeds to the sixty-odd pages of administrative and enforcement procedures established by the infamous Regulations No. 1. That regulation, not fully reproduced here, calls for a maze of affidavits, depositions, sworn statements, and constant Treasury Department police inspection in every instance that marihuana is bought, sold, used, raised, distributed, given away, and so on. Physicians who wish to purchase the one-dollar tax stamp so that they might prescribe it for their patients are forced to report such use to the Federal Bureau of Narcotics in sworn and attested detail, revealing the name and address of the patient, the nature of his ailment, the dates and amounts prescribed, and so on. If a physician for any reason fails to do so immediately, both he and his patient are liable to imprisonment and a heavy fine. Obviously, the details of that regulation make it far too risky for anyone to have anything to do with marihuana in any way whatsoever.

Regulations No. 1 was more than an invasion of the traditional right of privacy between patient and physician; it was a hopelessly involved set of rules that were obviously designed not merely to discourage but to prohibit the medical and popular use of marihuana. In addition to the Marihuana Tax Act and Regulations No. 1, the Bureau of Narcotics prepared a standard bill for marihuana that more than forty state legislatures enacted. This bill made possession and use of marihuana illegal per se, and so reinforced the federal act.

U. S. TREASURY DEPARTMENT

BUREAU OF NARCOTICS

REGULATIONS No. 1
RELATING TO THE
IMPORTATION, MANUFACTURE, PRODUCTION COMPOUNDING, SALE, DEALING IN, DISPENSING PRESCRIBING, ADMINISTERING, AND GIVING AWAY OF MARIHUANA
UNDER THE
ACT OF AUGUST 2, 1937
PUBLIC, No. 238, 75TH CONGRESS
NARCOTIC-INTERNAL REVENUE REGULATIONS
JOINT MARIHUANA REGULATIONS MADE BY THE COMMISSIONER OF NARCOTICS AND THE

COMMISSIONER OF
INTERNAL REVENUE WITH THE APPROVAL OF
THE SECRETARY OF THE TREASURY

———

EFFECTIVE DATE, OCTOBER 1, 1937

LAW AND REGULATIONS RELATING TO THE IM-
PORTATION, MANUFACTURE, PRODUCTION, COM-
POUNDING, SALE, DEALING IN, DISPENSING, PRE-
SCRIBING, ADMINISTERING, AND GIVING AWAY OF
MARIHUANA

———

THE LAW
(Act of Aug. 2, 1937, Public 238, 75th Congress)

*Be it enacted by the Senate and House of Representatives of
the United States of America in Congress assembled,* That
when used in this Act—

(a) The term "person" means an individual, a partnership,
trust, association, company, or corporation and includes an
officer or employee of a trust, association, company, or corporation, or a member or employee of a partnership, who, as
such officer, employee, or member, is under a duty to perform
any act in respect of which any violation of this Act occurs.

(b) The term "marihuana" means all parts of the plant
Cannabis sativa L., whether growing or not; the seeds thereof;
the resin extracted from any part of such plant; and every compound, manufacture, salt, derivative, mixture, or preparation
of such plant, its seeds, or resin; but shall not include the
mature stalks of such plant, fiber produced from such stalks,
oil or cake made from the seeds of such plant, any other compound, manufacture, salt, derivative, mixture, or preparation
of such mature stalks (except the resin extracted therefrom),
fiber, oil, or cake, or the sterilized seed of such plant which is
incapable of germination.

(c) The term "producer" means any person who (1) plants,
cultivates, or in any way facilitates the natural growth of marihuana; or (2) harvests and transfers or makes use of marihuana.

(d) The term "Secretary" means the Secretary of the Treasury and the term "collector" means collector of internal
revenue.

(e) The term "transfer" or "transferred" means any type
of disposition resulting in a change of possession but shall

not include a transfer to a common carrier for the purpose of transporting marihuana.

SEC. 2. (a) Every person who imports, manufactures, produces, compounds, sells, deals in, dispenses, prescribes, administers, or gives away marihuana shall (1) within fifteen days after the effective date of this Act, or (2) before engaging after the expiration of such fifteen-day period in any of the above-mentioned activities, and (3) thereafter, on or before July 1 of each year, pay the following special taxes respectively:

(1) Importers, manufacturers, and compounders of marihuana, $24 per year.

(2) Producers of marihuana (except those included within subdivision (4) of this subsection), $1 per year, or fraction thereof, during which they engage in such activity.

(3) Physicians, dentists, veterinary surgeons, and other practitioners who distribute, dispense, give away, administer, or prescribe marihuana to patients upon whom they in the course of their professional practice are in attendance, $1 per year or fraction thereof during which they engage in any of such activities.

(4) Any person not registered as an importer, manufacturer, producer, or compounder who obtains and uses marihuana in a laboratory for the purpose of research, instruction, or analysis, or who produces marihuana for any such purpose, $1 per year, or fraction thereof, during which he engages in such activities.

(5) Any person who is not a physician, dentist, veterinary surgeon, or other practitioner and who deals in, dispenses, or gives away marihuana, $3 per year: *Provided,* That any person who has registered and paid the special tax as an importer, manufacturer, compounder, or producer, as required by subdivisions (1) and (2) of this subsection, may deal in, dispense, or give away marihuana imported, manufactured, compounded, or produced by him without further payment of the tax imposed by this section.

(b) Where a tax under subdivision (1) or (5) is payable on July 1 of any year it shall be computed for one year; where any such tax is payable on any other day it shall be computed proportionately from the first day of the month in which the liability for the tax accrued to the following July 1.

(c) In the event that any person subject to a tax imposed by this section engages in any of the activities enumerated in subsection (a) of this section at more than one place, such person shall pay the tax with respect to each such place.

(d) Except as otherwise provided, whenever more than one of the activities enumerated in subsection (a) of this section is carried on by the same person at the same time, such person shall pay the tax for each such activity, according to the respective rates prescribed.

(e) Any person subject to the tax imposed by this section shall, upon payment of such tax, register his name or style and his place or places of business with the collector of the district in which such place or places of business are located.

(f) Collectors are authorized to furnish, upon written request, to any person a certified copy of the names of any or all persons who may be listed in their respective collection districts as special taxpayers under this section, upon payment of a fee of $1 for each one hundred of such names or fraction thereof upon such copy so requested.

Sec. 3. (a) No employee of any person who has paid the special tax and registered, as required by section 2 of this Act, acting within the scope of his employment, shall be required to register and pay such special tax.

(b) An officer or employee of the United States, any State, Territory, the District of Columbia, or insular possession, or political subdivision, who, in the exercise of his official duties, engages in any of the activities enumerated in section 2 of this Act, shall not be required to register or pay the special tax, but his right to this exemption shall be evidenced in such manner as the Secretary may by regulations prescribe.

Sec. 4. (a) It shall be unlawful for any person required to register and pay the special tax under the provisions of section 2 to import, manufacture, produce, compound, sell, deal in, dispense, distribute, prescribe, administer, or give away marihuana without having so registered and paid such tax.

(b) In any suit or proceeding to enforce the liability imposed by this section or section 2, if proof is made that marihuana was at any time growing upon land under the control of the defendant, such proof shall be presumptive evidence that at such time the defendant was a producer and liable under this section as well as under section 2.

Sec. 5. It shall be unlawful for any person who shall not have paid the special tax and registered, as required by section 2, to send, ship, carry, transport, or deliver any marihuana within any Territory, the District of Columbia, or any insular possession, or from any State, Territory, the District of Columbia, any insular possession of the United States, or the Canal Zone, into any other State, Territory, the District of Columbia, or insular possession of the United States: *Provided,* That nothing contained in this section shall apply to any common carrier engaged in transporting marihuana; or to any employee of any person who shall have registered and paid the special tax as required by section 2 while acting within the scope of his employment; or to any person who shall deliver marihuana which has been prescribed or dispensed by a physician, dentist, veterinary surgeon, or other practitioner registered under section 2, who has been employed to prescribe for the particular patient receiving such marihuana; or to any United States, State, county, municipal, District, Territorial, or insular officer or official acting within the scope of his official duties.

SEC. 6. (a) It shall be unlawful for any person, whether or not required to pay a special tax and register under section 2, to transfer marihuana, except in pursuance of a written order of the person to whom such marihuana is transferred, on a form to be issued in blank for that purpose by the Secretary.

(b) Subject to such regulations as the Secretary may prescribe, nothing contained in this section shall apply—

(1) To a transfer of marihuana to a patient by a physician, dentist, veterinary surgeon, or other practitioner registered under section 2, in the course of his professional practice only: *Provided,* That such physician, dentist, veterinary surgeon, or other practitioner shall keep a record of all such marihuana transferred, showing the amount transferred and the name and address of the patient to whom such marihuana is transferred, and such record shall be kept for a period of two years from the date of the transfer of such marihuana, and subject to inspection as provided in section 11.

(2) To a transfer of marihuana, made in good faith by a dealer to a consumer under and in pursuance of a written prescription issued by a physician, dentist, veterinary surgeon, or other practitioner registered under section 2: *Provided,* That such prescription shall be dated as of the day on which signed and shall be signed by the physician, dentist, veterinary surgeon, or other practitioner who issues the same; *Provided further,* That such dealer shall preserve such prescription for a period of two years from the day on which such prescription is filled so as to be readily accessible for inspection by the officers, agents, employees, and officials mentioned in section 11.

(3) To the sale, exportation, shipment, or delivery of marihuana by any person within the United States, any Territory, the District of Columbia, or any of the insular possessions of the United States, to any person in any foreign country regulating the entry of marihuana, if such sale, shipment, or delivery of marihuana is made in accordance with such regulations for importation into such foreign country as are prescribed by such foreign country, such regulations to be

promulgated from time to time by the Secretary of State of the United States.

(4) To a transfer of marihuana to any officer or employee of the United States Government or of any State, Territorial, District, county, or municipal or insular government lawfully engaged in making purchases thereof for the various departments of the Army and Navy, the Public Health Service, and for Government, State, Territorial, District, county, or municipal or insular hospitals or prisons.

(5) To a transfer of any seeds of the plant Cannabis sativa L. to any person registered under section 2.

(c) The Secretary shall cause suitable forms to be prepared for the purposes before mentioned and shall cause them to be distributed to collectors for sale. The price at which such forms shall be sold by said collectors shall be fixed by the Secretary, but shall not exceed 2 cents each. Whenever any collector shall sell any of such forms he shall cause the date of sale, the name and address of the proposed vendor, the name and address of the purchaser, and the amount of marihuana ordered to be plainly written or stamped thereon before delivering the same.

(d) Each such order form sold by a collector shall be prepared by him and shall include an original and two copies, any one of which shall be admissible in evidence as an original. The original and one copy shall be given by the collector to the purchaser thereof. The original shall in turn be given by the purchaser thereof to any person who shall, in pursuance thereof, transfer marihuana to him and shall be preserved by such person for a period of two years so as to be readily accessible for inspection by any officer, agent, or employee mentioned in section 11. The copy given to the purchaser by the collector shall be retained by the purchaser and preserved for a period of two years so as to be readily accessible to inspection by any officer, agent, or employee mentioned in section 11. The second copy shall be preserved in the records of the collector.

SEC. 7. (a) There shall be levied, collected, and paid upon all transfers of marihuana which are required by section 6 to be carried out in pursuance of written order forms taxes at the following rates:

(1) Upon each transfer to any person who has paid the special tax and registered under section 2 of this Act, $1 per ounce of marihuana or fraction thereof.

(2) Upon each transfer to any person who has not paid the special tax and registered under section 2 of this Act, $100 per ounce of marihuana or fraction thereof.

(b) Such tax shall be paid by the transferee at the time of securing each order form and shall be in addition to the price of such form. Such transferee shall be liable for the tax imposed by this section but in the event that the transfer is made in violation of section 6 without an order form and without payment of the transfer tax imposed by this section, the transferor shall also be liable for such tax.

(c) Payment of the tax herein provided shall be represented by appropriate stamps to be provided by the Secretary and said stamps shall be affixed by the collector or his representative to the original order form.

(d) All provisions of law relating to the engraving, issuance, sale, accountability, cancelation, and destruction of tax-paid stamps provided for in the internal-revenue laws shall, insofar as applicable and not inconsistent with this Act, be extended and made to apply to stamps provided for in this section.

(e) All provisions of law (including penalties) applicable in respect of the taxes imposed by the Act of December 17, 1914 (38 Stat. 785; U. S. C., 1934 ed., title 26, secs. 1040–1061, 1383–1391), as amended, shall, insofar as not inconsistent with this Act, be applicable in respect of the taxes imposed by this Act.

SEC. 8. (a) It shall be unlawful for any person who is a transferee required to pay the transfer tax imposed by section 7 to acquire or otherwise obtain any marihuana without having paid such tax; and proof that any person shall have had in his possession any marihuana and shall have failed, after reasonable notice and demand by the collector, to produce the order form required by section 6 to be retained by him, shall be presumptive evidence of guilt under this section and of liability for the tax imposed by section 7.

(b) No liability shall be imposed by virtue of this section upon any duly authorized officer of the Treasury Department engaged in the enforcement of this Act or upon any duly authorized officer of any State, or Territory, or of any political subdivision thereof, or the District of Columbia, or of any insular possession of the United States, who shall be engaged in the enforcement of any law or municipal ordinance dealing with the production, sale, prescribing, dispensing, dealing in, or distributing of marihuana.

SEC. 9. (a) Any marihuana which has been imported, manufactured, compounded, transferred, or produced in violation of any of the provisions of this Act shall be subject to seizure and forfeiture and, except as inconsistent with the provisions of this Act, all the provisions of internal-revenue laws relating to searches, seizures, and forfeitures are extended to include marihuana.

(b) Any marihuana which may be seized by the United

States Government from any person or persons charged with any violation of this Act shall upon conviction of the person or persons from whom seized be confiscated by and forfeited to the United States.

(c) Any marihuana seized or coming into the possession of the United States in the enforcement of this Act, the owner or owners of which are unknown, shall be confiscated by and forfeited to the United States.

(d) The Secretary is hereby directed to destroy any marihuana confiscated by and forfeited to the United States under this section or to deliver such marihuana to any department, bureau, or other agency of the United States Government, upon proper application therefor under such regulations as may be prescribed by the Secretary.

SEC. 10. (a) Every person liable to any tax imposed by this act shall keep such books and records, render under oath such statements, make such returns, and comply with such rules and regulations as the Secretary may from time to time prescribe.

(b) Any person who shall be registered under the provisions of section 2 in any internal-revenue district shall, whenever required so to do by the collector of the district, render to the collector a true and correct statement or return, verified by affidavits, setting forth the quantity of marihuana received or harvested by him during such period immediately preceding the demand of the collector, not exceeding three months, as the said collector may fix and determine. If such person is not solely a producer, he shall set forth in such statement or return the names of the persons from which said marihuana was received, the quantity in each instance received from such persons, and the date when received.

SEC. 11. The order forms and copies thereof and the prescriptions and records required to be preserved under the provisions of section 6, and the statements or returns filed in the office of the collector of the district under the provisions of section 10 (b) shall be open to inspection by officers, agents, and employees of the Treasury Department duly authorized for that purpose, and such officers of any State, or Territory, or of any political subdivision thereof, or the District of Columbia, or of any insular possession of the United States as shall be charged with the enforcement of any law or municipal ordinance regulating the production, sale, prescribing, dispensing, dealing in, or distributing of marihuana. Each collector shall be authorized to furnish, upon written request, copies of any of the said statements or returns filed in his office to any of such officials of any State or Territory, or political subdivision thereof, or the District of Columbia, or any insular possession of the United States as shall be entitled to inspect the said statements or returns filed in the office of the said collector, upon the payment of a fee of $1 for each 100 words or fraction thereof in the copy or copies so requested.

SEC. 12. Any person who is convicted of a violation of any provision of this Act shall be fined not more than $2,000 or imprisoned not more than five years, or both, in the discretion of the court.

SEC. 13. It shall not be necessary to negative any exemptions set forth in this Act in any complaint, information, indictment, or other writ or proceeding laid or brought under this Act and the burden of proof of any such exemption shall be upon the defendant. In the absence of the production of evidence by the defendant that he has complied with the provisions of section 6 relating to order forms, he shall be presumed not to have complied with such provisions of such sections, as the case may be.

SEC. 14. The Secretary is authorized to make, prescribe, and publish all necessary rules and regulations for carrying out the provisions of this Act and to confer or impose any of the rights, privileges, powers, and duties conferred or imposed upon him by this Act upon such officers or employees of the Treasury Department as he shall designate or appoint.

SEC. 15. The provisions of this Act shall apply to the several States, the District of Columbia, the Territory of Alaska, the Territory of Hawaii, and the insular possessions of the United States, except the Philippine Islands. In Puerto Rico the administration of this Act, the collection of the special taxes and transfer taxes, and the issuance of the order forms provided for in section 6 shall be performed by the appropriate internal-revenue officers of that government, and all revenues collected under this Act in Puerto Rico shall accrue intact to the general government thereof. The President is hereby authorized and directed to issue such Executive orders as will carry into effect in the Virgin Islands the intent and purpose of this Act by providing for the registration with appropriate officers and the imposition of the special and transfer taxes upon all persons in the Virgin Islands who import, manufacture, produce, compound, sell, deal in, dispense, prescribe, administer, or give away marihuana.

SEC. 16. If any provision of this Act or the application thereof to any person or circumstances is held invalid, the remainder of the Act and the application of such provision to other persons or circumstances shall not be affected thereby.

SEC. 17. This Act shall take effect on the first day of the second month during which it is enacted.

Sec. 18. This Act may be cited as the "Marihuana Tax Act of 1937."

(T. D. 28)

Order of the Secretary of the Treasury Relating to the Enforcement of the Marihuana Tax Act of 1937

September 1, 1937

Section 14 of the Marihuana Tax Act of 1937 (act of Congress approved August 2, 1937, Public, No. 238), provides as follows:

> The Secretary is authorized to make, prescribe, and publish all necessary rules and regulations for carrying out the provisions of this Act and to confer or impose any of the rights, privileges, powers, and duties conferred or imposed upon him by this Act upon such officers or employees of the Treasury Department as he shall designate or appoint.

In pursuance of the authority thus conferred upon the Secretary of the Treasury, it is hereby ordered:

I. Rights, Privileges, Powers, and Duties Conferred and Imposed Upon the Commissioner of Narcotics

1. There are hereby conferred and imposed upon the Commissioner of Narcotics, subject to the general supervision and direction of the Secretary of the Treasury, all the rights, privileges, powers, and duties conferred or imposed upon said Secretary by the Marihuana Tax Act of 1937, so far as such rights, privileges, powers, and duties relate to—

(*a*) Prescribing regulations, with the approval of the Secretary, as to the manner in which the right of public officers to exemption from registration and payment of special tax may be evidenced, in accordance with section 3 (b) of the act.

(*b*) Prescribing the form of written order required by section 6 (a) of the act, said form to be prepared and issued in blank by the Commissioner of Internal Revenue as hereinafter provided.

(*c*) Prescribing regulations, with the approval of the Secretary, giving effect to the exceptions, specified in subsection (b), from the operation of subsection (a) of section 6 of the act.

(*d*) The destruction of marihuana confiscated by and forfeited to the United States, or delivery of such marihuana to any department, bureau, or other agency of the United States

Government, and prescribing regulations, with the approval of the Secretary, governing the manner of application for, and delivery of such marihuana.

(*e*) Prescribing rules and regulations, with the approval of the Secretary, as to books and records to be kept, and statements and information returns to be rendered under oath, as required by section 10 (a) of the act.

(*f*) The compromise of any criminal liability (except as relates to delinquency in registration and delinquency in payment of tax) arising under the act, in accordance with section 3229 of the Revised Statutes of the United States (U. S. Code (1934 ed.) title 26, sec. 1661), and the recommendation for assessment of civil liability for internal-revenue taxes and ad valorem penalties under the act.

II. Rights, Privileges, Powers, and Duties Conferred and Imposed upon the Commissioner of Internal Revenue

1. There are hereby conferred and imposed upon the Commissioner of Internal Revenue, subject to the general supervision and direction of the Secretary of the Treasury, the rights, privileges, powers, and duties conferred or imposed upon said Secretary of the Marihuana Tax Act of 1937, not otherwise assigned herein, so far as such rights, privileges, powers, and duties relate to—

(*a*) Preparation and issuance in blank to collectors of internal revenue of the written orders, in the form prescribed by the Commissioner of Narcotics, required by section 6 (a) of the act. The price of the order form, as sold by the collector under section 6 (c) of the act shall be two cents for the original and one copy.

(*b*) Providing appropriate stamps to represent payment of transfer tax levied by section 7, and prescribing and providing appropriate stamps for issuance of special tax payers registering under section 2 of the act.

(*c*) The compromise of any civil liability involving delinquency in registration, delinquency in payment of tax, and ad valorem penalties, and of any criminal liability incurred through delinquency in registration and delinquency in payment of tax, in connection with the act and in accordance with Section 3229 of the Revised Statutes of the United States (U. S. Code (1934 ed.), title 26, sec. 1661); the determination of liability for and the assessment and collection of special and transfer taxes imposed by the act; the determination of liability for and the assessment and collection of the ad valorem penalties imposed by Section 3176 of the Revised Statutes, as modified by Section 406 of the Revenue Act of 1935 (U. S. Code (1934 ed.) title 26, secs. 1512–1525), for delinquency in registration; and the determination of liability for and the assertion of the specific penalty imposed by the act, for delinquency in registration and payment of tax.

General Provisions

The investigation and the detection, and presentation to prosecuting officers of evidence, of violations of the Marihuana Tax Act of 1937, shall be the duty of the Commissioner of Narcotics and the assistants, agents, inspectors, or employees under his direction. Except as specifically inconsistent with the terms of said act and of this order, the Commissioner of Narcotics and the Commissioner of Internal Revenue and the assistants, agents, inspectors, or employees of the Bureau of Narcotics and the Bureau of Internal Revenue, respectively, shall have the same powers and duties in safeguarding the revenue thereunder as they now have with respect to the enforcement of, and collection of the revenue under, the act of December 17, 1914, as amended (U. S. Code (1934 ed.), title 26, sec. 1049).

In any case where a general offer is made in compromise of civil and criminal liability ordinarily compromisable hereunder by the Commissioner of Internal Revenue and of criminal liability ordinarily compromisable hereunder by the Commissioner of Narcotics, the case may be jointly compromisable by those officers, in accordance with Section 3229 of the Revised Statutes of the United States (U. S. Code (1934 ed.), title 26, sec. 1661).

Power is hereby conferred upon the Commissioner of Narcotics to prescribe such regulations as he may deem necessary for the execution of the functions imposed upon him or upon the officers or employees of the Bureau of Narcotics, but all regulations and changes in regulations shall be subject to the approval of the Secretary of the Treasury.

The Commissioner of Internal Revenue and the Commissioner of Narcotics may, if they are of the opinion that the good of the service will be promoted thereby, prescribe regulations relating to internal revenue taxes where no violation of the Marihuana Tax Act of 1937 is involved, jointly, subject to the approval of the Secretary of the Treasury.

The right to amend or supplement this order or any provision thereof from time to time, or to revoke this order or any provision thereof at any time, is hereby reserved.

The effective date of this order shall be October 1, 1937, which is the effective date of the Marihuana Tax Act of 1937.

STEPHEN B. GIBBONS,
Acting Secretary of the Treasury.

REGULATIONS

Introductory

The Marihuana Tax Act of 1937, imposes special (occupational) taxes upon persons engaging in activities involving articles or material within the definition of "marihuana" contained in the act, and also taxes the transfer of such articles or material.

These regulations deal with details as to tax computation, procedure, the forms of records and returns, and similar matters. These matters in some degree are controlled by certain sections of the United States Revised Statutes and other statutes of general application. Provisions of these statutes, as well as of the Marihuana Tax Act of 1937 are quoted, in whole or in part, as the immediate or general basis for the regulatory provisions set forth. The quoted provisions are from the Marihuana Tax Act of 1937 unless otherwise indicated.

Provisions of the statutes upon which the various articles of the regulations are based generally have not been repeated in the articles. Therefore, the statutory excerpts preceding the several articles should be examined to obtain complete information.

Chapter 1

Laws Applicable

SEC. 7 (e) All provisions of law (including penalties) applicable in respect of the taxes imposed by the Act of December 17, 1914 (38 Stat. 785; U. S. C., 1934 ed., title 26, secs. 1040–1061, 1383–1391), as amended, shall, insofar as not inconsistent with this Act, be applicable in respect of the taxes imposed by this Act.

ART. 1. Statutes applicable.—All general provisions of the internal revenue laws, not inconsistent with the Marihuana Tax Act, are applicable in the enforcement of the latter.

Chapter II

Definitions

Sec. 1. That when used in this Act—

(a) The term "person" means an individual, a partnership, trust, association, company, or corporation and includes an officer or employee of a trust, association, company, or corporation, or a member or employee of a partnership, who as such officer, employee, or member is under a duty to perform any act in respect of which any violation of this Act occurs.

(b) The term "marihuana" means all parts of the plant Cannabis sativa L., whether growing or not; the seeds thereof; the resin extracted from any part of such plant; and every compound, manufacture, salt, derivative, mixture, or preparation of such plant, its seeds, or resins; but shall not include the mature stalks of such plant, fiber produced from such stalks, oil or cake made from the seeds of such plant, any other compound, manufacture, salt, derivative, mixture, or preparation of such mature stalks (except the resin extracted therefrom), fiber, oil, or cake, or the sterilized seed of such plant which is incapable of germination.

(c) The term "producer" means any person who (1) plants, cultivates, or in any way facilitates the natural growth of marihuana; or (2) harvests and transfers or makes use of marihuana.

(d) The term "Secretary" means the Secretary of the Treasury and the term "collector" means collector of internal revenue.

(e) The term "transfer" or "transferred" means any type of disposition resulting in a change of possession but shall not include a transfer to a common carrier for the purpose of transporting marihuana.

Art. 2. As used in these regulations:

(*a*) The term "act" or "this act" shall mean the Marihuana Tax Act of 1937, unless otherwise indicated.

(*b*) The term "United States" shall include the several States, the District of Columbia, the Territory of Alaska, the Territory of Hawaii, and the insular possessions of the United States except Puerto Rico and the Virgin Islands. It does not include the Canal Zone or the Philippine Islands.

(*c*) The terms "manufacturer" and "compounder" shall include any person who subjects marihuana to any process of separation, extraction, mixing, compounding, or other manufacturing operation. They shall not include one who merely gathers and destroys the plant, one who merely threshes out the seeds on the premises where produced, or one who in the conduct of a legitimate business merely subjects seeds to a cleaning process.

(*d*) The term "producer" means any person who induces in any way the growth of marihuana; and any person who harvests it, either in a cultivated or wild state, from his own or any other land, and transfers or makes use of it, including one who subjects the marihuana which he harvests to any processes rendering him liable also as a manufacturer or compounder. Generally all persons are included who gather marihuana for any purpose other than to destroy it. The term does not include one who merely plows under or otherwise destroys marihuana with or without harvesting. It does not include one who grows marihuana for use in his own laboratory for the purpose of research, instruction, or analysis and who does not use it for any other purpose or transfer it.

(*e*) The term "special tax" is used to include any of the taxes, pertaining to the several occupations or activities covered by the act, imposed upon persons who import, manufacture, produce, compound, sell, deal in, dispense, prescribe, administer, or give away marihuana.

(*f*) The term "person" occurring in these regulations is used to include individual, partnership, trust, association, company, or corporation; also a hospital, college of pharmacy, medical or dental clinic, sanatorium, or other institution or entity.

(*g*) Words importing the singular may include the plural; words importing the masculine gender may be applied to the feminine or the neuter.

(*h*) The definitions contained herein shall not be deemed exclusive.

(Sample—Warning card to be placed in R. R. Trains, Buses, Street Cars, etc.)

Beware! **Young and Old—People in All Walks of Life!**

This [ ] may be handed you

Marihuana Cigarette

by the <u>friendly stranger.</u> It contains the Killer Drug "Marihuana"—a powerful narcotic in which lurks *Murder! Insanity! Death!*

WARNING!

Dope peddlers are shrewd! They may put some of this drug in the *candy too* or or in the *cookie too* or in the tobacco cigarette.

WRITE FOR DETAILED INFORMATION, ENCLOSING 12 CENTS IN POSTAGE — MAILING COST

Address: THE INTER-STATE NARCOTIC ASSOCIATION

(Incorporated not for profit)

52 W. Jackson Blvd. Chicago, Illinois, U.S.A.

This crude poster is a typical example of the kind of propaganda device officially welcomed and encouraged by the *Federal Bureau of Narcotics* as part of (to quote the *Bureau*) "an educational campaign describing the drug, its identification, and evil effects." The epithet "Killer Drug" is entirely in keeping with the *Bureau's* mendacious description of marihuana as "a lethal weed."

INDEX

INDEX

Adams, Roger, 414, 432
addiction: to marihuana, xvii,
xviii, 39, 41, 49, 55, 66, 67, 68,
90, 91, 92, 93, 109, 236, 240,
241, 287, 295-96, 299, 307, 313,
396-98, 404, 407-8, 410, 414,
421, 442, 446, 448, 462, 463,
468; to other narcotics, xxvi, 48,
49, 55, 56, 61, 68, 93, 238, 296,
307, 326, 415. *See also* narcotics, marihuana's place among;
narcotics withdrawal, use of
marihuana in; tolerance
Africa, 141-42, 238, 284-85,
456, 459, 478-79
alcohol and marihuana compared, xiv, xxii, xxvii, 42, 49, 52-
53, 57, 91, 94-95, 104-5, 108,
109-10, 111-12, 115, 116, 119,
124, 237, 239, 240, 244, 249,
260, 271, 296, 412, 414, 442,
463, 468
alcoholism, treatment of, 431,
437-38
al-kief, 172
Allentuck, Samuel, xxvii, 59,
316, 332, 411, 466
American Medical Association,
xviii, xxvi, xxvii, 448, 490
Angola, 478
animals, effect of *cannabis* on,
409, 410
Anslinger, Harry J., xxv, xxvi,
xxvii, 41, 46, 51, 53, 54, 55, 58,
233, 239, 243, 247, 470, 473,
481
antidote to marihuana (sweets),
333

aphrodisiac, marihuana as, 44,
106, 459
apomorphine, 445
Arab world, 209-16 (story),
243, 456, 458
Arabia, 32
arrests for marihuana, xvi, 60-
61, 124, 297
Assassins, 33-34, 51, 108, 166,
467
Aubert-Roche, xix, 449

Babinski reflex, 267, 268
Baudelaire, Charles, 34, 42, 107,
179
Becker, Howard S., 65
Benabud, 466
benzedrine, 236
Bethea, Oscar, 431
bhakti, 112
bhang, 37, 39, 50, 103, 105, 456,
458, 462, 463, 464, 465, 468,
479
Boggs-Daniel Act (1956), xxvi,
xxviii, 124
Bowles, Paul, 209
Bowman, Karl, xxvii, 59, 411
Bromberg, Walter, 298, 309,
396, 411
Burroughs, William, 247, 440

cannabinols, 50, 399-403, 409,
422, 456
Cannabis indica, xix, 36, 39, 50,
193-95, 205-8, 249. *See also*
Marihuana, Uses

501

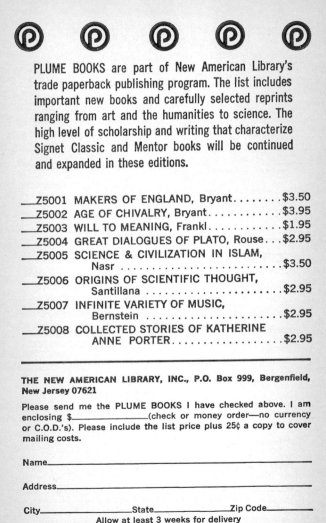

PLUME BOOKS are part of New American Library's trade paperback publishing program. The list includes important new books and carefully selected reprints ranging from art and the humanities to science. The high level of scholarship and writing that characterize Signet Classic and Mentor books will be continued and expanded in these editions.

___Z5001 MAKERS OF ENGLAND, Bryant........$3.50
___Z5002 AGE OF CHIVALRY, Bryant...........$3.95
___Z5003 WILL TO MEANING, Frankl...........$1.95
___Z5004 GREAT DIALOGUES OF PLATO, Rouse...$2.95
___Z5005 SCIENCE & CIVILIZATION IN ISLAM,
          Nasr $3.50
___Z5006 ORIGINS OF SCIENTIFIC THOUGHT,
          Santillana $2.95
___Z5007 INFINITE VARIETY OF MUSIC,
          Bernstein $2.95
___Z5008 COLLECTED STORIES OF KATHERINE
          ANNE PORTER.................$2.95

THE NEW AMERICAN LIBRARY, INC., P.O. Box 999, Bergenfield, New Jersey 07621

Please send me the PLUME BOOKS I have checked above. I am enclosing $_____(check or money order—no currency or C.O.D.'s). Please include the list price plus 25¢ a copy to cover mailing costs.

Name_____

Address_____

City_____State_____Zip Code_____
          Allow at least 3 weeks for delivery